Longman Mathematical

Differential vector ca

G000075813

Longman Mathematical Texts

Edited by Alan Jeffrey

Longman Mathematical Texts

Differential vector calculus

P.R. Baxandall and **H. Liebeck**

Department of Mathematics,
The University of Keele

Longman

London and New York

Longman Group Limited
Longman House
Burnt Mill, Harlow, Essex, UK

*Published in the United States of America
by Longman Inc., New York*

© Longman Group Limited 1981

First published 1981

British Library Cataloguing in Publication Data

Differential vector calculus. —(Longman
  mathematical texts).
  1. Calculus, Differential
  2. Vector analysis
  I. Baxandall, P
  II. Liebeck, Hans
  515′.63   QA304   80–41123
  ISBN   0–582–44193–5

Set in Monophoto Times New Roman
Printed in Great Britain by
Butler & Tanner Ltd, Frome and London

Contents

4: Vector-valued functions of $\mathbb{R}^m$

Preface

This book provides an introduction to advanced differential calculus
set against a background of linear algebra. It is designed as a first
or second year course for undergraduates who have some knowledge
of linear algebra and real analysis.

Traditionally linear algebra, vector analysis and calculus of
functions of several variables are taught as separate subjects. They
are, however, closely related. The underlying links are established by
defining the differentiability of a vector function at a point in its
domain in terms of the existence of an approximating linear transformation (differential). Many of the important classical results of
vector calculus are essentially concerned with the geometrical
properties of this differential and of its image and graph.
The Chain Rule for example, which plays an important part in the
development of the theory, is merely an expression of the fact that
the linear approximation to the composition of two functions is the
composition of their individual linear approximations. This theorem
enables us to study the relationship between different parametrizations of curves and surfaces.

In the study of vector functions from $\mathbb{R}^m$ to $\mathbb{R}^n$ the cases $m = 1$
and $n = 1$ warrant separate discussion. After a short introductory
chapter we proceed in Chapter 2 to consider functions from $\mathbb{R}$ to $\mathbb{R}^n$
(including the study of curves, differential geometry and dynamics).
Chapter 3 deals with functions from $\mathbb{R}^m$ to $\mathbb{R}$ (real-valued functions
of many variables, Taylor's Theorem and applications). Finally, the
general theory of functions from $\mathbb{R}^m$ to $\mathbb{R}^n$ is covered in Chapter 4. In
particular we prove the important inverse function and implicit
function theorems. Our approach has the advantage of introducing
the concept of differentiability of vector functions in easy stages.
Certain theorems (the Chain Rule in particular) appear at a number
of points in progressively more general form.

We have tried to give readable yet rigorous proofs (often omitted
from introductory texts) of some of the important classical
theorems. The reader is recommended to attempt as many of

the exercises as he can. Apart from the usual routine applications of definitions and theorems, many of the exercises explain by way of counter-example the significance of the hypotheses of the theorems.

We wish to express our thanks to Professor Alan Jeffrey editor of Longman Mathematical Texts for inviting us to contribute to the series. We are grateful to many colleagues and friends for fruitful discussions concerning the text and in particular to the son of one of the authors, Dr Martin Liebeck, who kindly read the whole manuscript and suggested many improvements. Finally, very special thanks are due to Miss Christine Williams for typing the manuscript, and for cheerfully retyping parts of it as the authors settled their differences.

Keele   P.R. Baxandall
March 1980   H. Liebeck

Basic linear algebra and analysis

1.1 Introduction

Basic analysis and linear algebra play a fundamental role in the generalization of elementary calculus to the theory of vector-valued functions. We shall assume familiarity with the analysis and linear algebra usually found in a first course. Most of this background material is summarized in this chapter.

A first course in calculus deals with real-valued functions of one real variable. Such a function $f : D \subseteq \mathbb{R} \to \mathbb{R}$ is defined on a domain D which is a subset of the real line $\mathbb{R}$. The value that f takes at $x \in D$ is a real number denoted by $f(x) \in \mathbb{R}$. For example, the rule

$$f(x) = \sqrt{(1 - x^2)}$$

can be taken to define a real-valued function $f : D \subseteq \mathbb{R} \to \mathbb{R}$, where D is the closed interval $[-1, 1] = \{x \in \mathbb{R} \mid -1 \leqslant x \leqslant 1\}$.

Let $\mathbb{R}^m$ denote the set of all m-tuples of real numbers $(x_1, x_2, \ldots, x_m)$, $x_i \in \mathbb{R}$, $i = 1, \ldots, m$. (In particular, $\mathbb{R}^1 = \mathbb{R}$.) We shall be concerned with the study of functions $f : D \subseteq \mathbb{R}^m \to \mathbb{R}^n$ defined on a subset D of $\mathbb{R}^m$ and taking values in $\mathbb{R}^n$. For example, the rule

1.1.1 $f(x_1, x_2, x_3) = (\sqrt{(1 - x_3^2)}, x_1 x_2 x_3)$

can be taken to define a function $f : D \subseteq \mathbb{R}^3 \to \mathbb{R}^2$, where D is the subset of $\mathbb{R}^3$ given by

1.1.2 $D = \{(x_1, x_2, x_3) \in \mathbb{R}^3 \mid -1 \leqslant x_3 \leqslant 1\}$.

The set $\mathbb{R}^m$ defined above is given the structure of a real vector space by defining an addition of m-tuples

1.1.3 $(x_1, \ldots, x_m) + (y_1, \ldots, y_m) = (x_1 + y_1, \ldots, x_m + y_m)$

and a multiplication by scalars in $\mathbb{R}$,

1.1.4 $k(x_1, \ldots, x_m) = (kx_1, \ldots, kx_m)$, $\qquad k \in \mathbb{R}$.

Viewed in this way, the rule 1.1.1 defines a funtion f on a subset D

of the vector space $\mathbb{R}^3$ such that the values that f takes lie in the vector space $\mathbb{R}^2$.

With $\mathbb{R}^m$ interpreted as a vector space, the study of functions $f : D \subseteq \mathbb{R}^m \to \mathbb{R}^n$ is appropriately called vector calculus. (The alternative title 'calculus of functions of several variables' is sometimes preferred when $m > 1$.) We observe that vector calculus includes the case $m = n = 1$ and so is a generalization of elementary calculus.

Exercise 1.1

1. Suggest a possible subset $D \subseteq \mathbb{R}^3$ as the domain of a function $f : D \subseteq \mathbb{R}^3 \to \mathbb{R}^2$ which is given by the rule
   (a) $f(x_1, x_2, x_3) = (x_1/x_2, \sqrt{(1 - x_3^2)})$;
   (b) $f(x, y, z) = (e^{1/x}\tan(xyz), x^2 + y^2 + z^2)$;
   (c) $f(x, y, z) = (1/(x^2 - z^2), \ln(xyz))$.

   Answers:
   (a) $\{(x_1, x_2, x_3) \in \mathbb{R}^3 | x_2 \neq 0, x_3 \in [-1, 1]\}$;
   (b) $\{(x, y, z) \in \mathbb{R}^3 | x \neq 0, xyz \neq (k + \frac{1}{2})\pi, \text{ for integers } k\}$;
   (c) $\{(x, y, z) \in \mathbb{R}^3 | x \neq \pm z, xyz > 0\}$.

1.2 The vector space $\mathbb{R}^m$

In section 1.1 we pointed out that the set $\mathbb{R}^m$ of all m-tuples $(x_1, \ldots, x_m)$, $x_i \in \mathbb{R}$, $i = 1, \ldots, m$, can be regarded as a vector space over $\mathbb{R}$ if we impose the rules 1.1.3, 1.1.4 of addition and scalar multiplication. We shall often denote a vector of $\mathbb{R}^m$ by a single letter in bold-face, thus: $\mathbf{x} = (x_1, \ldots, x_m)$. In $\mathbb{R}^2$ and $\mathbb{R}^3$ the familiar notation $\mathbf{r} = (x, y)$ and $\mathbf{r} = (x, y, z)$ is useful.

Consider the vectors in $\mathbb{R}^m$

$$\mathbf{e}_1 = (1, 0, \ldots, 0), \mathbf{e}_2 = (0, 1, \ldots, 0), \ldots, \mathbf{e}_m = (0, 0, \ldots, 1),$$

where $\mathbf{e}_i$ has 1 in the ith place and 0 elsewhere. The set $\{\mathbf{e}_1, \ldots, \mathbf{e}_m\}$ is clearly a basis of the vector space $\mathbb{R}^m$, since any $\mathbf{x} = (x_1, \ldots, x_m) \in \mathbb{R}^m$ has the unique expression $\mathbf{x} = x_1\mathbf{e}_1 + \cdots + x_m\mathbf{e}_m$ as a linear combination of the $\mathbf{e}_i$'s. In view of its simple form we call the set $\{\mathbf{e}_1, \ldots, \mathbf{e}_m\}$ the *standard* (or *natural*) *basis* of $\mathbb{R}^m$. No other bases of $\mathbb{R}^m$ are used in this book.

The vector spaces $\mathbb{R}^1 = \mathbb{R}$, $\mathbb{R}^2$ and $\mathbb{R}^3$ are conveniently pictured as a number line, as a plane and as three-dimensional space. For example, we picture $\mathbb{R}^2$ by choosing an ordered pair of perpendicular axes and a unit of length, and associating the vector $\mathbf{x} = (x_1, x_2) \in \mathbb{R}^2$

with the point in the plane whose coordinates relative to the axes are (x_1, x_2) in the usual way.

An important alternative way of picturing the vector $\mathbf{x} = (x_1, x_2)$ in the plane is by an arrow joining the origin $(0, 0)$ to the point labelled (x_1, x_2). Both ways of picturing vectors will frequently be used – sometimes in the same diagram. The arrow representation is particularly important in physical applications, for example when we wish to picture velocities, accelerations or forces.

In the arrow representation, the rule 1.1.3 of vector addition is the well known parallelogram law of vector addition. See Fig. 1.1(i). The arrows joining O to P and Q to R are identical in all respects except for their position in the plane. We therefore agree to picture $\mathbf{x} = (x_1, x_2)$ not only by the arrow $\overrightarrow{OP}$ but also by an arrow joining (y_1, y_2) to $(x_1 + y_1, x_2 + y_2)$, where y_1, y_2 are arbitrarily chosen real numbers.

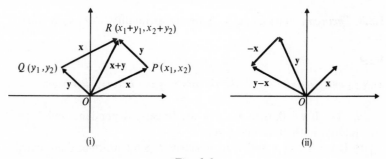

Fig. 1.1

Vector subtraction is illustrated in Fig. 1.1(ii). We have, by definition, $\mathbf{y} - \mathbf{x} = \mathbf{y} + (-\mathbf{x})$, where $-\mathbf{x} = (-x_1, -x_2)$.

Considerations similar to the above apply to a pictorial representation of $\mathbb{R}^3$ relative to three mutually perpendicular axes.

1.2.1 Definition. *Given vectors* $\mathbf{x} = (x_1, \ldots, x_m)$ *and* $\mathbf{y} = (y_1, \ldots, y_m)$ *in* $\mathbb{R}^m$, *the* dot *product (or* scalar *product) of* $\mathbf{x}$ *and* $\mathbf{y}$ *is defined to be the real number*

$$\mathbf{x} \cdot \mathbf{y} = x_1 y_1 + \cdots + x_m y_m.$$

The dot product has the following important properties

1.2.2   *Symmetry*: $\mathbf{x} \cdot \mathbf{y} = \mathbf{y} \cdot \mathbf{x}$, $\mathbf{x}, \mathbf{y} \in \mathbb{R}^m$

1.2.3   *Linearity*: $(k\mathbf{x} + l\mathbf{y}) \cdot \mathbf{z} = k(\mathbf{x} \cdot \mathbf{z}) + l(\mathbf{y} \cdot \mathbf{z})$,

$$\mathbf{x}, \mathbf{y}, \mathbf{z} \in \mathbb{R}^m, k, l \in \mathbb{R}$$

1.2.4   *Positivity*: $\mathbf{x} \cdot \mathbf{x} > 0$,   for all $\mathbf{x} \neq \mathbf{0}, \mathbf{x} \in \mathbb{R}^m$.

1.2.5 Definition. *The* norm *or* length *of* $\mathbf{x} \in \mathbb{R}^m$ *is the non-negative real number* $\|\mathbf{x}\| \geqslant 0$ *such that*

$$\|\mathbf{x}\|^2 = \mathbf{x} \cdot \mathbf{x} = x_1^2 + \ldots + x_m^2.$$

1.2.6 Example. If $\mathbf{a} = (2, 1)$, then $\|\mathbf{a}\|^2 = 2^2 + 1^2 = 5$ and $\|\mathbf{a}\| = \sqrt{5}$.
Note that $\|\mathbf{x}\| = 0$ if and only if $\mathbf{x} = \mathbf{0}$.

1.2.7 Example. It follows from Definition 1.2.5 that for $\mathbf{x} \in \mathbb{R}^m$, $k \in \mathbb{R}$,
$\|k\mathbf{x}\| = |k| \|\mathbf{x}\|$. For example, $\| - 2\mathbf{x}\| = 2 \|\mathbf{x}\|$.
  The following theorem will be used extensively in this book.

1.2.8 Theorem. The Cauchy–Schwarz inequality. *For any vectors*
$\mathbf{x}, \mathbf{y} \in \mathbb{R}^m$

1.2.9 $|\mathbf{x} \cdot \mathbf{y}| \leqslant \|\mathbf{x}\| \|\mathbf{y}\|$,

with equality if and only if the vectors $\mathbf{x}, \mathbf{y}$ *are linearly dependent.*

Proof. [*i*] If $\mathbf{y} = \mathbf{0}$, then $\mathbf{x}$ and $\mathbf{y}$ are linearly dependent, and 1.2.9 is
an equality, both sides being zero.
  [*ii*] If $\mathbf{y} \neq \mathbf{0}$ and $\mathbf{x}$ and $\mathbf{y}$ are linearly dependent, then there exists
$k \in \mathbb{R}$ such that $\mathbf{x} = k\mathbf{y}$. In this case 1.2.9 is an equality, both sides
being equal to $|k| \|\mathbf{y}\|^2$.
  [*iii*] The remaining case is that $\mathbf{x}$ and $\mathbf{y}$ are linearly independent.
Then, for any $k \in \mathbb{R}$, $\mathbf{x} + k\mathbf{y} \neq \mathbf{0}$ and, by the properties 1.2.2–1.2.4 of
the dot product,

$$0 < \|\mathbf{x} - k\mathbf{y}\|^2 = (\mathbf{x} + k\mathbf{y}) \cdot (\mathbf{x} + k\mathbf{y})$$
$$= \|\mathbf{x}\|^2 + 2k(\mathbf{x} \cdot \mathbf{y}) + k^2 \|\mathbf{y}\|^2.$$

With $k = -(\mathbf{x} \cdot \mathbf{y})/\|\mathbf{y}\|^2$, a simple calculation results in 1.2.9 as a
strict inequality.

  The Cauchy–Schwarz inequality is often stated in the form

1.2.10 $$\left(\sum_{i=1}^{m} x_i y_i \right)^2 \leq \sum_{i=1}^{m} x_i^2 \sum_{i=1}^{m} y_i^2.$$

This follows by squaring 1.2.9 and applying the definitions of dot product and norm.

1.2.11 *Theorem.* The Triangle Inequality. *For any vectors* $\mathbf{x}, \mathbf{y}$ *in* $\mathbb{R}^m$,

$$\|\mathbf{x} + \mathbf{y}\| \leqslant \|\mathbf{x}\| + \|\mathbf{y}\|.$$

Proof

1.2.12
$$\begin{aligned}
\|\mathbf{x} + \mathbf{y}\|^2 &= (\mathbf{x} + \mathbf{y}) \cdot (\mathbf{x} + \mathbf{y}) = \|\mathbf{x}\|^2 + 2\mathbf{x} \cdot \mathbf{y} + \|\mathbf{y}\|^2 \\
&\leqslant \|\mathbf{x}\|^2 + 2|\mathbf{x} \cdot \mathbf{y}| + \|\mathbf{y}\|^2 \\
&\leqslant \|\mathbf{x}\|^2 + 2\|\mathbf{x}\| \|\mathbf{y}\| + \|\mathbf{y}\|^2 \quad \text{by (1.2.9)} \\
&= (\|\mathbf{x}\| + \|\mathbf{y}\|)^2.
\end{aligned}$$

Taking square roots on both sides, we obtain the Triangle Inequality.

A picture for the cases $\mathbb{R}^2$ and $\mathbb{R}^3$ shows why Theorem 1.2.11 is called the Triangle Inequality, for it is related to the property of triangles that the sum of the lengths $\|\mathbf{x}\|$ and $\|\mathbf{y}\|$ of two sides of a triangle is not smaller than the length $\|\mathbf{x} + \mathbf{y}\|$ of the third side. (See Fig. 1.1.)

1.2.13 *Corollary.* **[i]** *For any* $\mathbf{x}$ *and* $\mathbf{y}$ *in* $\mathbb{R}^m$

1.2.14
$$|\|\mathbf{x}\| - \|\mathbf{y}\|| \leqslant \|\mathbf{x} - \mathbf{y}\| \leqslant \|\mathbf{x}\| + \|\mathbf{y}\|.$$

[ii] *For any* n *vectors* $\mathbf{a}_1, \ldots, \mathbf{a}_n \in \mathbb{R}^m$ *and scalars* $x_1, \ldots, x_n \in \mathbb{R}$,

1.2.15
$$\|x_1 \mathbf{a}_1 + \cdots + x_n \mathbf{a}_n\| \leqslant |x_1| \|\mathbf{a}_1\| + \cdots + |x_n| \|\mathbf{a}_n\|.$$

[iii] *For any* $\mathbf{x} = (x_1, \ldots, x_m) \in \mathbb{R}^m$,

1.2.16
$$\|(x_1, \ldots, x_m)\| \leqslant |x_1| + \cdots + |x_m|.$$

Proof. Exercise.

The well-known cosine rule applied to the triangle OPR of Fig. 1.1 gives

$$\|\mathbf{x} + \mathbf{y}\|^2 = \|\mathbf{x}\|^2 + \|\mathbf{y}\|^2 + 2\|\mathbf{x}\| \|\mathbf{y}\| \cos \theta,$$

where θ is the angle between the non-zero vectors $\mathbf{x}$ and $\mathbf{y}$. Comparing this expression with 1.2.12 we obtain

$$\cos \theta = \frac{\mathbf{x} \cdot \mathbf{y}}{\|\mathbf{x}\| \|\mathbf{y}\|}.$$

In particular, the vector **x** is perpendicular (or orthogonal) to **y** if and only if $\mathbf{x} \cdot \mathbf{y} = 0$. The following generalization applies to $\mathbb{R}^m$.

1.2.17 Definition.   *The vector* $\mathbf{x} \in \mathbb{R}^m$ *is* orthogonal *to the vector* $\mathbf{y} \in \mathbb{R}^m$ *if and only if* $\mathbf{x} \cdot \mathbf{y} = 0$.

Note that by the symmetry of the dot product, **x** is orthogonal to **y** if and only if **y** is orthogonal to **x**.

1.2.18 Example.   *Equation of a plane in* $\mathbb{R}^3$. A plane in $\mathbb{R}^3$ is specified by a point $\mathbf{q} \in \mathbb{R}^3$ in the plane and a non-zero vector $\mathbf{n} \in \mathbb{R}^3$ perpendicular (or *normal*) to the plane.

The point $\mathbf{r} = (x, y, z) \in \mathbb{R}^3$ lies in the plane if and only if $\mathbf{r} - \mathbf{q}$ is orthogonal to **n**, that is, if and only if

1.2.19 $(\mathbf{r} - \mathbf{q}) \cdot \mathbf{n} = 0$.

Equation 1.2.19 is called the equation of the plane containing the point **q** and having normal **n**.

For example, the equation of the plane containing $\mathbf{q} = (1, 1, 1)$ with normal $\mathbf{n} = (2, 4, 6)$ is $(x, y, z) \cdot (2, 4, 6) = (1, 1, 1) \cdot (2, 4, 6)$, that is,

$$2x + 4y + 6z = 12.$$

The dot product is defined on vectors in $\mathbb{R}^m$, where m is arbitrary. The following vector product is defined in $\mathbb{R}^3$ only.

1.2.20 Definition.   *The* vector product *of* $\mathbf{b} = (b_1, b_2, b_3)$ *and* $\mathbf{c} = (c_1, c_2, c_3)$ *in* $\mathbb{R}^3$ *is the vector*

$$\mathbf{b} \wedge \mathbf{c} = (b_2 c_3 - b_3 c_2, b_3 c_1 - b_1 c_3, b_1 c_2 - b_2 c_1).$$

The formula for $\mathbf{b} \wedge \mathbf{c}$ is conveniently obtained by expanding the formal determinant

1.2.21 $\mathbf{b} \wedge \mathbf{c} = \begin{vmatrix} \mathbf{e}_1 & \mathbf{e}_2 & \mathbf{e}_3 \\ b_1 & b_2 & b_3 \\ c_1 & c_2 & c_3 \end{vmatrix}$,

where $\mathbf{e}_1, \mathbf{e}_2, \mathbf{e}_3$ is the standard basis of $\mathbb{R}^3$. An alternative common notation for the standard basis of $\mathbb{R}^3$ is $\mathbf{i} = (1, 0, 0), \mathbf{j} = (0, 1, 0)$, $\mathbf{k} = (0, 0, 1)$ and we shall use it occasionally.

We state the following standard results about the vector product without proof.

1.2.22 Theorem.   *Let* **b** *and* **c** *be vectors in* $\mathbb{R}^3$. *Then*
   [i] *the vector* $\mathbf{b} \wedge \mathbf{c}$ *is orthogonal to* **b** *and to* **c**;

[ii] **b** *and* **c** *are linearly dependent if and only if* $\mathbf{b} \wedge \mathbf{c} = \mathbf{0}$;

[iii] *if* **b** and **c** *are linearly independent then relative to a right-handed coordinate system of* $\mathbb{R}^3$ *the vectors* **b**,**c**, $\mathbf{b} \wedge \mathbf{c}$ *from a right-handed triple of vectors*;

[iv] $\|\mathbf{b} \wedge \mathbf{c}\| = \|\mathbf{b}\| \, \|\mathbf{c}\| \sin \phi$,

where ϕ *is the angle between* **b** *and* **c**. *Thus* $\|\mathbf{b} \wedge \mathbf{c}\|$ *measures the area of the parallelogram with* **b** *and* **c** *as adjacent sides.*

Exercises 1.2

1. Prove Corollary 1.2.13. (Hint: to prove the right-hand inequality 1.2.14 apply Theorem 1.2.11 to $\mathbf{x} + (-\mathbf{y})$; for the left-hand inequality put $\mathbf{x} - \mathbf{y} = \mathbf{z}$.)

2. (a) Prove that the zero vector in $\mathbb{R}^m$ is orthogonal to every vector $\mathbf{x} \in \mathbb{R}^m$.
    (b) Prove that if $\mathbf{x} \in \mathbb{R}^m$ is orthogonal to the vectors $\mathbf{y}_1, \ldots, \mathbf{y}_r$ in $\mathbb{R}^m$, then **x** is orthogonal to every vector in the subspace of $\mathbb{R}^m$ spanned by $\mathbf{y}_1, \ldots, \mathbf{y}_r$.

3. Find the angle between (a) the vectors $(1, -1, 0)$ and $(-4, 1, 1)$; (b) the vectors $(1, -1, 0)$ and $(4, -1, -1)$. Compare.

Answer: (a) $\cos \theta = -\frac{5}{6}$;   (b) $\cos \phi = \frac{5}{6}$. $\theta + \phi = \pi$.

4. Prove that vectors $\mathbf{x} - \mathbf{y}$ and $\mathbf{x} + \mathbf{y}$ in $\mathbb{R}^m$ are orthogonal if and only if $\|\mathbf{x}\| = \|\mathbf{y}\|$. Illustrate this result in $\mathbb{R}^2$, and deduce that the diagonals of a parallelogram intersect at right angles if and only if the parallelogram is a rhombus.

5. Find the equation of the plane in $\mathbb{R}^3$
    (a) containing the point $(1, -1, 1)$ and with normal $\mathbf{n} = (0, 1, 1)$;
    (b) containing the points $(1, 0, 1)$, $(0, 1, 1)$ and $(1, 1, 0)$.

Answers: (a) $y + z = -2$;   (b) $x + y + z = 2$.

6. Prove from the definition of the vector product that
    (a) $\mathbf{b} \wedge \mathbf{c} = -\mathbf{c} \wedge \mathbf{b}$;   (b) $\mathbf{a} \wedge (\mathbf{b} \wedge \mathbf{c}) = (\mathbf{a} \cdot \mathbf{c})\mathbf{b} - (\mathbf{a} \cdot \mathbf{b})\mathbf{c}$.

7. Find a vector orthogonal to both $\mathbf{a} = (1, -1, 2)$ and $\mathbf{b} = (2, 0, 1)$.

Answer: any scalar multiple of the vector product $\mathbf{a} \wedge \mathbf{b} = (-1, 3, 2)$.

1.3   Linear functions

1.3.1 *Definition.* *A* linear *function* $L : \mathbb{R}^m \to \mathbb{R}^n$ *with domain* $\mathbb{R}^m$ *and codomain* $\mathbb{R}^n$ *is a rule that assigns to each* $\mathbf{x} \in \mathbb{R}^m$ *a unique vector* $L(\mathbf{x}) \in \mathbb{R}^n$ *such that for any* $\mathbf{x}, \mathbf{y} \in \mathbb{R}^m$ *and* $k, l \in \mathbb{R}$,

1.3.2 $$L(k\mathbf{x} + l\mathbf{y}) = kL(\mathbf{x}) + lL(\mathbf{y}).$$

It follows from 1.3.2 (by induction on r) that for any $\mathbf{a}_1, \ldots, \mathbf{a}_r \in \mathbb{R}^m$ and $k_1, \ldots, k_r \in \mathbb{R}$,

1.3.3 $$L(k_1\mathbf{a}_1 + \cdots + k_r\mathbf{a}_r) = k_1 L(\mathbf{a}_1) + \cdots + k_r L(\mathbf{a}_r).$$

1.3.4 Theorem. *A linear function $L : \mathbb{R}^m \to \mathbb{R}^n$ is completely determined by its effect on the standard basis $\mathbf{e}_1, \ldots, \mathbf{e}_m$ of $\mathbb{R}^m$. Moreover, an arbitrary choice of vectors $L(\mathbf{e}_1), \ldots, L(\mathbf{e}_m)$ in $\mathbb{R}^n$ determines a linear function $L : \mathbb{R}^m \to \mathbb{R}^n$.*

Proof.   Choose $L(\mathbf{e}_i) \in \mathbb{R}^n$ for each $i = 1, \ldots, n$. Then for $\mathbf{x} = (x_1, \ldots, x_m) \in \mathbb{R}^m$,

$$
\begin{aligned}
L(\mathbf{x}) &= L(x_1\mathbf{e}_1 + \cdots + x_m\mathbf{e}_m) \\
&= x_1 L(\mathbf{e}_1) + \cdots + x_m L(\mathbf{e}_m), \qquad \text{by (1.3.3)}.
\end{aligned}
$$

Therefore the image under L of any $\mathbf{x} \in \mathbb{R}^m$ is known, and so L is completely determined.

Note that a linear function has a vector space $\mathbb{R}^m$ as its domain, whereas a non-linear function may be defined on a subset of $\mathbb{R}^m$. See, for example, 1.1.1.

The *image* of a function $L : \mathbb{R}^m \to \mathbb{R}^n$ is defined as the set of all image vectors:

1.3.5 $$\operatorname{im} L = \{L(\mathbf{x}) \in \mathbb{R}^n \mid \mathbf{x} \in \mathbb{R}^m\}.$$

We say that L maps $\mathbb{R}^m$ *onto* $\mathbb{R}^n$ if $\operatorname{im} L = \mathbb{R}^n$.

The *kernel* of $L : \mathbb{R}^m \to \mathbb{R}^n$ is defined as the set of all $\mathbf{x} \in \mathbb{R}^m$ that are mapped by L to zero:

1.3.6 $$\ker L = \{\mathbf{x} \in \mathbb{R}^m \mid L(\mathbf{x}) = \mathbf{0} \in \mathbb{R}^n\}.$$

When $L : \mathbb{R}^m \to \mathbb{R}^n$ is linear, then $\operatorname{im} L$ is a subspace of $\mathbb{R}^n$, $\ker L$ is a subspace of $\mathbb{R}^m$, and the dimensions of $\operatorname{im} L$ and $\ker L$ are related by the celebrated formula (which we leave unproved)

1.3.7 $$\dim \operatorname{im} L + \dim \ker L = \dim \mathbb{R}^m = m.$$

1.3.8 Definition. *A function f defined on a domain D is said to be 1–1 (one-to-one) on D if distinct elements of D have distinct images under f; that is if, for any $\mathbf{x} \in D$, $\mathbf{y} \in D$, $\mathbf{x} \neq \mathbf{y}$ implies that $f(\mathbf{x}) \neq f(\mathbf{y})$.*

1.3.9 Theorem. *A linear function $L : \mathbb{R}^m \to \mathbb{R}^n$ is 1–1 if and only if $\ker L = \{\mathbf{0}\}$.*

Proof. Exercise.

We shall require (in section 4.6) the following definition and result concerning a linear function $L : \mathbb{R}^n \to \mathbb{R}^n$ whose domain and co-domain are the same space $\mathbb{R}^n$.

1.3.10 Definition. *An* isomorphism *on $\mathbb{R}^n$ is a linear function $L : \mathbb{R}^n \to \mathbb{R}^n$ mapping $\mathbb{R}^n$ onto itself.*

1.3.11 Theorem. *A linear function $L : \mathbb{R}^n \to \mathbb{R}^n$ is an isomorphism on $\mathbb{R}^n$ if and only if L is 1–1.*

Proof. By Definition 1.3.10, L is an isomorphism on $\mathbb{R}^n$ if and only if $\operatorname{im} L = \mathbb{R}^n$. By 1.3.7 (applied to $\mathbb{R}^n$ as domain) this is so if and only if $\ker L = \{\mathbf{0}\}$. The theorem follows from Theorem 1.3.9.

We now outline the procedure for representing a linear function $L : \mathbb{R}^m \to \mathbb{R}^n$ by a matrix. By Theorem 1.3.4, the function L is determined by the images under L of the standard basis $\mathbf{e}_1, \dots, \mathbf{e}_m$ of its domain $\mathbb{R}^m$. We must avoid confusing the standard bases of $\mathbb{R}^m$ and of $\mathbb{R}^n$, so let us denote the standard basis of $\mathbb{R}^n$ by $\mathbf{e}_1^*, \dots, \mathbf{e}_n^*$. Suppose that for each $j = 1, \dots, m$,

$$L(\mathbf{e}_j) = a_{1j}\mathbf{e}_1^* + \cdots + a_{nj}\mathbf{e}_n^*, \qquad a_{ij} \in \mathbb{R}, \quad i = 1, \dots, n.$$

Then for any $\mathbf{x} = (x_1, \dots, x_m) \in \mathbb{R}^m$, if $L(\mathbf{x}) = \mathbf{y} = (y_1, \dots, y_n) \in \mathbb{R}^n$,

1.3.12
$$y_i = \sum_{j=1}^{m} a_{ij} x_j, \qquad i = 1, \dots, n.$$

Formula 1.3.12 is conveniently written in matrix form

1.3.13
$$\begin{bmatrix} y_1 \\ \vdots \\ y_n \end{bmatrix} = \begin{bmatrix} a_{11} & \cdots & a_{1m} \\ \vdots & & \vdots \\ a_{n1} & \cdots & a_{nm} \end{bmatrix} \begin{bmatrix} x_1 \\ \vdots \\ x_m \end{bmatrix},$$

the evaluation being performed by the usual matrix multiplication.

We say that a vector $\mathbf{z} = (z_1, \dots, z_q) \in \mathbb{R}^q$ is represented relative to the standard basis of $\mathbb{R}^q$ by the column ($q \times 1$ matrix)

$$[\mathbf{z}] = \begin{bmatrix} z_1 \\ \vdots \\ z_q \end{bmatrix}$$

and that the linear function $L : \mathbb{R}^m \to \mathbb{R}^n$ discussed above is represented relative to the standard bases of $\mathbb{R}^m$ and $\mathbb{R}^n$ by the $n \times m$ matrix

$$[L] = A = \begin{bmatrix} a_{11} & \cdots & a_{1m} \\ \vdots & & \\ a_{n1} & \cdots & a_{nm} \end{bmatrix}.$$

Then the matrix representation 1.3.13 of the relation $\mathbf{y} = L(\mathbf{x})$ can be expressed in the form

1.3.14 $[\mathbf{y}] = A[\mathbf{x}],$

the evaluation being performed by the usual matrix multiplication. The matrix A is sometimes denoted by its general term: $A = [a_{ij}]$.

Note that the columns of the matrix $[L]$ are simply the representatives of $L(\mathbf{e}_1), \ldots, L(\mathbf{e}_m)$ relative to the standard basis of $\mathbb{R}^n$.

1.3.15 *Example.* The linear function $L : \mathbb{R}^3 \to \mathbb{R}^2$ specified by

$$L(1, 0, 0) = (2, 0), L(0, 1, 0) = (-1, 3), L(0, 0, 1) = (0, 2)$$

is represented relative to the standard bases of $\mathbb{R}^3$ and $\mathbb{R}^2$ by the 2×3 matrix

$$A = \begin{bmatrix} 2 & -1 & 0 \\ 0 & 3 & 2 \end{bmatrix}.$$

By the linearity of L we have

1.3.16 $(y_1, y_2) = L(x_1, x_2, x_3) = (2x_1 - x_2, 3x_2 + 2x_3).$

The relation 1.3.16 is conveniently remembered in the form 1.3.14.

1.3.17 *Example.* The identity function $\mathbf{l} : \mathbb{R}^n \to \mathbb{R}^n$ defined by

$$\mathbf{l}(\mathbf{x}) = \mathbf{x}, \qquad \mathbf{x} \in \mathbb{R}^n$$

is a linear function. We denote the matrix representing it by I.

Given linear functions $L : \mathbb{R}^m \to \mathbb{R}^n$ and $M : \mathbb{R}^n \to \mathbb{R}^q$, the composite function $(M \circ L) : \mathbb{R}^m \to \mathbb{R}^q$ is defined by the rule

1.3.18 $(M \circ L)(\mathbf{x}) = M(L(\mathbf{x})), \qquad \mathbf{x} \in \mathbb{R}^m.$

The $q \times m$ matrix representing $M \circ L$ relative to the standard bases of $\mathbb{R}^m$ and $\mathbb{R}^q$ is given by the matrix product

1.3.19 $[M \circ L] = [M][L],$

which is evaluated in the usual way.

Exercises 1.3

1. (a)   Which of the following functions $f : \mathbb{R}^3 \to \mathbb{R}^2$ are linear? If non-linear, demonstrate a breakdown of the conditions 1.3.2 or 1.3.3.

    (i) $f(x_1, x_2, x_3) = (3x_1 - x_3, x_1 + x_3)$;
    (ii) $f(x_1, x_2, x_3) = (x_1^2 - x_2, x_2 + x_3)$;
    (iii) $f(x_1, x_2, x_3) = (\sin(x_1 x_2 x_3), 0)$.

Answers: Only (i) is linear. (ii) $f(\mathbf{e}_1 + \mathbf{e}_1) \neq f(\mathbf{e}_1) + f(\mathbf{e}_1)$.
    (iii) $f(\mathbf{e}_1 + \mathbf{e}_2 + \mathbf{e}_3) \neq f(\mathbf{e}_1) + f(\mathbf{e}_2) + f(\mathbf{e}_3)$.

    (b)   Prove that a transformation $f : \mathbb{R}^3 \to \mathbb{R}^2$ is linear if and only if there exist $a_{ij} \in \mathbb{R}$, $i = 1, 2$, and $j = 1, 2, 3$, such that, for all $(x_1, x_2, x_3) \in \mathbb{R}^3$

$$f(x_1, x_2, x_3) = (a_{11}x_1 + a_{12}x_2 + a_{13}x_3, a_{21}x_1 + a_{22}x_2 + a_{23}x_3).$$

2. Let $L : \mathbb{R}^m \to \mathbb{R}^n$ be a linear function. Prove that $\ker L$ is a subspace of $\mathbb{R}^m$ and that $\operatorname{im} L$ is a subspace of $\mathbb{R}^n$.

3. A linear function $L : \mathbb{R}^4 \to \mathbb{R}^3$ is defined by the rule

$$L(x_1, x_2, x_3, x_4)$$
$$= (x_1 + 2x_2 - 2x_4, x_3 + x_4, x_1 + 2x_2 + x_3 - x_4).$$

    (a)   Write down the 3×4 matrix A representing L relative to the standard bases of $\mathbb{R}^4$ and $\mathbb{R}^3$.
    (b)   Calculate $\operatorname{im} L$. (*Hint*: $\operatorname{im} L$ is spanned by $L(\mathbf{e}_j), j = 1, 2, 3, 4$.)
    (c)   Calculate $\ker L$.
    (d)   Verify that $\dim \operatorname{im} L + \dim \ker L = 4$.

Answers: (a) $A = \begin{bmatrix} 1 & 2 & 0 & -2 \\ 0 & 0 & 1 & 1 \\ 1 & 2 & 1 & -1 \end{bmatrix}$,

    (b) $\operatorname{im} L = \operatorname{span} \{(1, 0, 1), (0, 1, 1)\} \subseteq \mathbb{R}^3$.
    This can be read off from the first and third columns of A, which represent $L(\mathbf{e}_1)$ and $L(\mathbf{e}_3)$. It will be seen that $L(\mathbf{e}_2) = 2L(\mathbf{e}_1)$ and $L(\mathbf{e}_4) = -2L(\mathbf{e}_1) + L(\mathbf{e}_3)$; (c) $\ker L = \operatorname{span} \{(2, 0, -1, 1), (-2, 1, 0, 0)\} \subseteq \mathbb{R}^4$.

4. Prove that if $L : \mathbb{R} \to \mathbb{R}^n$ is a linear function, then there exists a vector $\mathbf{c} \in \mathbb{R}^n$ such that $L(t) = t\mathbf{c}$ for all $t \in \mathbb{R}$.
    Hint: consider $L(1)$.

5. Prove that a linear function $L : \mathbb{R}^m \to \mathbb{R}^n$ is 1–1 if and only if $\ker L = \{\mathbf{0}\}$.
    Hint: If L is linear, then $L(\mathbf{x}) = L(\mathbf{y})$ if and only if $L(\mathbf{x} - \mathbf{y}) = \mathbf{0}$.

1.4   Quadratic forms

The material in this section is used in Section 3.12. We do little more than state the required results. Familiarity with diagonalizing a symmetric matrix is assumed.

1.4.1 Definition.   *A function $q : \mathbb{R}^m \to \mathbb{R}$ is called a* quadratic form *on $\mathbb{R}^m$ if there exists an $m \times m$ real symmetric matrix $A = [a_{ij}]$ (so $a_{ij} = a_{ji}$, for all $i, j = 1, \ldots, m$) such that*

1.4.2 $q(\mathbf{h}) = [\mathbf{h}]^t A [\mathbf{h}]$ $\mathbf{h} \in \mathbb{R}^m$

(evaluated using matrix multiplication), where $[\mathbf{h}]^t$ denotes the transpose of $[\mathbf{h}]$. We call q the quadratic form corresponding to the symmetric matrix A.

Multiplying out 1.4.2, we obtain the *quadratic polynomial*

$$q(\mathbf{h}) = \sum_{i=1}^{m} \sum_{j=1}^{m} a_{ij} h_i h_j = a_{11} h_1^2 + 2a_{12} h_1 h_2 + \cdots.$$

1.4.3 Example.   The quadratic form $q : \mathbb{R}^3 \to \mathbb{R}$ given by

$$q(\mathbf{h}) = -h_1^2 + 2h_2^2 - h_3^2 + 4h_1 h_2 + 8h_1 h_3 - 4h_2 h_3$$

corresponds to the symmetric matrix

$$A = \begin{bmatrix} -1 & 2 & 4 \\ 2 & 2 & -2 \\ 4 & -2 & -1 \end{bmatrix}.$$

1.4.4 Definition.   *A quadratic form q on $\mathbb{R}^m$ is (i)* positive definite, *(ii)* negative definite, *(iii)* indefinite *if*
   [i] $q(\mathbf{h}) > 0$ *for all $\mathbf{h} \in \mathbb{R}^m$, $\mathbf{h} \neq \mathbf{0}$,*
   [ii] $q(\mathbf{h}) < 0$ *for all $\mathbf{h} \in \mathbb{R}^m$, $\mathbf{h} \neq \mathbf{0}$,*
   [iii] $q(\mathbf{h})$ *takes both positive and negative values.*

We also say that a real symmetric matrix A is positive definite, negative definite or indefinite if the quadratic form corresponding to A has this property.

1.4.5 Example.   The quadratic form of Example 1.4.3 is indefinite, since $q(\mathbf{h}) = 27$ when $\mathbf{h} = (1, -2, 2)$ and $q(\mathbf{h}) = -54$ when $\mathbf{h} = (-2, 1, 2)$.

The following theorem provides the machinery for determining the nature of quadratic forms.

1.4.6 Theorem.   *Let A be an $m \times m$ real symmetric matrix. Then*

[i]   *the eigenvalues* $\lambda_1, \ldots, \lambda_m$ *of A are real;*

[ii]   *there exist pairwise orthogonal unit vectors* $\mathbf{c}_1, \ldots, \mathbf{c}_m$ *in* $\mathbb{R}^m$ *such that* $A[\mathbf{c}_i] = \lambda_i[\mathbf{c}_i]$, $i = 1, \ldots, m$;

[iii]   *if C is the* $m \times m$ *matrix whose columns are* $[\mathbf{c}_1], \ldots, [\mathbf{c}_m]$, *then C is orthogonal (that is,* $C^t = C^{-1}$) *and*

1.4.7
$$C^t A C = \begin{bmatrix} \lambda_1 & & 0 \\ & \vdots & \\ 0 & & \lambda_m \end{bmatrix}.$$

[iv]   *If* λ_{min} *and* λ_{max} *are the minimum and the maximum eigenvalues of A, then*

1.4.8 $\|\mathbf{h}\|^2 \lambda_{min} \leqslant [\mathbf{h}]^t A [\mathbf{h}] \leqslant \|\mathbf{h}\|^2 \lambda_{max}$, $\mathbf{h} \in \mathbb{R}^m$.

A proof of parts (i)–(iii) will be found in most textbooks on linear algebra.

Proof of part (iv).   Put $[\mathbf{h}] = C[\mathbf{k}]$. Then

1.4.9
$$\begin{cases} [\mathbf{h}]^t A [\mathbf{h}] = [\mathbf{k}]^t C^t A C [\mathbf{k}] = \lambda_1 k_1^2 + \cdots + \lambda_m k_m^2, \\ \|\mathbf{k}\|^2 = [\mathbf{h}]^t C^t C [\mathbf{h}] = [\mathbf{h}]^t [\mathbf{h}] = \|\mathbf{h}\|^2. \end{cases}$$

Now,

$$\|\mathbf{k}\|^2 \lambda_{min} = (k_1^2 + \cdots + k_m^2)\lambda_{min} \leqslant \lambda_1 k_1^2 + \cdots + \lambda_m k_m^2 \leqslant \|\mathbf{k}\|^2 \lambda_{max}.$$

The inequality 1.4.8 follows from 1.4.9.

1.4.10 *Example.* Consider the matrix A of Example 1.4.3. It will be found that the eigenvalues of A are 3, 3, -6 (solve the determinantal equation $\det(A - tI) = 0$) and that the orthogonal matrix

$$C = \frac{1}{3}\begin{bmatrix} 1 & 2 & -2 \\ -2 & 2 & 1 \\ 2 & 1 & 2 \end{bmatrix} \quad \text{is such that} \quad C^t A C = \begin{bmatrix} 3 & 0 & 0 \\ 0 & 3 & 0 \\ 0 & 0 & -6 \end{bmatrix}.$$

It follows that

1.4.11 $[\mathbf{h}]^t A [\mathbf{h}] = 3k_1^2 + 3k_2^2 - 6k_3^2$,   where $[\mathbf{h}] = C[\mathbf{k}]$.

The inequality 1.4.8 becomes

$$-6\|\mathbf{h}\|^2 \leqslant [\mathbf{h}]^t A [\mathbf{h}] \leqslant 3\|\mathbf{h}\|^2.$$

The formula 1.4.11 is useful in obtaining values of $\mathbf{h}$ for which $[\mathbf{h}]^t A [\mathbf{h}]$ takes a prescribed value. For example it is clear from 1.4.11 that $[\mathbf{h}]^t A [\mathbf{h}]$ takes the value -54 when $k_1 = k_2 = 0$, $k_3 = 3$. The corresponding value of $\mathbf{h}$

is given by

$$\begin{bmatrix} h_1 \\ h_2 \\ h_3 \end{bmatrix} = C \begin{bmatrix} 0 \\ 0 \\ 3 \end{bmatrix} = \begin{bmatrix} -2 \\ 1 \\ 2 \end{bmatrix}.$$

This calculation was used in Example 1.4.5.

1.4.12 Theorem. *The real symmetric matrix A is* [i] *positive definite,* [ii] *negative definite,* [iii] *indefinite if and only if the eigenvalues of A are* [i] *all positive,* [ii] *all negative,* [iii] *some positive and some negative.*

Proof.   Apply 1.4.9.

Exercises 1.4

1. Decide whether the following matrices are positive definite, negative definite or indefinite.

(a) $\begin{bmatrix} 2 & 1 & 0 \\ 1 & 2 & 0 \\ 0 & 0 & 2 \end{bmatrix}$,   (b) $\begin{bmatrix} 0 & 1 & 2 \\ 1 & 0 & 2 \\ 2 & 2 & 0 \end{bmatrix}$,   (c) $\begin{bmatrix} 0 & -1 & -1 \\ -1 & 0 & 0 \\ -1 & 0 & 0 \end{bmatrix}$,

(d) $\begin{bmatrix} -5 & 2 \\ 2 & -2 \end{bmatrix}$.

Answers: (a) positive-definite;   (b) indefinite;   (c) indefinite;
(d) negative-definite.

2. Let A be an $m \times m$ real symmetric matrix with eigenvalues $\lambda_1, \ldots, \lambda_m$. Prove that the determinant of A is equal to the product of its eigenvalues: $\det A = \lambda_1 \cdots \lambda_m$.

Hint: apply Theorem 1.4.6(iii).

3. A quadratic form $q : \mathbb{R}^m \to \mathbb{R}$ and its associated symmetric matrix A are said to be *positive semi-definite* (*negative semi-definite*) if $q(\mathbf{h}) \geqslant 0$ ($q(\mathbf{h}) \leqslant 0$) for all $\mathbf{h} \in \mathbb{R}^m$, but there exists $\mathbf{h} \neq \mathbf{0}$ such that $q(\mathbf{h}) = 0$.

Prove that q is positive semi-definite (negative semi-definite) if and only if the eigenvalues of the associated matrix A are all non-negative (non-positive) and at least one is zero.

Show that the symmetric matrix

$$A = \begin{bmatrix} 3 & -2 & 2 \\ -2 & 4 & 0 \\ 2 & 0 & 2 \end{bmatrix}$$

is positive semi-definite. Find $\mathbf{h} \neq \mathbf{0}$ such that $[\mathbf{h}]^t A [\mathbf{h}] = 0$.

Answer: $\mathbf{h} = (2, 1, -2)$, for example.

1.5 Functions from $\mathbb{R}^m$ to $\mathbb{R}^n$. Definitions and notation

In this section we collect together various definitions and notation that we shall require later in the book.

We shall be concerned with functions $f : D \subseteq \mathbb{R}^m \to \mathbb{R}^n$, where the domain D of f is a subset of $\mathbb{R}^m$. The *image* of f is the subset of the codomain $\mathbb{R}^n$ consisting of all vectors $f(\mathbf{x})$, $\mathbf{x} \in D$. We denote the image of f by $f(D)$.

In Chapter 2, where we consider functions $f : D \subseteq \mathbb{R} \to \mathbb{R}^n$, the domain D of f is usually taken to be an interval in $\mathbb{R}$. An *open interval* in $\mathbb{R}$ is of one of the following forms:

$$] - \infty, a[, \qquad]a, b[, \qquad]b, \infty[\qquad \text{and} \qquad \mathbb{R},$$

where, for example, $]a, b[= \{t \in \mathbb{R} | a < t < b\}$. A *closed interval* has the form

$$] - \infty, a], \qquad [a, b], \qquad [b, \infty[\qquad \text{and} \qquad \mathbb{R},$$

where, for example, $[a, b] = \{t \in \mathbb{R} | a \leqslant t \leqslant b\}$. The half-open intervals $]a, b]$ and $[a, b[$ are defined similarly. In later chapters we study functions whose domains are subsets of $\mathbb{R}^m$, $m \geqslant 2$. The most usual domains then are *open sets*. These are defined in Section 3.2. The domain of a function is often conveniently expressed as a Cartesian product. Given $A \subseteq \mathbb{R}^p$, $B \subseteq \mathbb{R}^q$, the *Cartesian product* of A and B is the set

$$A \times B = \{(\mathbf{a}, \mathbf{b}) \in \mathbb{R}^{p + q} | \mathbf{a} \in A, \mathbf{b} \in B\}.$$

1.5.1 *Example.* [i] $\mathbb{R} \times \mathbb{R} = \mathbb{R}^2$, and more generally $\mathbb{R}^p \times \mathbb{R}^q = \mathbb{R}^{p + q}$

[ii] The set D given by 1.1.2 is equal to $\mathbb{R}^2 \times [-1, 1]$.

1.5.2 *Definition.* *Corresponding to any function $f : D \subseteq \mathbb{R}^m \to \mathbb{R}^n$ we define* coordinate functions $f_i : D \subseteq \mathbb{R}^m \to \mathbb{R}$, $i = 1, \ldots, n$ *by means of the expression*

$$f(\mathbf{x}) = (f_1(\mathbf{x}), \ldots, f_n(\mathbf{x})), \qquad \mathbf{x} \in \mathbb{R}^m.$$

1.5.3 *Example.* The coordinate functions of $f : \mathbb{R}^3 \to \mathbb{R}^2$ given by $f(x_1, x_2, x_3) = (x_1 x_2, x_2 x_3)$ are $f_i : \mathbb{R}^3 \to \mathbb{R}$, $i = 1, 2$, where

$$f_1(x_1, x_2, x_3) = x_1 x_2, \qquad f_2(x_1, x_2, x_3) = x_2 x_3.$$

The following definition gives a number of important ways of combining functions.

1.5.4 Definition.   Given $f : D \subseteq \mathbb{R}^m \to \mathbb{R}^n$, $g : D \subseteq \mathbb{R}^m \to \mathbb{R}^n$ and $\phi : D \subseteq \mathbb{R}^m \to \mathbb{R}$, we define

[i]   the sum and difference functions $f \pm g : D \subseteq \mathbb{R}^m \to \mathbb{R}^n$ by

$$(f + g)(\mathbf{x}) = f(\mathbf{x}) \pm g(\mathbf{x}), \qquad \mathbf{x} \in D;$$

[ii]   the product $\phi f : D \subseteq \mathbb{R}^m \to \mathbb{R}^n$ by

$$(\phi f)(\mathbf{x}) = \phi(\mathbf{x})f(\mathbf{x}) = (\phi(\mathbf{x})f_1(\mathbf{x}), \dots, \phi(\mathbf{x})f_n(\mathbf{x})), \qquad \mathbf{x} \in D;$$

[iii]   the dot product $f \cdot g : D \subseteq \mathbb{R}^m \to \mathbb{R}$ by

$$(f \cdot g)(\mathbf{x}) = f_1(\mathbf{x})g_1(\mathbf{x}) + \cdots + f_n(\mathbf{x})g_n(\mathbf{x}), \qquad \mathbf{x} \in D,$$

where $f_i : D \subseteq \mathbb{R}^m \to \mathbb{R}$ and $g_i : D \subseteq \mathbb{R}^m \to \mathbb{R}$, $i = 1, \dots, n$ are the coordinate functions of f and g;

[iv] for the case $f : D \subseteq \mathbb{R}^m \to \mathbb{R}^3$, $g : D \subseteq \mathbb{R}^m \to \mathbb{R}^3$, the vector product function $h = f \wedge g : D \subseteq \mathbb{R}^m \to \mathbb{R}^3$ by its coordinate functions

$$h_1 = f_2 g_3 - f_3 g_2, \qquad h_2 = f_3 g_1 - f_1 g_3, \qquad h_3 = f_1 g_2 - f_2 g_1.$$

1.5.5 Example.   Given $f : \mathbb{R}^2 \to \mathbb{R}^3$ and $g : \mathbb{R}^2 \to \mathbb{R}^3$ such that

$$f(x, y) = (x, y, xy) \quad and \quad g(x, y) = (-y, x, 0), \qquad (x, y) \in \mathbb{R}^2$$

then

$$(f \cdot g)(x, y) = -xy + yx + 0 = 0$$

and

$$(f \wedge g)(x, y) = (0 - x^2 y, -xy^2 - 0, x^2 + y^2)$$
$$= (-x^2 y, -xy^2, x^2 + y^2).$$

1.5.6 Definition.   Let $g : E \subseteq \mathbb{R}^l \to \mathbb{R}^m$ and $f : D \subseteq \mathbb{R}^m \to \mathbb{R}^n$ be such that the domain D of f contains the image $g(E)$ of g. The composite function $f \circ g : E \subseteq \mathbb{R}^l \to \mathbb{R}^n$ is defined by

$$(f \circ g)(\mathbf{x}) = f(g(\mathbf{x})), \qquad \mathbf{x} \in E.$$

1.5.7 Example.   Define functions $g : \mathbb{R}^3 \to \mathbb{R}^2$ and $f : \mathbb{R}^2 \to \mathbb{R}^2$ by

$$g(t_1, t_2, t_3) = (t_1 t_2, t_2 t_3) \qquad (t_1, t_2, t_3) \in \mathbb{R}^3,$$
$$f(x_1, x_2) = (\sin x_1, x_1 x_2) \qquad (x_1, x_2) \in \mathbb{R}^2.$$

Then

$$(f \circ g)(t_1, t_2, t_3) = (\sin(t_1 t_2), t_1 t_2^2 t_3).$$

We conclude with a short list describing further notation used in the book.

$\mathbb{N}, \mathbb{Z}$ the natural numbers, integers

$A\backslash B$ $\{x \in A \mid x \notin B\}$

$f : U \to V$ function on domain U, codomain V,
            with $f(U) \subseteq V$.

$\mathbb{R}^+, \mathbb{R}^-$ positive, negative real numbers.

Exercises 1.5

1. Let $f_i : D \subseteq \mathbb{R}^m \to \mathbb{R}$, $i = 1, \ldots, n$ be the coordinate functions of the function $f : D \subseteq \mathbb{R}^m \to \mathbb{R}^n$. Prove that

    $$f_i(\mathbf{x}) = f(\mathbf{x}) \cdot \mathbf{e}_i, \qquad \mathbf{x} \in \mathbb{R}^m, \quad i = 1, \ldots, n,$$

    where $\mathbf{e}_1, \ldots, \mathbf{e}_n$ is the standard basis of $\mathbb{R}^n$. By way of illustration consider Example 1.5.3.

2. Let $f : \mathbb{R}^3 \to \mathbb{R}^3$ and $g : \mathbb{R}^3 \to \mathbb{R}^3$ be defined by

    $$f(x_1, x_2, x_3) = (x_2, -x_3, x_1),$$
    $$g(x_1, x_2, x_3) = (x_1 x_3, x_1 x_2, x_2 x_3).$$

    Determine the functions $f \cdot g$, $f \wedge g$, $g \wedge f$, $f \circ g$ and $g \circ f$. (Note that $f \circ g$ and $g \circ f$ are both defined. In Example 1.5.7 this is not the case.)

Answers: $(f \cdot g)(\mathbf{x}) = x_1 x_2 x_3$;
    $(f \wedge g)(\mathbf{x}) = (-x_2(x_1^2 + x_3^2), x_3(x_1^2 - x_2^2), x_1(x_2^2 + x_3^2))$;
    $g \wedge f = -f \wedge g$; $(f \circ g)(t_1, t_2, t_3) = (t_1 t_2, -t_2 t_3, t_1 t_3)$;
    $(g \circ f)(t_1, t_2, t_3) = (t_1 t_2, -t_2 t_3, -t_1 t_3)$.

1.6   Elementary real analysis and calculus

In this section we summarize the material from elementary analysis on which we base our generalizations. Proofs can be found, for example, in *Elementary Mathematical Analysis* by Iain T. Adamson.

1.6.1 Definition.   *A set E of real numbers is* bounded above (below) *if there exists $b \in \mathbb{R}$ such that $b \geqslant x$ ($b \leqslant x$) for all $x \in E$. The smallest (largest) number b with this property is called the* least upper bound *of E (greatest lower bound of E).*

1.6.2 Example.   The open interval $D =]-\infty, 5[$ is bounded above but not below. Its least upper bound is 5. Note that $5 \notin D$. In general, an interval is open if and only if it contains neither its greatest lower bound nor its least upper bound (if these exist).

We next consider sequences $a_1, a_2, a_3, \ldots$ of real numbers, which we denote in short by (a_k).

1.6.3 Definition. [i] *The sequence (a_k) of real numbers* converges *to $a \in \mathbb{R}$ if to each $\varepsilon > 0$ there corresponds $N \in \mathbb{N}$ such that*

$$|a_k - a| < \varepsilon \quad \text{whenever} \quad k > N.$$

In this case we write $a_k \to a$ and also $\lim_{k \to \infty} a_k = a$.
[ii] *The sequence (a_k) of real numbers is a* Cauchy *sequence if to each $\varepsilon > 0$ there corresponds $N \in \mathbb{N}$ such that*

$$|a_k - a_l| < \varepsilon \quad \text{whenever} \quad k, l > N.$$

1.6.4 Theorem.   *A Cauchy sequence is convergent.*

An interval in $\mathbb{R}$ is said to be *compact* if it is closed and bounded. Thus the compact intervals are of the form $[a, b]$.

1.6.5 Theorem. (*Bolzano–Weierstrass*) *Every sequence of real numbers in a compact interval $[a, b]$ has a subsequence that converges to a limit in $[a, b]$.*

We shall find that functions which are 1–1 on their domains play an important role in vector calculus. Suppose that $f : D \subseteq \mathbb{R}^m \to \mathbb{R}^n$ is 1–1 on D. Then we can define a (unique) function $g : f(D) \to D$ which reverses the effect of f, by the rule

$$g(f(\mathbf{x})) = \mathbf{x}, \qquad f(\mathbf{x}) \in f(D).$$

Thus if f maps $\mathbf{x}$ to $\mathbf{y}$ then g maps $\mathbf{y}$ back to $\mathbf{x}$. The function g is called the *inverse* of f and the function f is said to be *invertible*. For example, the function $f : [-1, 0] \subseteq \mathbb{R} \to \mathbb{R}$ given by the rule

$$f(x) = x^2, \qquad x \in [-1, 0]$$

is invertible, and the inverse function is $g : [0, 1] \to [-1, 0]$, where

$$g(y) = -\sqrt{y}, \qquad y \in [0, 1].$$

In contrast, the rule $f(x) = x^2$, $x \in [-1, 1]$ does not define an invertible function, since f is not 1–1 on the extended domain. Note that if f is invertible (on its domain) then the inverse function g is also invertible and the inverse of g is f.

We shall study inverse functions in some detail in Sections 4.5 and 4.6. The following results are needed for applications in Chapter 2.

1.6.6 *Definition.* Let D be an interval in $\mathbb{R}$. A function $f : D \subseteq \mathbb{R} \to \mathbb{R}$ is strictly increasing (strictly decreasing) if $f(b) > f(a)$ $(f(b) < f(a))$ whenever $b > a$, where $a, b \in D$. A function is strictly monotone if it is either strictly increasing or strictly decreasing.

1.6.7 *Theorem.* Let $f : D \subseteq \mathbb{R} \to \mathbb{R}$ be a differentiable function on an interval D such that f has positive (negative) derivative throughout D. Then f is 1–1 and strictly increasing (strictly decreasing). Its inverse function $f^{-1} : f(D) \subseteq \mathbb{R} \to \mathbb{R}$ is also differentiable and has positive (negative) derivative throughout $f(D)$.

Our next results concern continuity and differentiability. These concepts are defined for functions $f : D \subseteq \mathbb{R} \to \mathbb{R}^n$ in Chapter 2. We will require the following classical theorems about real-valued functions.

1.6.8 *The Intermediate Value Theorem.* Let $f : [a, b] \subseteq \mathbb{R} \to \mathbb{R}$ be a continuous function. If t is any point between the points $f(a)$ and $f(b)$ then there exists a point $x \in [a,b]$ such that $f(x) = t$.

1.6.9 *The Mean-Value Theorem.* Let p and $h > 0$ be real numbers, and suppose that $f : [p, p+h] \to \mathbb{R}$ is a real-valued function such that (a) f is continuous on $[p, p+h]$, and (b) f is differentiable at every point of the open interval $]p, p+h[$. Then there exists a point c in the open interval $]p, p+h[$ such that

$$f(p+h) = f(p) + hf'(c).$$

1.6.10 *The Generalized Mean-Value Theorem* (Taylor's Theorem). Let $f : D \subseteq \mathbb{R} \to \mathbb{R}$ be a real-valued function on an open interval D in $\mathbb{R}$, and suppose that f is n times differentiable at every point of D. If p and $p+h$ are points of D, then there exists in D a point $c = p + \theta h$, $0 < \theta < 1$, such that

$$f(p+h) = f(p) + hf'(p) + \frac{h^2}{2!}f''(p) + \cdots$$

$$+ \frac{h^{n-1}}{(n-1)!}f^{(n-1)}(p) + \frac{h^n}{n!}f^{(n)}(c).$$

1.6.11 *Theorem.* The Chain Rule. Let $g : E \subseteq \mathbb{R} \to \mathbb{R}$ and $f : D \subseteq \mathbb{R} \to \mathbb{R}$ be defined on open intervals E and D such that $g(E) \subseteq D$.

Suppose that g is differentiable at $a \in E$ and that f is differentiable at $g(a) \in D$. Then the composite function $F = f \circ g : E \subseteq \mathbb{R} \to \mathbb{R}$ is differentiable at $a \in E$ and

$$F'(a) = (f \circ g)'(a) = f'(g(a))g'(a).$$

1.6.12 Remark. The Chain Rule is sometimes presented in the following form 1.6.13, which is easily remembered but lacks the precision of the above statement of the rule. In the expression

$$F(t) = (f \circ g)(t) = f(g(t)), \qquad t \in E,$$

put $u = g(t)$. Then $F(t) = f(u)$ and

1.6.13
$$\frac{\mathrm{d}F}{\mathrm{d}t} = \frac{\mathrm{d}f}{\mathrm{d}u}\frac{\mathrm{d}u}{\mathrm{d}t}.$$

1.6.14 Example. Consider the function $F : \mathbb{R} \to \mathbb{R}$ defined by $F(t) = \sin(t^2)$, $t \in \mathbb{R}$. Then $F = f \circ g$, where $f(u) = \sin u$ and $g(t) = t^2$. By the Chain Rule

$$F'(a) = \cos(g(a))2a = 2a\cos(a^2).$$

Alternatively, Formula 1.6.13 can be applied by putting $u = t^2$ and $f(u) = \sin u$.

We shall need the following two classical theorems of elementary calculus.

1.6.15 The Fundamental Theorem of Calculus. *Let $f : [p, q] \subseteq \mathbb{R} \to \mathbb{R}$ be such that the derivative f' is continuous. Then*

$$\int_p^q f'(x)\mathrm{d}x = f(q) - f(p).$$

1.6.16 The Integral Mean-Value Theorem. *If $f : [a, b] \subseteq \mathbb{R} \to \mathbb{R}$ is continuous then there exists $\xi \in]a, b[$ such that*

$$\int_a^b f(x)\mathrm{d}x = (b - a)f(\xi).$$

The concept of uniform continuity is also important. Specifically we shall require the following result and its generalization.

1.6.17 Definition. *A function $f : D \subset \mathbb{R} \to \mathbb{R}$ is uniformly continuous on D if to each $\varepsilon > 0$ there corresponds $\delta > 0$ (depending only on ε) such* *that*

$$|f(t) - f(s)| < \varepsilon \quad \text{whenever} \quad |t - s| < \delta, \quad t, s \in D.$$

1.6.18 Theorem. *A function $f : [a, b] \subseteq \mathbb{R} \to \mathbb{R}$ which is continuous on the closed bounded interval $[a, b]$ is uniformly continuous on $[a, b]$.*

We shall use the following well-known comparison theorem.

1.6.19 Theorem. *Let $g : [c, d] \subseteq \mathbb{R} \to \mathbb{R}$ be a bounded function and suppose that $m \leqslant g(y) \leqslant M$ for all $y \in [c, d]$. If g is integrable over $[c, d]$, then*

$$m(d - c) \leqslant \int_c^d g(y)\mathrm{d}y \leqslant M(d - c).$$

Exercises 1.6

1. Prove that (a) $\lim_{k \to \infty} (1/k)\sin k = 0$;   (b) $\lim_{k \to \infty} k\sin(1/k) = 1$.

2. Prove that if (a_k) and (b_k) are convergent sequences of real numbers such that $a_k \to a$ and $b_k \to b$, then the sequences $(a_k + b_k)$ and $(a_k b_k)$ are convergent and $a_k + b_k \to a + b$, $a_k b_k \to ab$.

   Suppose $b_k \neq 0$ for all $k \in \mathbb{N}$. What can you say about the sequence (a_k/b_k)?

   Hint: Consider for example the sequences (b_k) where
   (a) $b_k = (1 + k)/k$ and (b) $b_k = 1/k$.

3. Suppose that $f :]a, b[\subseteq \mathbb{R} \to \mathbb{R}$ is differentiable, and $f'(x) = 0$ for all $x \in]a, b[$. Prove that f is constant on $]a, b[$.

   Hint: take $p, q \in]a, b[$ and use the Mean Value Theorem to prove that $f(p) = f(q)$.

4. Prove that when $a > 0$ and $|h| < a, \sqrt{(a^2 + h)}$ differs from $a + \frac{1}{2}(h/a)$ by an amount less than $h^2/8a^3$. Show in particular that

   $$10.392 < \sqrt{108} < 10.400.$$

   Hint: Apply Taylor's Theorem.

5. Apply the Chain Rule to find $F'(\pi)$, given that

   $$F(t) = (\sin t)^2 + e^{\sin t}, \qquad t \in \mathbb{R}.$$

   Answer: -1.

6. Let $f :]0, 1[\subseteq \mathbb{R} \to \mathbb{R}$ be defined by $f(t) = 1/t, t \in]0, 1[$.
   (a) Prove that f is continuous at every point $p \in]0, 1[$. (Show that given

$\varepsilon > 0$, however small, there exists $\delta > 0$ such that $|f(t) - f(p)| < \varepsilon$ whenever $t \in]0, 1[$ and $|t - p| < \delta$.)

(b)   Prove that f is not uniformly continuous on $]0, 1[$.

Answer: for a given $\varepsilon > 0$, the choice of δ in part (a) depends on the point p. A possible choice is, for example, $\delta = \min\{\frac{1}{2}p, \frac{1}{2}\varepsilon p^2\}$, for then if $|t - p| < \delta$ it follows that $t > \frac{1}{2}p$ and

$$|f(t) - f(p)| = |t - p|/|tp| < \tfrac{1}{2}\varepsilon p^2 / \tfrac{1}{2}p^2 = \varepsilon.$$

(b)   Take $\varepsilon = \frac{1}{2}$, for example. Then it is not possible to choose a $\delta > 0$ to satisfy the continuity condition for all $p \in]0, 1[$. However δ is chosen, there exists an integer $n > 1$ such that $\delta > 1/n$. Consider $p = 1/n$, $t = 1/(n + 1)$. Then $|t - p| < \delta$, but $|f(t) - f(p)| = 1 > \varepsilon$.)

7.   Prove the following generalization of the Fundamental Theorem of Calculus 1.6.15. Let $f : [a, b] \subseteq \mathbb{R} \to \mathbb{R}$ be continuous and suppose that there exists a subdivision $a = p_0 < p_1 < \cdots < p_r = b$ of $[a, b]$ such that for each $k = 1, \ldots, r$ the function f restricted to the subinterval $[p_{k-1}, p_k]$ has continuous derivative. Prove that

$$\int_a^b f'(x)\,dx = f(b) - f(a),$$

where the integral is given the natural interpretation

$$\int_a^b f'(x)\,dx = \sum_{k=1}^r \int_{p_{k-1}}^{p_k} f'(x)\,dx.$$

(Note that $f'(x)$ is not necessarily defined at $x = p_k$, but the left-hand and right-hand derivatives of f exist at such points. The function f is said to be *piecewise continuously differentiable*.)

8.   (a) Illustrate Exercise 7 with the continuous function $f : [-1, 2] \subseteq \mathbb{R} \to \mathbb{R}$ defined by $f(x) = |x|, x \in [-1, 2]$.

Answer: $\displaystyle\int_{-1}^2 f'(x)\,dx = f(2) - f(-1) = 1.$

(b) Comment on the condition that f be continuous in Exercise 7. (Consider, for example, the discontinuous function $f : [-1, 2] \subseteq \mathbb{R} \to \mathbb{R}$ defined by

$$f(x) = \begin{cases} -x + 1, & \text{when } -1 \leqslant x \leqslant 0 \\ x, & \text{when } 0 < x \leqslant 2.) \end{cases}$$

Vector-valued functions of $\mathbb{R}$

2.1 Introduction

Linear algebra is the study of linear functions from one vector space into another. In this book we shall be concerned with functions from $\mathbb{R}^m$ into $\mathbb{R}^n$ that can be approximated (in a sense to be made precise) by linear functions. This is the main theme of differential vector calculus.

In the present chapter we confine ourselves to the study of vector-valued functions $f : D \subseteq \mathbb{R} \to \mathbb{R}^n$ where D is an interval in $\mathbb{R}$ and the dimension n of the codomain is open to choice. We shall see that such functions are significant in both geometry and dynamics. Geometrically, if f is 'continuous' on an interval D, then the image of f is a curve and the 'derivatives' of f describe the way the curve twists and turns in $\mathbb{R}^n$. In dynamics, on the other hand, the position of a particle moving in space is a function of time, so that with respect to suitable frames of reference we have a corresponding function $f : D \subseteq \mathbb{R} \to \mathbb{R}^3$ where at time t the position vector of the particle is $f(t)$. The 'derivatives' of f relate to the velocity and acceleration of the particle. Before having a closer look at geometry and dynamics, however, we must explain precisely what is meant by the continuity and differentiability of vector-valued functions of $\mathbb{R}$.

In the following definitions we introduce three fundamental ideas and then explore their relationship by considering some simple examples.

2.1.1 Definition. *Corresponding to any function $f : D \subseteq \mathbb{R} \to \mathbb{R}^n$ we define* coordinate functions *$f_i : D \subseteq \mathbb{R} \to \mathbb{R}$, $i = 1, \ldots, n$, by means of the expression*

$$f(t) = (f_1(t), \ldots, f_n(t)), \qquad t \in D.$$

Our knowledge of calculus applied to the real-valued functions f_i will lead to the calculus of the vector-valued function f.

2.1.2 Definition. *The* image *of a function $f : D \subseteq \mathbb{R} \to \mathbb{R}^n$ is the* *subset of* $\mathbb{R}^n$ *given by* $\{f(t) \in \mathbb{R}^n | t \in D\}$. *The expressions*

$$x_1 = f_1(t), \ldots, x_n = f_n(t), \qquad t \in D$$

are said to give a parametrization *of the image of f with parameter t.*

2.1.3 *Definition.* *The* graph *of a function* $f : D \subseteq \mathbb{R} \to \mathbb{R}^n$ *is the subset of* $\mathbb{R}^{n+1}$ *given by* $\{(t, f_1(t), \ldots, f_n(t)) | t \in D\}$. *We could also express the graph as the set* $\{(t, f(t)) | t \in D\} \subseteq \mathbb{R}^{n+1}$.

For the case $n = 1$, Definition 2.1.3 reduces to the usual high-school concept of the graph of $f : \mathbb{R} \to \mathbb{R}$ as a subset of $\mathbb{R}^2$. For example, the graph of the sine function consists of all points $(t, \sin t)$ in $\mathbb{R}^2$, that is, all points (t, y) such that $y = \sin t$.

2.1.4 *Example.* The rule

$$f(t) = (1, 2, -3) + t(2, 0, 1), \qquad t \in \mathbb{R}$$

defines a function $f : \mathbb{R} \to \mathbb{R}^3$ whose image is the straight line in $\mathbb{R}^3$ through $(1, 2, -3)$ in direction $(2, 0, 1)$. The coordinate functions of f are given by

$$f_1(t) = 1 + 2t, \qquad f_2(t) = 2, \qquad f_3(t) = t - 3, \qquad t \in \mathbb{R},$$

and the corresponding parametrization of the straight line is $x = 1 + 2t$, $y = 2, z = t - 3$.

2.1.5 *Example.* The function $g : \mathbb{R} \to \mathbb{R}^2$ defined by

$$g(t) = (\cos t, \sin t), \qquad t \in \mathbb{R}$$

has image the unit circle $x^2 + y^2 = 1$ in $\mathbb{R}^2$ (see Fig. 2.1).

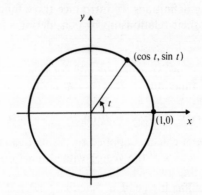

Fig. 2.1 Image of $g(t) = (\cos t, \sin t)$

The coordinate functions of g are given by $g_1(t) = \cos t$ and $g_2(t) = \sin t$, and the corresponding parametrization of the unit circle is $x = \cos t$, $y = \sin t$. The function g is periodic for, since $g(t + 2\pi) = g(t)$ for all t in $\mathbb{R}$, the values of $g(t)$ repeat regularly. The *period* of g is 2π, since this is the smallest positive number p such that $g(t + p) = g(t)$ for all t.

2.1.6 Example. Compare the function g of Example 2.1.5 with the function $h : \mathbb{R} \to \mathbb{R}^2$ defined by

$$h(t) = (\cos 2t, \sin 2t), \qquad t \in \mathbb{R}.$$

The image of h is the unit circle of Fig. 2.1 and yet g and h are different functions (for example $g(\pi) \neq h(\pi)$). Like g, the function h is periodic but unlike g its period is π. As t passes from 0 to 2π, $g(t)$ performs one revolution of the circle whereas $h(t)$ performs two revolutions. Although the functions g and h have the same image, they can be distinguished pictorially by sketching their respective graphs.

2.1.7 Example. The graphs of the functions g and h of Example 2.1.5 and 2.1.6 are respectively the set of points $(t, \cos t, \sin t)$ and $(t, \cos 2t, \sin 2t)$, for all t in $\mathbb{R}$. Just as the graph of a real-valued function (such as the sine function) can be sketched in the plane, so we can also sketch the graph of our function $g : \mathbb{R} \to \mathbb{R}^2$ (see Fig. 2.2). The graph of g is called a *circular helix*. The graph of h is also a circular helix, the windings being around the same circular cylinder but with half the pitch.

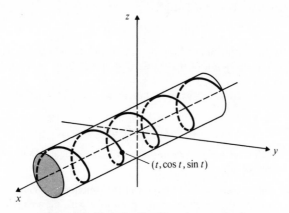

Fig. 2.2 Graph of $g(t) = (\cos t, \sin t)$

We have seen that two different functions can have the same image. It is not difficult to see that there is an infinity of different parametrizations of any non-empty subset of $\mathbb{R}^n$. The unit circle in

$\mathbb{R}^2$ for example has parametrization

$$x = \cos(kt + c), \qquad y = \sin(kt + c), \qquad\qquad t \in \mathbb{R},$$

for any c and $k \neq 0$ in $\mathbb{R}$.

In contrast, a function is uniquely determined by its graph. That is, two different functions have different graphs (Exercise 2.1.8). The following theorem provides a useful way of thinking about the graph of a function.

2.1.8 Theorem. *The graph of a function $f : D \subseteq \mathbb{R} \to \mathbb{R}^n$ is the image of the function $f^* : D \subseteq \mathbb{R} \to \mathbb{R}^{n+1}$ given by*

$$f^*(t) = (t, f_1(t), \ldots, f_n(t)) = (t, f(t)) \in \mathbb{R}^{n+1}, \qquad\qquad t \in D.$$

Proof. The theorem follows immediately from Definitions 2.1.2 and 2.1.3.

Exercises 2.1

1. Find a vectorial equation of the straight line in $\mathbb{R}^3$ through $(1, 0, -4)$ in the direction $(-1, 2, 3)$. Prove that the point (x, y, z) lies on the line if and only if

    $$\frac{x-1}{-1} = \frac{y}{2} = \frac{z+4}{3}.$$

2. The function $g : \mathbb{R} \to \mathbb{R}^2$ defined by

    $$g(t) = (2\cos t, \sin t)$$

    has as its image the ellipse $\frac{1}{4}x^2 + y^2 = 1$. Sketch the ellipse. Find a second parametrization of the ellipse that corresponds to a function of period 4π.

    Does there exist a non-periodic function $h : \mathbb{R} \to \mathbb{R}^2$ whose image is the ellipse?

    Hint: consider, for example, $h(t) = (2\cos(t^2), \sin(t^2))$.

3. Prove that there is an infinity of different parametrizations of any non-empty subset of $\mathbb{R}^n$.

4. Describe the largest possible domain of the function f, where $f(t) = (\sqrt{(4 - t^2)}, t)$. Sketch its image. Compare with the image of g, where $g(t) = (-\sqrt{(4 - t^2)}, t)$.

5. Sketch (a) the image and (b) the graph of $f : \mathbb{R} \to \mathbb{R}^2$ given by $f(t) = (t, t^2)$.

    Note: a rough sketch only is possible for the graph of f, since it is a subset of $\mathbb{R}^3$.

6. Find the period of the function $g : \mathbb{R} \to \mathbb{R}^2$ defined by
   $g(t) = (\cos 2t, \cos 3t)$.

7. Is it true that if the coordinate functions of $f : D \subseteq \mathbb{R} \to \mathbb{R}^n$ are periodic, then f is periodic?

8. Prove that a function $f : D \subseteq \mathbb{R} \to \mathbb{R}^n$ is uniquely determined by its graph, that is that two different functions on D have different graphs.

Hint: If f and g are different functions on D then there exists $t \in D$ such that $f(t) \neq g(t)$.

2.2   Sequences and limits

The reader will find in Chapter 1 a definition (1.6.3) of convergence for sequences of real numbers. The following theorem is an immediate consequence of that definition. Recall that we denote the sequence $a_1, a_2, a_3, \ldots$, by (a_k).

2.2.1 Theorem. *The sequence (a_k) of real numbers converges to $a \in \mathbb{R}$ if and only if $\lim_{k \to \infty} |a_k - a| = 0$.*

This theorem suggests that we can define the convergence of a sequence of vectors in $\mathbb{R}^n$ by generalizing the idea of absolute value to vectors in $\mathbb{R}^n$. The required generalization is the norm or length $\|x\|$ of a vector $\mathbf{x} \in \mathbb{R}^n$ which we defined (Definition 1.2.5) by

$$\|\mathbf{x}\| = \|(x_1, \ldots, x_n)\| = (x_1^2 + \cdots + x_n^2)^{1/2}.$$

We note that in $\mathbb{R}^n$

2.2.2 $$\|\mathbf{x} - \mathbf{y}\|^2 = \sum_{r=1}^{n} (x_r - y_r)^2, \qquad \mathbf{x}, \mathbf{y} \in \mathbb{R}^n$$

and that accordingly in $\mathbb{R}$

2.2.3 $$\|x - y\| = |x - y|, \qquad x, y \in \mathbb{R}.$$

We refer to the real number $\|\mathbf{x} - \mathbf{y}\|$ as the *distance* between the vectors $\mathbf{x}$ and $\mathbf{y}$ in $\mathbb{R}^n$. This generalizes the familiar concept of distance in physical space. If $\mathbf{x}$ and $\mathbf{y}$ are the position vectors of physical points P and Q relative to a rectangular coordinate system, then $\mathbf{x} - \mathbf{y}$ is the vector $\overrightarrow{QP}$ (see Fig. 2.3(i)). The distance between P and Q is $\|\mathbf{x} - \mathbf{y}\|$ units.

Intuitively a sequence of vectors $(\mathbf{a}_k)$ in $\mathbb{R}^n$ converges to $\mathbf{a} \in \mathbb{R}^n$ if the

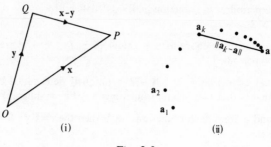

Fig. 2.3

distance between $\mathbf{a}_k$ and $\mathbf{a}$ tends to 0 as k tends to infinity
(Fig. 2.3(ii)). The following definition captures this idea and is a
natural extension of Theorem 2.2.1.

2.2.4 Definition.   *The sequence* $(\mathbf{a}_k)$ *in* $\mathbb{R}^n$ *is said to* convert to $\mathbf{a} \in \mathbb{R}^n$
if $\lim_{k \to \infty} \|\mathbf{a}_k - \mathbf{a}\| = 0$ *in* $\mathbb{R}$. *The convergence of* $(\mathbf{a}_k)$ *to* $\mathbf{a}$ *is denoted by*
$\lim_{k \to \infty} \mathbf{a}_k = \mathbf{a}$ *or by* $\mathbf{a}_k \to \mathbf{a}$. *If the sequence* $(\mathbf{a}_k)$ *does not converge to* $\mathbf{a}$
we write $\mathbf{a}_k \nrightarrow \mathbf{a}$.

2.2.5 Example.   The sequence defined by $\mathbf{a}_k = (1, k/(k+1), 1/k)$, $k \in \mathbb{N}$ converges to $(1, 1, 0)$ in $\mathbb{R}^3$ since

$$\|\mathbf{a}_k - (1, 1, 0)\| = \left\|\left(0, \frac{1}{k+1}, \frac{1}{k}\right)\right\| = \left(\left(\frac{1}{k+1}\right)^2 + \left(\frac{1}{k}\right)^2\right)^{1/2} \to 0.$$

The following theorem is an immediate consequence of the
definition of convergence in $\mathbb{R}$.

2.2.6 Theorem.   *The sequence* $(\mathbf{a}_k)$ *in* $\mathbb{R}^n$ *converges to* $\mathbf{a} \in \mathbb{R}^n$ *if and
only if to each* $\varepsilon > 0$ *there corresponds a natural number* K *such that*

$$\|\mathbf{a}_k - \mathbf{a}\| < \varepsilon \quad whenever \quad k > K.$$

The techniques we have for studying convergence in $\mathbb{R}$ can be
used to study the more general situation by appealing to the following fundamental theorem.

2.2.7 Theorem.   *Let* $(\mathbf{a}_k)$ *be a sequence in* $\mathbb{R}^n$ *with* $\mathbf{a}_k = (a_{k1}, \ldots, a_{kn})$
for all $k \in \mathbb{N}$ *and let* $\mathbf{a} = (a_1, \ldots, a_n) \in \mathbb{R}^n$. *Then* $\mathbf{a}_k \to \mathbf{a}$ *if and only if* a_{ki}
$\to a_i$ *for each* $i = 1, \ldots, n$. *In other words, the convergence of* $(\mathbf{a}_k)$ *is
equivalent to the convergence of each of its coordinate sequences.*

Proof. It follows from 2.2.2 that for each $k \in \mathbb{N}$

2.2.8
$$\|\mathbf{a}_k - \mathbf{a}\|^2 = \sum_{i=1}^{n} (a_{ki} - a_i)^2.$$

Suppose that $a_{ki} \to a_i$ for each $i = 1, \ldots, n$. Choose any $\varepsilon > 0$.
To each $i = 1, \ldots, n$ there corresponds a number $K_i \in \mathbb{N}$ which depends on ε, such that

$$|a_{ki} - a_i| < \left(\frac{\varepsilon}{n}\right)^{1/2} \qquad \text{whenever} \quad k > K_i.$$

Let $K = \max \{K_1, \ldots, K_n\}$. By 2.2.8,

$$\|\mathbf{a}_k - \mathbf{a}\|^2 = \sum_{i=1}^{n} (a_{ki} - a_i)^2 < n\left(\frac{\varepsilon}{n}\right) = \varepsilon \qquad \text{whenever} \quad k > K.$$

This establishes that $\|\mathbf{a}_k - \mathbf{a}\|^2 \to 0$ and hence that $\|\mathbf{a}_k - \mathbf{a}\| \to 0$.
Therefore $\mathbf{a}_k \to \mathbf{a}$.
The proof of the converse is left as an exercise.

2.2.9 Example. [i] $\lim_{k \to \infty} (k/1 + k), k/(1 + k^2)) = (1, 0)$.
[ii] The sequence $(\mathbf{a}_k)$ where $\mathbf{a}_k = ((-1)^k, 1/k)$ does not converge in $\mathbb{R}^2$.

Exercises 2.2

1. Show that $\lim_{k \to \infty} (k \sin(1/k), (1/k)\sin k) = (1, 0)$.

2. Prove that a convergent sequence $(\mathbf{a}_k)$ in $\mathbb{R}^n$ has a unique limit in $\mathbb{R}^n$.

3. Let (a_k) be the sequence of real numbers defined by $a_k = 10^{-k}[10^k \sqrt{2}]$, where $[r]$ denotes the integer part of the real number r. Verify that the first four terms of the sequence are $a_1 = 1, a_2 = 1.4, a_3 = 1.41, a_4 = 1.414$.
   Prove that (a_k) is a convergent sequence of rational numbers with limit $\sqrt{2}$.

Hint: given $\varepsilon > 0$, prove that $|a_k - \sqrt{2}| < \varepsilon$ for all k such that $1/10^k < \varepsilon$.

4. Let $(\mathbf{a}_k)$ and $(\mathbf{b}_k)$ be convergent sequences in $\mathbb{R}^n$. Prove that if $\mathbf{a}_k \to \mathbf{a}$ and $\mathbf{b}_k \to \mathbf{b}$ then $\mathbf{a}_k + \mathbf{b}_k \to \mathbf{a} + \mathbf{b}$. Show also that for any constant c, the sequence $(c\mathbf{a}_k)$ is convergent, and $c\mathbf{a}_k \to c\mathbf{a}$.

5. Prove that the definition of distance between $\mathbf{x}$ and $\mathbf{y}$ is symmetric in $\mathbf{x}$ and $\mathbf{y}$. (Show that $\|\mathbf{x} - \mathbf{y}\| = \|\mathbf{y} - \mathbf{x}\|$.)

6. A sequence $(\mathbf{a}_k)$ in $\mathbb{R}^n$ is a Cauchy sequence if to each $\varepsilon > 0$ there corresponds $N \in \mathbb{N}$ such that

$$\|\mathbf{a}_k - \mathbf{a}_l\| < \varepsilon \qquad \text{whenever } k, l > N.$$

Prove that a Cauchy sequence in $\mathbb{R}^n$ is convergent.

Hint: Apply the ideas in the proof of Theorem 2.2.7 and Theorem 1.6.4.

2.3   Continuity

A function $f : D \subseteq \mathbb{R} \to \mathbb{R}$ is *discontinuous* at $p \in D$ if we can find a sequence (a_k) in D such that $a_k \to p$, but $f(a_k) \not\to f(p)$. If no such sequence can be found we say that f is continuous at p. Thus we have the following definition of continuity, generalized to functions with codomain $\mathbb{R}^n$ for arbitrary dimension n.

2.3.1 Definition.   *The function* $f : D \subseteq \mathbb{R} \to \mathbb{R}^n$ *is said to be* continuous *at* $p \in D$ *if* $f(a_k) \to f(p)$ *whenever* $a_k \to p$, *where* $a_k \in D$ *for all* $k \in \mathbb{N}$.

The following theorem about continuity corresponds to Theorem 2.2.7 about limits.

2.3.2 Theorem.   *The function* $f : D \subseteq \mathbb{R} \to \mathbb{R}^n$ *is continuous at* $p \in D$ *if and only if for each* $i = 1, \ldots, n$, *the coordinate function* $f_i : D \subseteq \mathbb{R} \to \mathbb{R}$ *is continuous at* p.

Proof.   Let (a_k) be a sequence in D with $a_k \to p$. By definition of coordinate functions $f(a_k) = (f_1(a_k), \ldots, f_n(a_k))$ for each $k \in \mathbb{N}$, and $f(p) = (f_1(p), \ldots, f_n(p))$. By Theorem 2.2.7, $f(a_k) \to f(p)$ if and only if $f_i(a_k) \to f_i(p)$ for each $i = 1, \ldots, n$. The result follows.

2.3.3 Example.   The function $f : \mathbb{R} \to \mathbb{R}^2$ given by $f(t) = (t, t^2)$ is continuous at all points in $\mathbb{R}$.

2.3.4 Example.   The function $f : \mathbb{R} \to \mathbb{R}^2$ given by

$$f(t) = \begin{cases} (2t-1, 2t-1) & \text{when } t \leq 2, \\ (3-t, 5-t) & \text{when } t > 2, \end{cases}$$

is not continuous at 2 since the coordinate function f_1 is not continuous there. On the other hand the coordinate function f_2 is continuous everywhere.

2.3.5 Corollary.   *Consider functions* $f : D \subseteq \mathbb{R} \to \mathbb{R}^n$, $g : D \subseteq \mathbb{R} \to \mathbb{R}^n$ *and* $\phi : D \subseteq \mathbb{R} \to \mathbb{R}$. *If* f, g *and* ϕ *are continuous at* $p \in D$, *then so are the functions* ϕf, $f + g$, $f \cdot g$ *and, provided* $n = 3$, *so is* $f \wedge g$.

Proof. Exercise.

2.3.6 Definition. *A function* $f : D \subseteq \mathbb{R} \to \mathbb{R}^n$ *is said to be* continuous *if it is continuous at p for every* $p \in D$.

Theorem 2.3.2 establishes that f is continuous if and only if all its coordinate functions are continuous.

Exercises 2.3

1. (a) Let $f : \mathbb{R} \to \mathbb{R}$ be the linear function defined by $f(t) = ct$, where c is a constant. Prove from first principles that f is continuous.
    (b) Prove that a linear function $f : \mathbb{R} \to \mathbb{R}^n$ is continuous.

Hint: consider the coordinate functions of f.

2. Prove that the function $f : \mathbb{R} \to \mathbb{R}^2$ defined by

$$f(t) = \begin{cases} (t, 3t - 2) & \text{when } t \leqslant 1 \\ (2t - 1, t + a) & \text{when } t > 1 \end{cases}$$

is continuous on $\mathbb{R}$ if and only if $a = 0$.

3. Prove Corollary 2.3.5.

Hint: consider the coordinate functions, and apply Exercise 1.6.2.

2.4 Limits and continuity

We have seen that the continuity of the function $f : D \subseteq \mathbb{R} \to \mathbb{R}^n$ at $p \in D$ depends upon how f behaves near to p as well as upon the value that f takes at p. In this section we study how f behaves near p by considering what f does to sequences (a_k) in D which converge to p but are such that $a_k \neq p$ for all $k \in \mathbb{N}$. Remember that we are restricting ourselves to functions whose domain is an interval of some sort.

2.4.1 Definition. *The* cluster points *of an interval D in* $\mathbb{R}$ *are the points of D together with its end points.*

2.4.2. Example
  (i) The cluster points of $[-2, 1[$ form $[-2, 1]$.
  (ii) The cluster points of $]-\infty, 3[$ form $]-\infty, 3]$.

2.4.3 Theorem. *A point* $p \in \mathbb{R}$ *is a cluster point of an interval D if* *and only if there is a sequence* (a_k) *in* D *such that* $a_k \to p$ *but* $a_k \neq p$ *for all* $k \in \mathbb{N}$.

Proof.   Exercise.

2.4.4 Example.   Let $D = [-2, 1[$. The sequences $(-2 + k^{-1})$, (k^{-1}) and $(1 - k^{-1})$ in D converge to cluster points $-2, 0$, and 1 respectively.

2.4.5 Definition.   *Consider a function* $f : D \subseteq \mathbb{R} \to \mathbb{R}^n$, *a cluster point* p *of* D *and a point* $\mathbf{q}$ *in* $\mathbb{R}^n$. *We write* $\lim_{t \to p} f(t) = \mathbf{q}$ *if* $f(a_k) \to \mathbf{q}$ *whenever* (a_k) *is a sequence in* D *such that* $a_k \to p$ *and* $a_k \neq p$ *for all* $k \in \mathbb{N}$.

For this type of limit we have the coordinate result that we have come to expect.

2.4.6 Theorem.   *Given* $f : D \subseteq \mathbb{R} \to \mathbb{R}^n$ *and* p *a cluster point of* D, *then* $\lim_{t \to p} f(t) = \mathbf{q}$ *if and only if* $\lim_{t \to p} f_i(t) = q_i$ *for each* $i = 1, \ldots, n$.

Proof.   From Theorem 2.2.7, for any sequence (a_k) in D, $f(a_k) \to \mathbf{q}$ if and only if $f_i(a_k) \to q_i$ for all $i = 1, \ldots, n$. This equivalence still holds if we confine ourselves to sequences such that $a_k \to p$ and $a_k \neq p$ for all $k \in \mathbb{N}$.

2.4.7 Example.   Define $f : \mathbb{R} \to \mathbb{R}^2$ by

$$f(t) = \begin{cases} (1 + t, 2 + t) & \text{when } t \geqslant 0, \\ (1 + t, 1 - t) & \text{when } t < 0. \end{cases}$$

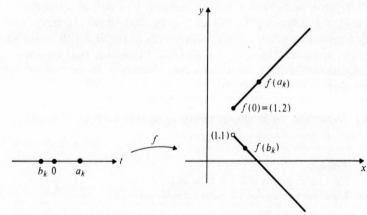

Fig. 2.4 Image of function f (Example 2.4.7)

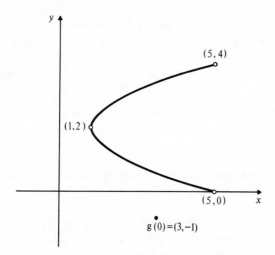

Fig. 2.5 Image of function g (Example 2.4.8)

Let $a_k = k^{-1}$ and $b_k = -k^{-1}$. Then $a_k \to 0$ and $b_k \to 0$ but $\lim_{k \to \infty} f(a_k) = (1, 2)$ and $\lim_{k \to \infty} f(b_k) = (1, 1)$. Hence $\lim_{t \to 0} f(t)$ does not exist. The situation is sketched in Fig. 2.4. In particular $\lim_{t \to 0} f_1(t) = 1$ but $\lim_{t \to 0} f_2(t)$ does not exist.

2.4.8 Example. Figure 2.5 is a sketch of the image of the function $g:\,]-2,2[\to \mathbb{R}^2$ defined by $g(0) = (3, -1)$ and $g(t) = (t^2 + 1, t + 2)$ when $t \neq 0$. The image of 0 is separated from the rest of the image, but $\lim_{t \to 0} g(t)$ exists and, by Theorem 2.4.6,

$$\lim_{t \to 0} g(t) = \left(\lim_{t \to 0} t^2 + 1,\ \lim_{t \to 0} t + 2 \right) = (1, 2).$$

Notice also that, even though 2 is not in the domain of g, $\lim_{t \to 2} g(t)$ exists and

$$\lim_{t \to 2} g(t) = \left(\lim_{t \to 2} t^2 + 1,\ \lim_{t \to 2} t + 2 \right) = (5, 4).$$

The fact that the domains of the functions considered in Examples 2.4.7 and 2.4.8 are intervals but that their images are not in one piece indicates that the functions are not continuous. We can explore this property further by using the following theorem relating the limit concept and continuity.

2.4.9 Theorem. *The function $f : D \subseteq \mathbb{R} \to \mathbb{R}^n$ is continuous at $p \in D$ if and only if $\lim_{t \to p} f(t) = f(p)$.*

Proof. It is clear that if $f(a_k) \to f(p)$ whenever $a_k \to p$, with $a_k \neq p$ for all $k \in \mathbb{N}$, then $f(a_k) \to f(p)$ whenever $a_k \to p$ without that restriction.

2.4.10 Example. [i] The function g of Example 2.4.8 is not continuous at 0 since $\lim_{t \to 0} g(t) = (1, 2) \neq (3, -1) = g(0)$. If, however, we redefine the value of g at 0 to be $(1, 2)$, then the new function is continuous at 0.

[ii] The function f of Example 2.4.7 is not continuous at 0 since $\lim_{t \to 0} f(t)$ does not exist. Furthermore, f cannot be made continuous by changing its value at 0.

The following result provides an important tool for manipulating with limits.

2.4.11 Theorem. *Consider a function* $f : D \subseteq \mathbb{R} \to \mathbb{R}^n$, *a cluster point* p *of* D *and a point* $\mathbf{q} \in \mathbb{R}^n$. *Then* $\lim_{t \to p} f(t) = \mathbf{q}$ *if and only if to each* $\varepsilon > 0$ *there corresponds* $\delta > 0$ *such that*

2.4.12 $\| f(t) - \mathbf{q} \| < \varepsilon$ *whenever* $t \in D$ *and* $0 < |t - p| < \delta$.

Proof. Suppose firstly that the ε, δ condition is satisfied. Let (a_k) be any sequence in D such that $a_k \to p$ and $a_k \neq p$ for all $k \in \mathbb{N}$. Given any $\varepsilon > 0$ there corresponds, by 2.4.12, a $\delta > 0$ such that

2.4.13 $\| f(a_k) - \mathbf{q} \| < \varepsilon$ whenever $0 < |a_k - p| < \delta$.

But $a_k \to p$ and $a_k \neq p$ for all $k \in \mathbb{N}$, and so there exists $k \in \mathbb{N}$ such that

2.4.14 $0 < |a_k - p| < \delta$ whenever $k > K$.

Expressions 2.4.13 and 2.4.14 together establish that $\lim_{k \to \infty} f(a_k) = \mathbf{q}$. Since this is true for all suitable sequences (a_k) it follows from Definition 2.4.5 that $\lim_{t \to p} f(t) = \mathbf{q}$.

To prove the converse we will show that the failure of the ε, δ condition 2.4.12 implies that $\lim_{t \to \infty} f(t) \neq \mathbf{q}$. Failure of the condition implies that there exists an $\varepsilon > 0$ such that no corresponding δ can be found. In particular $\delta = 1/k$ will not do for any $k \in \mathbb{N}$. For any $k \in \mathbb{N}$, therefore, there exists $a_k \in D$ such that

2.4.15 $0 < |a_k - p| < 1/k$ but $\| f(a_k) - \mathbf{q} \| \geqslant \varepsilon$.

The first part of 2.4.15 tells us that the sequence (a_k) converges to p and that $a_k \neq p$ for all $k \in \mathbb{N}$. The second part of 2.4.15 tells us that $\lim_{k \to \infty} f(a_k) \neq \mathbf{q}$. This is the required contradiction.

The ε, δ condition of Theorem 2.4.11 means that given any required level of approximation, the value of $f(t)$ is approximately equal to $\mathbf{q}$ for all $t \neq p$ sufficiently close to p.

2.4.16 Corollary. *Given $f : D \subseteq \mathbb{R} \to \mathbb{R}^n$ and $p \in D$, then f is continuous at p if and only if to each $\varepsilon > 0$ there corresponds $\delta > 0$ such that $\| f(t) - f(p) \| < \varepsilon$ whenever $t \in D$ and $|t - p| < \delta$.*

Proof. Immediate from Theorem 2.4.9 and Theorem 2.4.11.

2.4.17 Remark. The limit $\lim_{t \to p} f(t)$ defined in Definition 2.4.5 is related to a function f whose domain is an interval D in $\mathbb{R}$. The definition still makes sense if D is *any* non-empty subset of $\mathbb{R}$ and $p \in \mathbb{R}$ is any point such that there is a sequence (a_k) in D for which $a_k \to p$ and $a_k \neq p$ for all $k \in \mathbb{N}$.

2.4.18 Example. Define $g : \mathbb{R} \backslash \{0\} \to \mathbb{R}$ by $g(t) = (\sin t)/t$. Then $\lim_{t \to 0} g(t)$ is defined and in fact $\lim_{t \to 0} g(t) = 1$ since, for all small t,

$$\left| t - \frac{t^3}{6} \right| \leqslant |\sin t| \leqslant |t|.$$

Exercises 2.4

1. Apply the test for continuity of Corollary 2.4.16 to prove that
   (a) the function $f : \mathbb{R} \to \mathbb{R}^n$ given by $f(t) = (t, t^2)$ $t \in \mathbb{R}$, is continuous at 0;
   (b) a linear function $f : \mathbb{R} \to \mathbb{R}^2$ is continuous at $p \in \mathbb{R}$.

2. Prove that the real-valued function $f : \mathbb{R} \to \mathbb{R}$ defined by $f(t) = \sin(1/t)$, $t \neq 0$, $f(0) = 0$, is discontinuous at 0 by showing that the test for continuity of Corollary 2.4.16 breaks down.

   (*Hint*: choose $\varepsilon = \frac{1}{2}$ and show that for any $\delta > 0$ there exists $0 < x < \delta$ such that $|f(x) - f(0)| > \varepsilon$. In fact, it is possible to choose $0 < x < \delta$ such that $f(x) = 1$.)

3. A function $f : D \subseteq \mathbb{R} \to \mathbb{R}^n$ is said to have a *removable discontinuity* at $p \in D$ if f is not continuous at p but there exists $\mathbf{q} \in \mathbb{R}^n$ such that $\lim_{t \to p} f(t) = \mathbf{q}$. This means that f can be made continuous at p by changing its value there. Show that 0 is a removable discontinuity of the function g of Example 2.4.8 but 0 is not a removable discontinuity of the function f of Example 2.4.7.

4. Given a function $f : D \subseteq \mathbb{R} \to \mathbb{R}^n$, consider the function $\| f \| : D \subseteq \mathbb{R} \to \mathbb{R}$ where $\| f \| (t) = \| f(t) \|$, $t \in D$. Prove that if f is continuous then $\| f \|$ is continuous. Is the converse true?

2.5   Differentiability and tangent lines

The derivative of a function $\phi : \mathbb{R} \to \mathbb{R}$ at $p \in \mathbb{R}$ is defined to be

2.5.1
$$\phi'(p) = \lim_{h \to 0} \frac{\phi(p+h) - \phi(p)}{h},$$

if this limit exists.

In generalizing this definition to a function $f : D \subseteq \mathbb{R} \to \mathbb{R}^n$ at a point $p \in \mathbb{R}$ we consider vectors of the form

2.5.2
$$\frac{1}{h}(f(p+h) - f(p)) \in \mathbb{R}^n,$$

where $h \in \mathbb{R}$ is non-zero and is such that $p + h \in D$. Since the vector given in 2.5.2 is a multiple of $f(p+h) - f(p)$ it is parallel to the line joining $f(p)$ and $f(p+h)$. It is pictured (for the case $h > 0$) in Fig. 2.4(i) as lying along this line and based at $f(p)$.

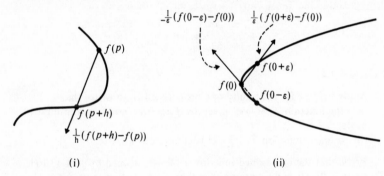

Fig. 2.6

2.5.3 *Example.* Consider the function $f : \mathbb{R} \to \mathbb{R}^2$ defined by $f(t) = (t^2 + 1, t + 2)$. Taking $p = 0$, for any $\varepsilon > 0$ the two vectors in $\mathbb{R}^2$ obtained from 2.5.2 by taking $h = \varepsilon$ and $h = -\varepsilon$ are respectively

$$\frac{1}{\varepsilon}(f(0+\varepsilon) - f(0)) = (\varepsilon, 1) \quad \text{and} \quad \frac{1}{-\varepsilon}(f(0-\varepsilon) - f(0)) = (-\varepsilon, 1).$$

These vectors are drawn, together with the image of f, in Fig. 2.6(ii). The image of f is the parabola $(y - 2)^2 = (x - 1)$ in $\mathbb{R}^2$.

2.5.4 *Definition.* *Let p be a point in an interval D. Then the interval D_p is defined by*

$$D_p = \{h \in \mathbb{R} \mid p + h \in D\}.$$

The interval D_p is merely the translation of D through $(-p)$. Since p lies in D, 0 lies in D_p. In view of Remark 2.4.17 the following definition makes sense.

2.5.5 Definition.   *The function* $f : D \subseteq \mathbb{R} \to \mathbb{R}^n$ *is said to be* differentiable *at* $p \in D$ *if the limit*

$$\lim_{h \to 0} \frac{1}{h}(f(p+h) - f(p)), \qquad h \in D_p \backslash \{0\}$$

exists in $\mathbb{R}^n$. *If the limit does exist then it is called the* derivative *of* f *at* p *and is denoted by* $f'(p)$.

We can say, as in the elementary case, that $f'(p)$ measures the rate of change of f at p. Notice, however, that in this case $f'(p)$ is a vector in $\mathbb{R}^n$.

2.5.6 Example.   For the function f of Example 2.5.3 with $p = 0$ and $h \neq 0$,

$$\frac{1}{h}(f(p+h) - f(p)) = (h, 1)$$

and Definition 2.5.5 gives $f'(0) = \lim_{h \to 0}(h, 1) = (0, 1) \in \mathbb{R}^2$. This vector is drawn in Fig. 2.7(i) based at $f(0) = (1, 2)$. Compare this figure with Fig. 2.6(ii). In particular, note that as ε tends to zero, the two vectors drawn in Fig. 2.6(ii) tend to the vector $f'(0)$ drawn in Fig. 2.7(i).

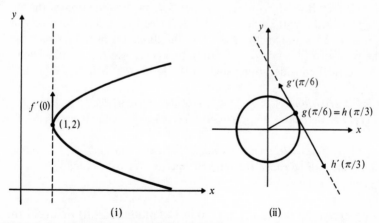

Fig. 2.7 (i) Tangent vector $f'(0) = (0, 1)$;
(ii) Point $g(\pi/6) = h(\pi/3) = (\tfrac{1}{2}\sqrt{3}, \tfrac{1}{2})$
Tangent vectors $g'(\pi/6) = \tfrac{1}{2}(-1, \sqrt{3})$ and $h'(\pi/3) = (1, -\sqrt{3})$

2.5.7 Theorem. *The function* $f : D \subseteq \mathbb{R} \to \mathbb{R}^n$ *is differentiable at* $p \in D$ *if and only if for each* $i = 1, \ldots, n$ *the coordinate function* $f_i : D \subseteq \mathbb{R} \to \mathbb{R}$ *is differentiable at* p. *Furthermore, if* f *is differentiable at* p, *then*

$$f'(p) = (f_1'(p), \ldots, f_n'(p)).$$

Proof. Apply Theorem 2.4.6.

2.5.8 *Example.* (i) The function $g : \mathbb{R} \to \mathbb{R}^2$ defined by $g(t) = (\cos t, \sin t)$ has as its image the unit circle centre $(0, 0)$ in $\mathbb{R}^2$. The function is differentiable at $\pi/6$ with derivative

$$g'\left(\frac{\pi}{6}\right) = \left(-\sin\frac{\pi}{6}, \cos\frac{\pi}{6}\right) = \left(-\frac{1}{2}, \frac{\sqrt{3}}{2}\right).$$

This vector is drawn in Fig. 2.7(ii) based at $g(\pi/6) = (\sqrt{3}/2, 1/2)$.

(ii) The function $h : \mathbb{R} \to \mathbb{R}^2$ defined by $h(u) = (\sin 2u, \cos 2u)$ has image the same unit circle in $\mathbb{R}^2$. The function h is differentiable at $\pi/3$ with derivative

$$h'\left(\frac{\pi}{3}\right) = \left(2\cos\frac{2\pi}{3}, -2\sin\frac{2\pi}{3}\right) = (1, -\sqrt{3}).$$

This derivative is also drawn in Fig. 2.7(ii) based, as was $g'(\pi/6)$, at $h(\pi/3) = (\sqrt{3}/2, 1/2)$.

In Example 2.5.8 the vectors $g'(\pi/6)$ and $h'(\pi/3)$ are linearly dependent and are orthogonal to the radius vector $g(\pi/6) = h(\pi/3) = (\sqrt{3}/2, 1/2)$. Both derivatives are therefore in the direction of the tangent to the unit circle at $(\sqrt{3}/2, 1/2)$ (see Fig. 2.7(ii)). Similarly, in Example 2.5.3, the vector $f'(0)$ is in the direction of the tangent to the parabola $(y - 2)^2 = (x - 1)$ at $f(0) = (1, 2)$ (see Fig. 2.7(i)). Such geometrical considerations suggest the following definitions.

2.5.9 *Definition.* Let $f : D \subseteq \mathbb{R} \to \mathbb{R}^n$ *be differentiable at* $p \in D$.
[i] *The derivative* $f'(p)$ *will also be called the* tangent vector *to* f *at* p.
[ii] *If* $f'(p) \neq \mathbf{0}$, *then the straight line in* $\mathbb{R}^n$ *through* $f(p)$ *in direction* $f'(p)$ *will be called the* tangent line *to* f *at* p. *It is the set* $\{f(p) + sf'(p) | s \in \mathbb{R}\} \subseteq \mathbb{R}^n$.

By excluding the case $f'(p) = 0$ in Definition 2.5.9(ii) we avoid the tangent line degenerating to a single point. Notice that the tangent vector and tangent line are defined in terms of a function and not in terms of its image.

2.5.10 *Example*. The tangent vector to the function f of Example 2.5.6 at 0 is $(0, 1) \in \mathbb{R}^2$. The tangent line at 0 is the line $\{(1, 2) + s(0, 1)|s \in \mathbb{R}\} \subseteq \mathbb{R}^2$. It is the line $x = 1$ sketched as a broken line in Fig. 2.7(i).

2.5.11 *Example*. The functions g and h of Example 2.5.8 both have image the unit circle centre $\mathbf{0}$ in $\mathbb{R}^2$. Although $g(\pi/6) = h(\pi/3)$ the two tangent vectors $g'(\pi/6)$ and $h'(\pi/3)$ are different. The tangent line to g at $\pi/6$ is the set

$$\{(\sqrt{3}/2, 1/2) + s(-1/2, \sqrt{3}/2)|s \in \mathbb{R}\} \subseteq \mathbb{R}^2.$$

It is the straight line $y + \sqrt{3}x = 2$ sketched as a broken line in Fig. 2.7(ii). Since $h(\pi/3) = g(\pi/6)$ and since $h'(\pi/3)$ is a non-zero multiple of $g'(\pi/6)$, the tangent line to h at $\pi/3$ is the same straight line in $\mathbb{R}^2$. Our earlier work on the geometry of Fig. 2.7(ii) shows that this tangent line is the tangent to the circle at $(\sqrt{3}/2, 1/2)$.

We shall have a second look at the relationship between tangent lines to a function and the image of the function in the next section.

2.5.12 *Definition*. *The function $f : D \subseteq \mathbb{R} \to \mathbb{R}^n$ is said to be* differentiable *if it is differentiable at each point $p \in D$. The function $f' : D \subseteq \mathbb{R} \to \mathbb{R}^n$ whose image at $p \in D$ is the vector $f'(p) \in \mathbb{R}^n$ is called the* derivative *of f. If f' is itself differentiable, then its derivative is denoted by $f'' : D \subseteq \mathbb{R} \to \mathbb{R}^n$.*

With the help of Theorem 2.5.7 many theorems of elementary calculus are readily generalized.

2.5.13 *Theorem*. *Consider functions $f : D \subseteq \mathbb{R} \to \mathbb{R}^n$, $g : D \subseteq \mathbb{R} \to \mathbb{R}^n$ and $\phi : D \subseteq \mathbb{R} \to \mathbb{R}$. If f, g and ϕ are differentiable, then so are the following functions with the stated derivatives.*
  [i]   *The sum function:* $(f + g)' = f' + g'$.
  [ii] *The dot product* $(f \cdot g)' = (f' \cdot g) + (f \cdot g')$
  [iii] *(For the case $n = 3$) the vector product:*
       $(f \wedge g)' = (f' \wedge g) + (f \wedge g')$
  [iv] *The product function:* $(\phi f)' = \phi' f + \phi f'$.

Proof. For each $t \in D$ express $(f + g)(t)$, $(f \cdot g)(t)$, $(f \wedge g)(t)$ and $(\phi f)(t)$ in terms of coordinate functions of f and of g. Now apply Theorem 2.5.7 and use results from elementary calculus to obtain the required results.

The following theorem is an important application of Theorem 2.5.13(ii).

2.5.14 *Theorem.*   Let $h : D \subseteq \mathbb{R} \rightarrow \mathbb{R}^n$ *be a differentiable function such that* $\|h(t)\| = 1$ *for all* $t \in D$. *Then* $h(t)$ *and* $h'(t)$ *are orthogonal for all* $t \in D$.

Proof.   The image of h lies on the unit sphere centre **0** in $\mathbb{R}^n$. For all $t \in D$

2.5.15 $$h(t) \cdot h(t) = \|h(t)\|^2 = 1.$$

Using Theorem 2.5.13(ii) we find, on differentiating 2.5.15, that

$$h(t) \cdot h'(t) + h'(t) \cdot h(t) = 2h(t) \cdot h'(t) = 0, \qquad \text{for all } t \in D.$$

Therefore the tangent vector $h'(t)$ is orthogonal to the radius vector $h(t)$.

In particular, if $n = 2$ and if $h'(p) \neq \mathbf{0}$ then the tangent line to h at p is just the tangent to the unit circle centre $\mathbf{0} \in \mathbb{R}^2$ at $h(p)$. We have already seen this to be true in the particular cases considered in Example 2.5.11.

Despite their geometrical significance, differentiability, tangent vectors and tangent lines are defined in terms of functions rather than in terms of their images. The following two examples should serve to warn the reader against jumping to conclusions about a function merely on the basis of looking at its image.

2.5.16 *Example.*   Consider the continuous functions f, g and h from $\mathbb{R}$ into $\mathbb{R}^2$ defined for each $t \in \mathbb{R}$ by

$$g(t) = (t, t^2), \quad f(t) = (t^3, t^6), \quad h(t) = \begin{cases} (t, t^2) & \text{for } t \geqslant 0, \\ (t^3, t^6) & \text{for } t < 0. \end{cases}$$

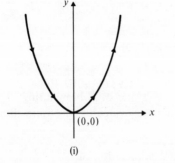

(i)

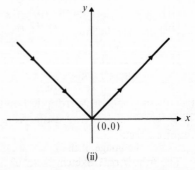

(ii)

Fig. 2.8

All three functions have the same image (the parabola $y = x^2$ in $\mathbb{R}^2$ — see Fig. 2.8(i)) and all take the value $(0, 0)$ at 0. Furthermore they cover the points of this curve in the same order as t increases (indicated by the arrows in Fig. 2.8(i)). The function g is differentiable at 0 with tangent vector $g'(0)$ $= (1, 0)$ and tangent line $y = 0$ there. The function f is also differentiable but f has no tangent line at 0 since $f'(0) = (0, 0)$. Even more striking is the fact that, since the coordinate function h_1 is not differentiable at 0, the function h is not differentiable at 0. This is so despite the smoothness of the image of h.

2.5.17 *Example*.   The image of a continuous function $g : \mathbb{R} \to \mathbb{R}^2$ where $g(t) = (t|t|, t^2), t \in \mathbb{R}$, is sketched in Fig. 2.8(ii). It is the set $y = |x|$ in $\mathbb{R}^2$. The coordinate functions of g are given by

$$g_1(t) = \begin{cases} t^2 & \text{when } t \geqslant 0 \\ -t^2 & \text{when } t < 0 \end{cases} \quad \text{and} \quad g_2(t) = t^2, \qquad t \in \mathbb{R}.$$

Both g_1 and g_2 are differentiable at 0. Therefore g is differentiable at 0 and has a tangent vector there despite the fact that the image has a 'corner' at $g(0) = (0, 0)$. Since the tangent vector at 0 is $g'(0) = (0, 0)$, there is no associated tangent line.

In elementary calculus the differentiability of a function $\phi : \mathbb{R} \to \mathbb{R}$ is usually thought of in terms of the smoothness of the graph of ϕ. It is very important in deducing properties of $f : D \subseteq \mathbb{R} \to \mathbb{R}^n$ from a sketch of its image to remember that it is just the image and not the graph of f. This point is amply supported in Examples 2.5.16 and 2.5.17.

Exercises 2.5

1. Find the tangent vector (a) at 0 (b) at $\frac{1}{2}\pi$ to the function $g : \mathbb{R} \to \mathbb{R}^2$ defined by $g(t) = (2\cos t, \sin t)$. Determine the corresponding tangent lines. Sketch these and the image of g (the ellipse of Exercise 2.1.2).

2. Sketch the images of the following differentiable functions $f : \mathbb{R} \to \mathbb{R}^2$ and indicate the tangent vectors and tangent lines (if they exist) to f (i) at $t = 0$; (ii) at $t = 1$.
    (a) $f(t) = (t + t^2, t - t^2)$
    (b) $f(t) = (t^2, t^3)$

3. Illustrate Theorem 2.5.14 and its proof with the function $h : \mathbb{R} \to \mathbb{R}^2$ defined by $h(t) = (\cos(t^2), \sin(t^2))$. Calculate $h'(t)$ and sketch the corresponding tangent lines for various values of t.

4. Sketch the image of the differentiable function $g : \mathbb{R} \to \mathbb{R}^2$ given by $g(t) = (t, t^3), t \in \mathbb{R}$. Sketch the tangent vector and tangent line at $t = 0$ and at $t = 1$.

Using the idea of Example 2.5.16, construct a function h with the same image as g and such that $g(0) = h(0)$, but h is not differentiable at 0.

Answer: for example $h(t) = (t^{1/3}, t)$, $t \in \mathbb{R}$.

5. Prove that the function $f : \mathbb{R} \to \mathbb{R}$ defined by $f(t) = |t|$ is continuous but not differentiable at 0.

6. Verify Theorem 2.5.13 for the functions $f : \mathbb{R} \to \mathbb{R}^3$, $g : \mathbb{R} \to \mathbb{R}^3$ and $\phi : \mathbb{R} \to \mathbb{R}$, where

$$f(t) = (e^t, t, 1), \quad g(t) = (0, -t, t^2 + 1), \quad \phi(t) = t^2.$$

7. Sketch the image of the differentiable function $f : \mathbb{R} \to \mathbb{R}^2$ defined by

$$f(t) = (e^{kt} \cos t, e^{kt} \sin t), \qquad t \in \mathbb{R},$$

where k is a constant. Prove that

$$\frac{f'(t) \cdot f(t)}{\|f'(t)\| \, \|f(t)\|} = k, \qquad t \in \mathbb{R}.$$

Deduce that the angle between the tangent vector $f'(t)$ and the line joining the origin and the point $f(t)$ is the same for all t. The image of f is called an *equiangular spiral*.

2.6   Curves and simple arcs

Cartesian geometry and calculus developed during the first half of the seventeenth century through the study of some special curves and in particular through attempts to solve problems concerning their tangents, their length and the areas associated with them.

Intuitively one thinks of a curve as a wavy copy of an interval, with possible self-intersections and corners. It seems reasonable to define a curve in $\mathbb{R}^n$ as the image of an interval D under a continuous function $f : D \subseteq \mathbb{R} \to \mathbb{R}^n$. The point $f(t) \in \mathbb{R}^n$ would then trace the curve as the parameter t moves along the interval. This definition, however, is too general to be useful. There is, for example, such a continuous function defined on a compact interval $[a, b]$ whose image fills out a square in $\mathbb{R}^2$. See Apostol, *Mathematical Analysis*, Section 13.8. We therefore impose extra conditions on f, although many of our results are also true if they are weakened.

2.6.1 Definition.   *A function $f : D \subseteq \mathbb{R} \to \mathbb{R}^n$ is said to be continuously differentiable, or a C^1 function, if f is differentiable and if*

f' is continuous. *In general a C^k function is one whose kth derivative exists and is continuous.*

2.6.2 Definition.   *A subset C of $\mathbb{R}^n$ is a curve if there is a C^1 function $f : D \subseteq \mathbb{R} \to \mathbb{R}^n$, where D is an interval, such that $f(D) = C$. The function f is called a C^1 parametrization of the curve.*

2.6.3 Example.   The function $f(t) = (t^2 + 1, t + 2)$ of Example 2.5.3 defines a C^1 parametrization of the curve (parabola) $(y - 2)^2 = (x - 1)$ in $\mathbb{R}^2$. The functions $g(t) = (\cos t, \sin t)$ and $h(t) = (\sin 2t, \cos 2t)$ of Example 2.5.8 define two different C^1 parametrizations of the curve (circle) $x^2 + y^2 = 1$ in $\mathbb{R}^2$. Notice that g and h trace the circle in opposite directions.

2.6.4 Example.   The function $f : \mathbb{R} \to \mathbb{R}^3$ defined by $f(t) = (t, \cos t, \sin t)$ is a C^1 parametrization of the circular helix curve sketched in Fig. 2.2.

2.6.5 Example.   The function $g : \mathbb{R} \to \mathbb{R}^2$ defined by $g(t) = (\sin t, \sin 2t)$ is a C^1 parametrization of the 'figure 8' curve sketched in Fig. 2.9. The arrows in Fig. 2.9 indicate the direction in which $g(t)$ traces the curve as t increases. Clearly g has period 2π and indeed the curve is traced just once in each interval of length 2π.

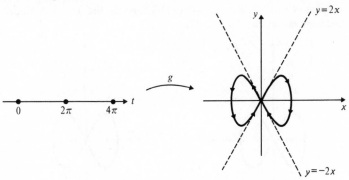

Fig. 2.9 $g(t) = (\sin t, \sin 2t), t \in \mathbb{R}$

In this section we shall consider the possibility of using a parametrization of a curve to define the tangent lines to it as we did in Examples 2.5.10 and 2.5.11. Example 2.5.16 indicates that care is needed, as do the following examples.

2.6.6 Example.   The function $g : \mathbb{R} \to \mathbb{R}^2$ defined by $g(t) = (t|t|, t^2)$ as in Example 2.5.17 is a C^1 parametrization of the curve $y = |x|$ in $\mathbb{R}^2$ sketched in Fig. 2.8(ii). There is no tangent line at 0.

2.6.7 *Example*.   Consider the C^1 parametrization $g(t) = (\sin t, \sin 2t)$ of the 'figure 8' curve defined in Example 2.6.5. In considering the properties of this curve at the cross-over point $(0, 0)$ we observe that $g(0) = g(\pi) = (0, 0)$. The derivative of g is given by

$$g'(t) = (\cos t, 2\cos 2t), \qquad t \in \mathbb{R}.$$

Hence $g'(0) = (1, 2)$ and the tangent line to g at 0 is $y = 2x$. On the other hand $g'(\pi) = (-1, 2)$ and the tangent line to g at π is $y = -2x$. These two lines are sketched in Fig. 2.9 as dotted lines through $g(0) = g(\pi) = (0, 0)$.

In general, $y = 2x$ is the tangent line to g at points of the form $2k\pi \in \mathbb{R}$, $k \in \mathbb{Z}$, and $y = -2x$ is the tangent line to g at points of the form $(2k + 1)\pi$, $k \in \mathbb{Z}$.

2.6.8 *Example*.   (i) The function g of Example 2.6.7 restricted to the open interval $]-\pi, \pi[$ leads to a 1–1 C^1 function $f :]-\pi, \pi[\subseteq \mathbb{R} \to \mathbb{R}^2$ defined by $f(t) = (\sin t, \sin 2t)$. The image of f is the same 'figure 8' curve sketched in Fig. 2.9. However, the only value of t for which $f(t) = (0, 0)$ is $t = 0$. The tangent line to f at 0 is $y = 2x$. The other significant line through $(0, 0)$, $y = -2x$, is not revealed by this parametrization of the curve. See Fig. 2.10 (i).

(ii) By restricting g to the open interval $]0, 2\pi[$, we obtain a 1–1 C^1 function $h :]0, 2\pi[\subseteq \mathbb{R} \to \mathbb{R}^2$ defined by $h(u) = (\sin u, \sin 2u)$. Again the image of h is the 'figure 8' curve. The only value of u for which $h(u) = (0, 0)$ is $u = \pi$. The tangent line to h at π is $y = -2x$. This time the line $y = 2x$ is hidden by the parametrization. See Fig. 2.10(ii).

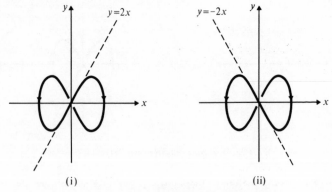

Fig. 2.10 (i) $f(t) = (\sin t, \sin 2t)$, $t \in]-\pi, \pi[$;
(ii) $h(u) = (\sin u, \sin 2u)$, $u \in]0, 2\pi[$

Nevertheless, we would expect that if two parametrizations of a curve are related in some way then they will associate the same tangent lines with points of the curve. Accordingly we define the following equivalence relation between parametrizations.

2.6.9 Definition. Two C^1 *parametrizations* $f : D \subseteq \mathbb{R} \to \mathbb{R}^n$ *and* $h : E \subseteq \mathbb{R} \to \mathbb{R}^n$ *of a curve C in $\mathbb{R}^n$ are* equivalent *if there is a differentiable function ϕ from E onto D such that*

[i] $h = f \circ \phi$ *and*

[ii] *either $\phi'(u) > 0$ for all $u \in E$ or $\phi'(u) < 0$ for all $u \in E$.*

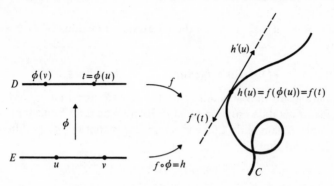

Fig. 2.11 Equivalent parametrizations of f and h with opposite orientations

See Fig. 2.11. Notice that ϕ may be strictly increasing (in which case f and h trace the curve in the same direction) or ϕ may be strictly decreasing (in which case they trace the curve in opposite directions). In the former case we say that f and h are *properly equivalent* or *equivalent with the same orientation* and in the latter case that they are *equivalent with opposite orientations*.

2.6.10 Example. The functions g and h considered in Example 2.5.8 were given by $g(t) = (\cos t, \sin t)$, $t \in \mathbb{R}$, and $h(u) = (\sin 2u, \cos 2u)$, $u \in \mathbb{R}$. They are both C^1 parametrizations of the unit circle in $\mathbb{R}^2$. Let $\phi : \mathbb{R} \to \mathbb{R}$ be defined by $\phi(u) = \frac{1}{2}\pi - 2u$, $u \in \mathbb{R}$. Then $h = g \circ \phi$ and $\phi'(u) < 0$ for all $u \in \mathbb{R}$. Hence g and h are equivalent parametrizations with opposite orientation – they trace the circle in opposite directions.

In order to relate the properties of equivalent parametrizations we need to know how their derivatives are related. The required result is a Chain Rule of the following type.

2.6.11 Theorem. (Chain Rule). *Let $\phi : E \subseteq \mathbb{R} \to \mathbb{R}$ and $f : D \subseteq \mathbb{R} \to \mathbb{R}^n$ be differentiable functions and let $\phi(E) \subseteq D$. Then $f \circ \phi : E \subseteq \mathbb{R} \to \mathbb{R}^n$ is differentiable, and for each $u \in E$,*

2.6.12 $$(f \circ \phi)'(u) = (f'(\phi(u)))\phi'(u).$$

Remark. We have written the scalar $\phi'(u)$ on the right of the vector $f'(\phi(u))$ in 2.6.12 in order to relate this theorem firstly to the elementary Chain Rule (Theorem 1.6.11) and secondly to generalizations in subsequent chapters.

Proof. For each $i = 1, \ldots, n$ the coordinate functions of $f \circ \phi$ and f satisfy

2.6.13 $$(f \circ \phi)_i(u) = f_i(\phi(u)), \qquad \text{for all } u \in E.$$

We are given that ϕ is differentiable at $u \in E$, and that f (and therefore f_i) is differentiable at $\phi(u)$. Expression 2.6.13 and the elementary Chain Rule 1.6.11 together imply that $(f \circ \phi)_i$ is differentiable at u and that

$$(f \circ \phi)_i'(u) = f_i'(\phi(u))\phi'(u).$$

The required conclusion follows from Theorem 2.5.7.

2.6.14 Example. Let $\phi : \mathbb{R} \to \mathbb{R}$ and $f : \mathbb{R} \to \mathbb{R}^3$ be defined by $\phi(u) = \sin u$, $u \in \mathbb{R}$ and $f(t) = (2t, t^3, 1)$, $t \in \mathbb{R}$. Then $(f \circ \phi)(u) = (2\sin u, \sin^3 u, 1)$, $u \in \mathbb{R}$. We have by way of illustration of the Chain Rule,

$$f'(\phi(u)) = (2, 3\sin^2 u, 0), \quad \phi'(u) = \cos u, \text{ and}$$
$$(f \circ \phi)'(u) = (2\cos u, 3\sin^2 u \cos u, 0), \qquad u \in \mathbb{R}.$$

The relationship $h = f \circ \phi$ will occur frequently when we compare the properties of two parametrizations f and h of a curve, as in the following theorem.

2.6.15 Theorem. *Let* $f : D \subseteq \mathbb{R} \to \mathbb{R}^n$ *and* $h : E \subseteq D \to \mathbb{R}^n$ *be equivalent* C^1 *parametrizations of a given curve C in $\mathbb{R}^n$ related by a differentiable function* $\phi : E \to D$ *with the properties given in Definition 2.6.9. Then, whenever* $\phi(u) = t$,

[i] *the tangent vector to f at t is in the same (opposite) direction as the tangent vector to h at u when f and h have the same (opposite) orientations;*

[ii] *the tangent lines to f at t and to h at u are the same if either of them exists.*

Proof. Immediate from the Chain Rule 2.6.11. The theorem is illustrated in Fig. 2.11, where f and h have opposite orientations, the tangent vectors being in opposite directions.

2.6.16 *Example.* The functions

$$g(t) = (\cos t, \sin t) \quad \text{and} \quad h(u) = (\sin 2u, \cos 2u)$$

considered in Example 2.6.10 are C^1 parametrizations of the unit circle with opposite orientations. For all $u \in \mathbb{R}$, $h(u) = g(\phi(u))$, where $\phi(u) = \frac{1}{2}\pi - 2u$, and the tangent vectors

$$h'(u) = (2\cos 2u, -2\sin 2u) \quad \text{and} \quad g'(\phi(u)) = (-\cos 2u, \sin 2u)$$

are in opposite directions. The tangent lines to h at u and to g at $\phi(u)$ are the same.

2.6.17 *Example.* Consider the functions

$$f(t) = (\sin t, \sin 2t),\ t \in]-\pi, \pi[$$

and

$$h(u) = (\sin u, \sin 2u),\ u \in]0, 2\pi[$$

of Example 2.6.8 which parametrize the 'figure 8' curve. If there were a differentiable function $\phi :]0, 2\pi[\to]-\pi, \pi[$ such that $h = f \circ \phi$ then, since $(0,0) = h(\pi) = f(\phi(\pi))$, we would have to have $\phi(\pi) = 0$. Furthermore by Theorem 2.6.15 (ii) the tangent line to h at π would be the same as the tangent line to f at $\phi(\pi) = 0$. But $h'(\pi) = (-1, 2)$ and $f'(0) = (1, 2)$, hence the tangent lines are different (see Fig. 2.10). Therefore no such ϕ exists.

So far, both in this section and the previous one, we have considered tangent lines to functions which parametrize curves. Intuitively, however, provided a curve C does not have a 'corner' at $\mathbf{q} \in C$ and provided C does not cross itself at $\mathbf{q}$, the tangent line to C at $\mathbf{q}$ exists and is independent of parametrization. We can exclude the possibility of corners by requiring that the parametrization should have non-zero derivative (see Example 2.5.17). We can exclude the possibility of crossovers by firstly requiring the parametrization to be 1–1 (see Example 2.6.7) and secondly requiring that its domain should be a compact interval $[a, b]$ (compare Example 2.6.8.).

2.6.18 *Definition.* *A function $f : D \subseteq \mathbb{R} \to \mathbb{R}^n$ is said to be* smooth *if it is C^1 (continuously differentiable) and if $f'(t) \neq \mathbf{0}$ for all $t \in D$.*

2.6.19 *Example.* There is no smooth parametrization of the curve $y = |x|$ in $\mathbb{R}^2$. See Fig. 2.8(ii).

2.6.20 Definition. *A curve C in* $\mathbb{R}^n$ *is a* (smooth) simple arc *if C has a* 1–1 (smooth) C^1 *parametrization of the form* $f : [a, b] \subseteq \mathbb{R} \to \mathbb{R}^n$. *The points* $f(a)$ *and* $f(b)$ *are then called the* end-points *of the arc.*

2.6.21 Example. Let $g : [a, b] \subseteq \mathbb{R} \to \mathbb{R}$ be a C^1 function. The graph G of g is a smooth simple arc in $\mathbb{R}^2$ parametrized by the smooth, 1–1 C^1 function $f : [a, b] \subseteq \mathbb{R} \to \mathbb{R}^2$ defined by

2.6.22 $$f(t) = (t, g(t)), \qquad t \in [a, b].$$

The end points of G are $(a, g(a))$ and $(b, g(b))$.

2.6.23 Theorem. *Let C be a smooth simple arc in* $\mathbb{R}^n$ *parametrized by a smooth* 1–1 *function* $f : [a, b] \subseteq \mathbb{R} \to \mathbb{R}^n$. *Then any smooth parametrization* $h : [c, d] \subseteq \mathbb{R} \to \mathbb{R}^n$ *of C is* 1–1 *and is equivalent to* f.

Proof. The function $\phi = f^{-1} \circ h$ is well defined, maps $[c, d]$ onto $[a, b]$ and satisfies $h = f \circ \phi$. See Fig. 2.12. Choose any $p \in [c, d]$.

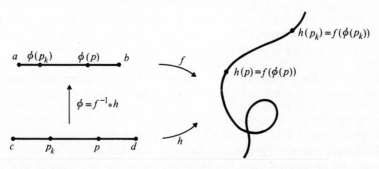

Fig. 2.12

(i) We begin by showing that ϕ is continuous at p. If it were not then there would be a sequence $p_k \to p$ in $[c, d]$ such that $\phi(p_k) \nrightarrow \phi(p)$ in $[a, b]$. Since $[a, b]$ is compact we may assume (by taking a subsequence if necessary – see Theorem 1.6.5) that

2.6.24 $$\phi(p_k) \to r \quad \text{in} \quad [a, b] \quad \text{and} \quad r \neq \phi(p).$$

But f is 1–1 and continuous, and $f \circ \phi = h$. Therefore, applying f to 2.6.24,

$$h(p_k) \to f(r) \quad \text{in} \quad C \quad \text{and} \quad f(r) \neq h(p).$$

This contradicts the continuity of h at p.

(ii) We next consider the differentiability of ϕ at p. Consider a sequence

2.6.25 $p_k \to p$ in $[c, d]$ with $p_k \neq p$ for all $k \in \mathbb{N}$.

We need to know that, for large k, $\phi(p_k) \neq \phi(p)$. This follows from the smoothness of h by considering the limit

$$\lim_{k \to \infty} \frac{f(\phi(p_k)) - f(\phi(p))}{p_k - p} = \lim_{k \to \infty} \frac{h(p_k) - h(p)}{p_k - p} \neq 0$$

Now, since f is smooth, we assume without loss of generality that $f_1'(\phi(p)) \neq 0$. Consider the identity

2.6.26 $\dfrac{h_1(p_k) - h_1(p)}{p_k - p} = \dfrac{f_1(\phi(p_k)) - f_1(\phi(p))}{\phi(p_k) - \phi(p)} \dfrac{\phi(p_k) - \phi(p)}{p_k - p}.$

Since ϕ is continuous at p, letting k tend to infinity in 2.6.26 establishes that ϕ is differentiable at p.

(iii) The above argument shows that ϕ is differentiable throughout $[a, b]$. Since $h = f \circ \phi$ the Chain Rule implies that

$$h'(u) = f'(\phi(u))\phi'(u), \qquad u \in [c, d].$$

Since h is smooth, it follows that $\phi'(u) \neq 0$ for all $u \in [c, d]$. Hence (by Rolle's Theorem) the functions ϕ and $h = f \circ \phi$ are 1–1. Finally, since ϕ is continuous and 1–1, ϕ is either strictly increasing (in which case ϕ' is positive) or strictly decreasing (in which case ϕ' is negative).

2.6.27 Corollary. *Let* **q** *be a point on a smooth simple arc* C *in* $\mathbb{R}^n$. *Then all smooth parametrizations of* C *associate the same tangent line with* **q**.

Remark.   In view of this corollary we can talk about the tangent line to a smooth simple arc C at a point **q** on C.

Proof.   Theorem 2.6.23 implies that two smooth parametrizations of C are equivalent and so the result follows from Theorem 2.6.15.

2.6.28 Example.   Consider again the smooth simple arc G which is the graph of a C^1 function $g : [a, b] \subseteq \mathbb{R} \to \mathbb{R}$ (see Example 2.6.21). From 2.6.22 the tangent line to G at $(t, g(t))$ is in direction $(1, g'(t))$.

If G is smoothly parametrized by $(x(u), y(u))$, then the tangent line at $(x(u), y(u))$ has direction $(x'(u), y'(u))$. Hence

2.6.29
$$g'(x(u)) = \frac{y'(u)}{x'(u)}.$$

Informally, 2.6.29 expresses the fact that if a graph $y = g(x)$ is smoothly parametrized by $(x(u), y(u))$ then

$$\frac{dy}{dx} = \frac{dy/du}{dx/du}.$$

Since, by Theorem 2.6.23, any two smooth parametrizations of a smooth simple arc are equivalent, the smooth parametrizations of such an arc divide into two classes according to their orientation.

2.6.30 Definition. *Let C be a smooth simple arc in* $\mathbb{R}^n$ *parametrized by a smooth function* $f : [a, b] \subseteq \mathbb{R} \to \mathbb{R}^n$. *The pair* $\{C, [f]\}$, *where* $[f]$ *is the set of all smooth parametrizations of C which are properly equivalent to f, is called an* oriented simple arc.

To every smooth simple arc C there correspond precisely two oriented simple arcs. If **a** and **b** are the end points of C, the two possible orientations can be described as being from **a** to **b** and from **b** to **a** respectively. See Fig. 2.13.

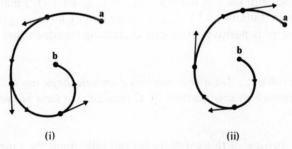

(i)   (ii)

Fig. 2.13 Smooth simple arc with two possible orientations
  (i) Orientation from **a** to **b**
  (ii) Orientation from **b** to **a**

Exercises 2.6

1. Verify that the following subsets C of $\mathbb{R}^2$ are curves in $\mathbb{R}^2$ according to Definition 2.6.2. In each case find a C^1 parametrization of C and sketch the curve.
    (a) The y-axis, $x = 0$;

(b) part of the y-axis, $x = 0$, $-1 \leqslant y \leqslant 2$;

(c) the parabola $y + 1 = (x - 2)^2$;

(d) the circle $(x - 1)^2 + (y - 2)^2 = 4$;

(e) the ellipse $4x^2 + y^2 = 1$;

(f) the subset C defined by $x = |y|$;

(g) the subset C defined by $x = |y|$, $0 \leqslant x \leqslant 1$;

(h) the subset C defined by $y^2 = x^3$, $0 \leqslant x \leqslant 1$;

(i) the subset C parametrized by

$$f(t) = (\sin 2t \cos t, \sin 2t \sin t), \qquad 0 \leqslant t \leqslant 2\pi.$$

Answers: (a) $(0, t)$, $t \in \mathbb{R}$, alternatively $(0, t^3)$, $t \in \mathbb{R}$. For each example there are many possibilities;   (b) $(0, t)$, $-1 \leqslant t \leqslant 2$;   (c) $(t, (t - 2)^2 - 1)$, alternatively $(t + 2, t^2 - 1)$;   (d) $(1 + 2\cos t, 2 + 2\sin t)$; (e) $(\frac{1}{2}\cos t, \sin t)$;   (f) $(t^2, t|t|)$;   (g) $(t^2, t|t|)$, $-1 \leqslant t \leqslant 1$; (h) (t^2, t^3), $-1 \leqslant t \leqslant 1$;   (i)$C^1$ parametrization as given. The curve has four 'petals' meeting at the origin.

2. Which of the curves in Exercise 1 can be smoothly parametrized?

Answer: all except (f), (g), (h).

3. Which of the curves in Exercise 1 are simple arcs? Which are smooth simple arcs?

Answer: (b), (g), (h) are simple arcs; of these, only (b) is smooth.

4. For each of the curves C of Exercise 1 find, where appropriate, the equation of the tangent line to C at the point $\mathbf{q} = (a, b)$ on C. Indicate points on C where no tangent line exists.

(*Hint*: using an appropriate parametrization, apply the method of Section 2.5.)

Answers: (a) $x = 0$,

   (c) $y - b = (2a - 4)(x - a)$, where $b = (a - 2)^2 + 1$;

   (e) $(x, y) = (\frac{1}{2}\cos \alpha, \sin \alpha) + s(-\frac{1}{2}\sin \alpha, \cos \alpha)$, $s \in \mathbb{R}$, where $a = \frac{1}{2}\cos \alpha$, $b = \sin \alpha$. For example, the tangent line to C at $(\frac{1}{2}, 0)$ is $x = \frac{1}{2}$, and the tangent line to C at $(\frac{1}{4}, -\frac{1}{2}\sqrt{3})$ is $y + \frac{1}{2}\sqrt{3} = (2/\sqrt{3})(x - \frac{1}{4})$. No tangent lines to C at $(0, 0)$ in examples (f) – (i) inclusive.)

5. Indicate on your sketches of the curves C of Exercise 1 the orientation assigned to C by your choice of C^1 parametrization $f : D \subseteq \mathbb{R} \to \mathbb{R}^n$. (Use arrows to indicate the direction in which C is traced.)

   Obtain in each case an equivalent parametrization $h = f \circ \phi$ where $\phi(u) = -u$, and verify that the orientation assigned to C by h is opposite to that assigned to C by f.

6. Sketch the simple arc C parametrized by the (not smooth) C^1 function

$f:[-1, 1] \subseteq \mathbb{R} \to \mathbb{R}^2$ defined by $f(t) = (t^3, t^5)$. By finding a suitable smooth C^1 re-parametrization of C, show that C is a smooth simple arc.

Answer: $h(u) = (u, u^{5/3})$, $u \in [-1, 1]$.

7. Sketch the curve C in $\mathbb{R}^2$ smoothly parametrized by

$$g(t) = ((2\cos t - 1)\cos t, (2\cos t - 1)\sin t), t \in [0, 2\pi].$$

Show that $(0, 0) = g(\pi/3) = g(5\pi/3)$, but $g'(\pi/3) \neq g'(5\pi/3)$. Interpret this on your sketch.

Using the method of Examples 2.6.7 and 2.6.8, obtain $1-1$ C^1 parametrizations f and h of C such that (a) for $p \in \mathbb{R}$ such that $f(p) = (0, 0)$, $f'(p) = g'(\pi/3)$, (b) for $q \in \mathbb{R}$ such that $h(q) = (0, 0)$, $h'(q) = g'(5\pi/3)$.

8. Prove that the equivalence of C^1 parametrizations given in Definition 2.6.9 is an equivalence relation on the class of all C^1 parametrizations of curves in $\mathbb{R}^n$.

Hint: Prove symmetry by applying Theorem 1.6.7.

9. Given that $\phi(u) = \sin u$, $u \in E \subseteq \mathbb{R}$, and $f(t) = (t^2, \sqrt{t})$, $t \geq 0$, find a suitable interval E such that $f \circ \phi$ is defined and differentiable on E. Apply the Chain Rule 2.6.11 to calculate $(f \circ \phi)'(u)$, $u \in E$.

10. Apply the Chain Rule 2.6.11 to calculate $h'(u)$, where
   (a) $h(u) = (\exp(\sin u), 2(\sin u)^2)$, $u \in \mathbb{R}$;
   (b) $h(u) = (2\cos\sqrt{u}, \sin\sqrt{u})$, $u > 0$.

11. Sketch the curve C parametrized by $f: \mathbb{R} \to \mathbb{R}^2$, where $f(t) = (t - \sin t, 1 - \cos t), t \in \mathbb{R}$ (The curve C is called a *cycloid*. A point fixed on the rim of a unit circle traces C when the circle rolls along the x-axis.) Prove that C is not the graph of a differentiable function.

Hint: consider the points $t = 2k\pi$, $k \in \mathbb{N}$.

12. Let C be a curve smoothly parametrized by a C^1 function $f(t) = (f_1(t), f_2(t))$, $t \in D$, where $f'_1(t) > 0$ for all $t \in D$. Prove that C is the graph of a C^1 function $g: D_1 \subseteq \mathbb{R} \to \mathbb{R}$, where $D_1 = f_1(D)$.

(*Hint*: apply Theorem 1.6.7. The required function is the composite function $f_2 \circ f_1^{-1}$.)

Deduce that the part of the cycloid (Exercise 11) which is the image of f on the open interval $]0, 2\pi[$ is the graph of a differentiable function.

13. The following exercise illustrates Example 2.6.28. Sketch the simple arc G which is the graph of the C^1 function

$$g(t) = \sqrt{(1 - t^2)}, \qquad t \in [-\tfrac{1}{2}, \tfrac{1}{2}].$$

Indicate the tangent lines to G at $(t, g(t))$ for the cases $t = -\frac{1}{2}$, $t = 0$ and $t = \frac{1}{2}$.

Verify that G is smoothly parametrized by

$$(x(\theta), y(\theta)) = (\cos\theta, \sin\theta), \qquad \theta \in [\pi/3, 2\pi/3],$$

and that

$$g'(x(\theta)) = \frac{y'(\theta)}{x'(\theta)} = -\cot\theta.$$

2.7 Path length and length of simple arcs

As a particle moves about in space its position can be regarded as a function of time. Choosing coordinate systems for space and time enables us to describe the motion of the particle over a finite time interval by a function $f : [a, b] \subseteq \mathbb{R} \to \mathbb{R}^3$, where the particle has position vector $f(t)$ at time t units. In most applications there will be no instantaneous jumps in the motion and so the corresponding function will be continuous. This leads us to the following definition.

2.7.1 Definition.   *A continuous function $f : [a, b] \subseteq \mathbb{R} \to \mathbb{R}^n$ is called a path in $\mathbb{R}^n$ from $f(a)$ to $f(b)$. The path is differentiable, C^1 or smooth if the function f is respectively differentiable, C^1 or smooth.*

The image of a C^1 path is a curve and the image of a $1-1$ smooth path is a smooth simple arc.

When a C^1 path f describes the motion of a particle in $\mathbb{R}^n$, the distance travelled by the particle in the time interval between t and $t + \Delta t$, for small positive Δt, is approximately $\| f(t + \Delta t) - f(t) \|$. This distance, by definition of the derivative, is approximately $\| f'(t) \| \Delta t$. Accordingly, the length of the path is defined as follows.

2.7.2 Definition.   *Let $f : [a, b] \subseteq \mathbb{R} \to \mathbb{R}^n$ be a C^1 path in $\mathbb{R}^n$. The length of f is defined to be*

$$l(f) = \int_a^b \| f'(t) \| \, \mathrm{d}t.$$

2.7.3 Example.   The function $g : [-r, r] \subseteq \mathbb{R} \to \mathbb{R}^2$ defined by

$$g(u) = (u, \sqrt{(r^2 - u^2)}), \qquad u \in [-r, r]$$

is a path in $\mathbb{R}^2$ whose image is a semi-circle of radius $r > 0$. However, g is not a C^1 path (why?).

We can reparametrize the semi-circle by defining a C^1 path $f : [0, \pi] \subseteq \mathbb{R} \to \mathbb{R}^2$ by

$$f(t) = (-r\cos t, r\sin t), \qquad t \in [0, \pi].$$

We have $f'(t) = (r\sin t, r\cos t)$, and so $\|f'(t)\| = r$. Hence

$$l(f) = \int_0^\pi r\,\mathrm{d}t = \pi r.$$

2.7.4 Example. The function $f : [0, 2\pi] \subseteq \mathbb{R} \to \mathbb{R}^2$ defined by

$$f(t) = (\cos 2t, \sin 2t), \qquad t \in [0, 2\pi]$$

is a C^1 path parametrizing the unit circle, and

$$\|f'(t)\| = 2\|(-\sin 2t, \cos 2t)\| = 2.$$

Hence

$$l(f) = \int_0^{2\pi} 2\,\mathrm{d}t = 4\pi.$$

As expected, $l(f)$ is twice the circumference of the unit circle which $f(t)$ traverses twice.

2.7.5 Example. The 1-1 C^1 path $f : [-1, 1] \subseteq \mathbb{R} \to \mathbb{R}^2$ defined by

$$f(t) = (t^2, t^3), \qquad t \in [-1, 1]$$

has image curve lying in the semi-cubical parabola $y^2 = x^3$ (see Fig. 2.14). We have $f'(t) = (2t, 3t^2)$, and so

$$l(f) = \int_{-1}^1 \sqrt{(4t^2 + 9t^4)}\,\mathrm{d}t = 2\int_0^1 t\sqrt{4 + 9t^2}\,\mathrm{d}t.$$

The substitution $u(t) = 4 + 9t^2$ leads to $l(f) = \frac{2}{27}(13\sqrt{13} - 8)$.

We would expect that if two C^1 paths trace the points of a curve in the same order, then their lengths would be the same. Similarly, we would expect that the length of a C^1 path is the same as the length of the C^1 path which traces the points of the curve in the reverse order. These impressions are confirmed by the following theorem.

2.7.6 Theorem. *Let* $f : [a, b] \subseteq \mathbb{R} \to \mathbb{R}^n$ *and* $h : [c, d] \subseteq \mathbb{R} \to \mathbb{R}^n$ *be two equivalent* C^1 *paths parametrizing a curve* C *in* $\mathbb{R}^n$. *Then* $l(f) = l(h)$.

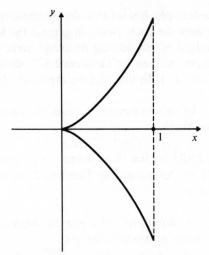

Fig. 2.14 Image of $f(t) = (t^2, t^3)$, $t \in [-1, 1]$

Proof. Since f and h are equivalent, there exists a $1-1$ differentiable function ϕ mapping $[c, d]$ onto $[a, b]$ such that $h = f \circ \phi$. Furthermore, either $\phi'(u) > 0$ for all $u \in [c, d]$, in which case $a = \inf \phi = \phi(c)$ and $b = \sup \phi = \phi(d)$, or $\phi'(u) < 0$ for all $u \in [c, d]$, in which case $b = \phi(c)$ and $a = \phi(d)$.

It follows from the Chain Rule (Theorem 2.6.11) that

$$\|h'(u)\| = \|f'(\phi(u))\| \, |\phi'(u)|, \qquad u \in [c, d].$$

Therefore, since h and f are smooth and one of the above alternatives is true, ϕ' is continuous. Hence, by the substitution rule (treating the above alternatives separately),

$$l(h) = \int_c^d \|h'(u)\| \, du = \int_c^d \|f'(\phi(u))\| \, |\phi'(u)| \, du$$

$$= \int_a^b \|f'(t)\| \, dt = l(f).$$

2.7.7 Example. The function $h : [-2\pi, 2\pi] \subseteq \mathbb{R} \to \mathbb{R}^2$ defined by

$$h(u) = (\cos u, \, -\sin u), \qquad u \in [-2\pi, 2\pi],$$

is a C^1 path parametrizing the unit circle. It is equivalent to the C^1 path f defined in Example 2.7.4 (consider $\phi(u) = \pi - \frac{1}{2}u$). As expected

$$l(h) = \int_{-2\pi}^{2\pi} \|h'(u)\| \, du = 4\pi = l(f).$$

In the previous example, $l(h)$ is twice the circumference of the unit circle because h traces the circle twice. In general the length of a C^1 path cannot be judged by considering its image curve C. However, if C is a smooth simple arc then by Theorem 2.6.23 all smooth parametrizations of C are 1–1. In this case we expect the following result.

2.7.8 Corollary.   *All smooth parametrizations of a smooth simple arc in* $\mathbb{R}^n$ *have the same length.*

Proof.   Theorem 2.6.23 implies that all smooth parametrizations of a smooth simple arc are equivalent. By Theorem 2.7.6, they therefore have the same length.

2.7.9 Definition.   *The* length $l(C)$ *of a smooth simple arc* C *in* $\mathbb{R}^n$ *is the length of any smooth parametrization of* C.

2.7.10 Example.   Let G be the graph of the C^1 function $g:[a, b] \subseteq \mathbb{R} \to \mathbb{R}$ considered in Example 2.6.28. Suppose that G is smoothly parametrized by $(x(u), y(u))$, $u \in [c, d]$. Then

$$l(G) = \int_a^b \sqrt{(1 + g'(x)^2)}\,dx = \int_c^d \sqrt{(x'(u)^2 + y'(u)^2)}\,du.$$

The natural parametrization of a curve (the one which would be chosen by a small creature living on the curve!) is one in which the parameter s measures the distance along the curve from some fixed base point p. Such a parametrization $h : E \subseteq \mathbb{R} \to \mathbb{R}^n$, if it exists, is readily identified since it requires that for all a and b in E the distance traversed from $s = a$ to $s = b$ is given by

$$\int_a^b \|h'(s)\|\,ds = b - a.$$

An equivalent requirement is that $\|h'(s)\| = 1$ for all $s \in E$ (Exercise 2.7.9). This motivates the following definition.

2.7.11 Definition.   *A* C^1 *parametrization* $h : E \subseteq \mathbb{R} \to \mathbb{R}^n$ *of a curve* C *in* $\mathbb{R}^n$ *is a* path-length parametrization *of* C *if* $\|h'(s)\| = 1$ *for all* $s \in E$. Clearly such a parametrization is smooth.

2.7.12 Example.   The function $h : \mathbb{R} \to \mathbb{R}^2$ defined by

$$h(s) = \left(r\cos\frac{s}{r}, r\sin\frac{s}{r} \right), \qquad s \in \mathbb{R},$$

is a path-length parametrization of the circle in $\mathbb{R}^2$ with centre $(0, 0)$ and radius r. The length of the path between $s = a$ and $s = b$ is $b - a$.

We shall now show that general smooth parametrizations can be studied by considering equivalent path-length parametrizations.

2.7.13 Definition. *Let $f : D \subseteq \mathbb{R} \to \mathbb{R}^n$ be a smooth parametrization of a curve C in $\mathbb{R}^n$. Choose a base point $p \in D$. The* path-length *function based at p is the function $\lambda : D \subseteq \mathbb{R} \to \mathbb{R}$ defined by*

2.7.14
$$\lambda(t) = \int_p^t \| f'(u) \| \, du, \qquad t \in D.$$

Thinking of f as representing the motion of a particle in $\mathbb{R}^n$ over a time interval D, the number $s = \lambda(t)$ indicates the distance travelled by the particle in the time interval between p and t (with the convention that if $t < p$ then the distance is negative). We find from 2.7.14 that the speed of f at t is given by

2.7.15
$$\lambda'(t) = \| f'(t) \| > 0, \qquad t \in D.$$

This derivative clearly does not depend upon the base point chosen.

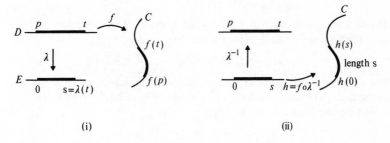

(i)   (ii)

Fig. 2.15

Definition 2.7.13 is illustrated in Fig. 2.15(i). Since λ is continuous, the set $E = \lambda(D)$ is an interval in $\mathbb{R}$. Furthermore, by 2.7.15, λ is a $1-1$ function whose inverse function $\lambda^{-1} : E \to D$ has positive derivative throughout E. Comparison of Fig. 2.15(i) and Fig. 2.11 suggests that we can use s as a parameter in a parametrization of C that is properly equivalent to f.

2.7.16 Theorem. *For any smooth parametrization $f : D \subseteq \mathbb{R} \to \mathbb{R}^n$ of a* *curve C in $\mathbb{R}^n$ there is a path-length parametrization $h : E \subseteq \mathbb{R} \to \mathbb{R}^n$ of C which is properly equivalent to f.*

Proof.   The proof is illustrated in Fig. 2.15(ii). Chose a base point $p \in D$ and let $\lambda : D \subseteq \mathbb{R} \to \mathbb{R}$ be the path-length function based at p given by 2.7.14. Let $E = \lambda(D)$ and define $h = f \circ \lambda^{-1} : E \subseteq \mathbb{R} \to \mathbb{R}^n$. By 2.7.15, h is properly equivalent to f. Also, since $f = h \circ \lambda$, it follows from the Chain Rule and 2.7.15 that

$$\| f'(t) \| = \| h'(\lambda(t)) \| \, |\lambda'(t)| = \| h'(\lambda(t)) \| \, \| f'(t) \|.$$

Therefore $\| h'(s) \| = 1$ for all $s \in E$.

2.7.17 Example.   The image of the continuously differentiable function $f : \mathbb{R} \to \mathbb{R}^3$ defined by

$$f(t) = (at, \, b\cos \omega t, \, b\sin \omega t), \qquad t \in \mathbb{R},$$

where $b > 0$ and $\omega > 0$, is a helix wound around a cylinder of radius b whose axis is the x-axis in $\mathbb{R}^3$. The helix corresponding to $a = b = \omega = 1$ is sketched in Fig. 2.2. Now

$$f'(t) = (a, \, -b\omega \sin \omega t, \, b\omega \cos \omega t), \qquad t \in \mathbb{R},$$

and

$$\| f'(t) \| = (a^2 + b^2 \omega^2)^{1/2}, \qquad t \in \mathbb{R}.$$

Hence f is smooth, since $a^2 + b^2 \omega^2 \neq 0$. Choose $0 \in \mathbb{R}$ as base point. The path-length function $\lambda : \mathbb{R} \to \mathbb{R}$ is defined by

$$\lambda(t) = (a^2 + b^2 \omega^2)^{1/2} t, \qquad t \in \mathbb{R}.$$

For example, the image of any closed interval of length $2\pi/\omega$ is a single twist of the helix, and hence the length of a single twist is $2\pi(a^2 + b^2 \omega^2)^{1/2}\omega$.

The inverse function $\lambda^{-1} : \mathbb{R} \to \mathbb{R}$ is given by

$$\lambda^{-1}(s) = (a^2 + b^2 \omega^2)^{-1/2} s, \qquad s \in \mathbb{R}.$$

Let $c = (a^2 + b^2 \omega^2)^{1/2}$. A path-length parametrization properly equivalent to f is given by

$$h(s) = f(\lambda^{-1}(s)) = \left[\frac{as}{c}, \, b\cos \frac{\omega s}{c}, \, b\sin \frac{\omega s}{c} \right], \qquad s \in \mathbb{R}.$$

As expected (from Theorem 2.7.16), for all $s \in \mathbb{R}$,

$$\| h'(s) \| = \left\| \left(\frac{a}{c}, \, -\frac{b\omega}{c} \sin \frac{\omega s}{c}, \frac{b\omega}{c} \cos \frac{\omega s}{c} \right) \right\| = \left[\frac{a^2 + b^2 \omega^2}{c^2} \right]^{1/2} = 1.$$

Finally in this section we consider how the above material can be adjusted to cope with parametrizations which fail to be C^1 at a finite number of points.

2.7.18 *Example*. Consider the path $f : [-1, 1] \subseteq \mathbb{R} \to \mathbb{R}^2$ defined by

$$f(t) = (t, |t|), \qquad t \in [-1, 1],$$

whose image is shown in Fig. 2.8(ii). The path f is not a C^1 path because f is not differentiable at 0. However, we may regard f as being composed of two pieces, each a C^1 path, $f_1 : [-1, 0] \subseteq \mathbb{R} \to \mathbb{R}^2$ and $f_2 : [0, 1] \subseteq \mathbb{R} \to \mathbb{R}^2$, where $f_1(t) = f(t) = (t, -t)$ when $t \in [-1, 0]$ and $f_2(t) = f(t) = (t, t)$ when $t \in [0, 1]$.

We define

$$l(f) = l(f_1) + l(f_2) = \int_{-1}^{0} \| f_1'(t) \| \, dt + \int_{0}^{1} \| f_2'(t) \| \, dt$$

$$= \int_{-1}^{1} \| f'(t) \| \, dt,$$

where in the last integral the integrand is undefined at $t = 0$. Since $\| f'(t) \| = \sqrt{2}, \; t \neq 0$, it follows that $l(f) = 2\sqrt{2}$.

Example 2.7.18 illustrates a piecewise C^1 path. The general definition is as follows.

2.7.19 *Definition*. *A path $f : [a, b] \subseteq \mathbb{R} \to \mathbb{R}^n$ is said to be* piecewise continuously differentiable (piecewise C^1) *if there is a subdivision $a = p_0 < p_1 < \cdots < p_r = b$ of $[a, b]$ such that for each $k = 1, \ldots, r$ the function f restricted to the sub-interval $[p_{k-1}, p_k]$ is C^1.*

The length *of the piecewise C^1 path f is defined to be*

$$l(f) = \sum_{1}^{r} \int_{p_{k-1}}^{p_k} \| f'(t) \| \, dt = \int_{a}^{b} \| f'(t) \| \, dt.$$

Notice that the piecewise C^1 function f considered in Definition 2.7.19 may not be differentiable at p_k for $k = 1, \ldots, r - 1$. However, the fact that f is differentiable on $[p_{k-1}, p_k]$ and on $[p_k, p_{k+1}]$ requires that both the left-hand and right-hand derivatives of f at p_k must exist.

2.7.20 *Example*. The path $f : [-1, 1] \subseteq \mathbb{R} \to \mathbb{R}^2$ considered in Example 2.7.18 is piecewise C^1 (consider the partition $-1 < 0 < 1$ of $[-1, 1]$). The function f is not differentiable at 0. However, the left-hand derivative of f at 0 is $(1, -1)$ and the right-hand derivative of f at 0 is $(1, 1)$.

The image curve C of the path f is sketched in Fig. 2.8(ii). Compare this parametrization of C with the parametrization $g : [-1, 1] \subseteq \mathbb{R} \rightarrow \mathbb{R}^2$ of C given by

$$g(t) = \begin{cases} (-t^2, t^2) & \text{when } t \in [-1, 0], \\ (t^2, t^2) & \text{when } t \in [0, 1]. \end{cases}$$

The function g is a C^1 parametrization of C.

Furthermore f and g have a weaker form of proper equivalence, since if $\phi : [-1, 1] \rightarrow [-1, 1]$ is defined by

$$\phi(t) = \begin{cases} -\sqrt{-t} & \text{when } t \in [-1, 0] \\ \sqrt{t} & \text{when } t \in [0, 1], \end{cases}$$

then ϕ is strictly increasing and differentiable except at 0, and $g = f \circ \phi$.

2.7.21 Remark. The process adopted in Example 2.7.20 may be thought of as smoothing out a piecewise C^1 parametrization to give a 'properly equivalent' C^1 parametrization of the same curve in the weaker sense described above. In fact, given any piecewise C^1 parametrization of a curve there is a C^1 parametrization which is 'properly equivalent' to it in this sense. The reader is recommended to prove this statement, by developing an appropriate 'smoothing process'.

Exercises 2.7

1. Calculate the lengths of the following smooth simple arcs in $\mathbb{R}^3$.
    (a) The circular helix parametrized by

    $$f(t) = (t, \cos t, \sin t), \qquad t \in [a, b];$$

    (b) the curve parametrized by

    $$f(t) = (e^t \cos t, e^t \sin t, e^t) \qquad t \in [0, k].$$

    Answers: (a) $\sqrt{2}(b - a);$ (b) $\sqrt{3}(e^k - 1)$.

2. Sketch the following smooth simple arcs in $\mathbb{R}^2$ and calculate their length.
    (a) The curve parametrized by $f(t) = (e^t \cos t, e^t \sin t), t \in [1, 2]$;
    (b) the graph (catenary) $y = \cosh x = \frac{1}{2}(e^x + e^{-x})$ between $x = -1$ and $x = 1$;
    (c) the portion of the parabola $y^2 = 16x$ which lies between the lines $x = 0$ and $x = 4$.

    Answers: (a) $\sqrt{2}(e^2 - e);$ (b) $e - e^{-1};$ (c) $2\sqrt{2} + 2\ln(\sqrt{2} + 1)$.

3. Which of the following two paths in $\mathbb{R}^3$ from $(0, 0, 0)$ to $(1, 1, 1)$ is the longer? (a) $f(t) = (t, t, t^2), 0 \le t \le 1$; (b) $g(t) = (t, t^2, t^2), 0 \le t \le 1$.

4. The semi-ellipse E with equation

$$\frac{x^2}{a^2} + \frac{y^2}{b^2} = 1, \qquad y \geqslant 0,$$

is smoothly parametrized by $f(t) = (a\cos t, b\sin t), 0 \leqslant t \leqslant \pi$. Prove that if $a > b$, then the length of E is given by

$$l(E) = 2a \int_0^{(1/2)\pi} \sqrt{(1 - k^2\sin^2 t)}\,dt,$$

where $k^2 = (a^2 - b^2)/a^2$. The integral is called an *elliptic integral*. There exist tables of elliptic integrals from which its value can be obtained for various values fo k.

5. (a) Sketch the simple arc C

$$x^{2/3} + y^{2/3} = 1, \qquad 0 \leqslant y \leqslant 1.$$

Verify that C is parametrized by the 1–1 C^1 path

$$f(t) = (\cos^3 t, \sin^3 t), \qquad 0 \leqslant t \leqslant \pi.$$

Show that C is not a smooth simple arc. (Consider the point $f(\tfrac{1}{2}\pi)$.)
(b) Call a simple arc C in $\mathbb{R}^n$ piecewise smooth if it has a 1–1 C^1 parametrization $f : [a, b] \subseteq \mathbb{R} \to \mathbb{R}^n$ such that $f'(t) = 0$ for at most a finite number of $t \in [a, b]$. Prove that all piecewise smooth parametrizations of C have the same length. Hence frame a definition of the length $l(C)$ of C.
(c) Find the length of the simple arc of part (a) of this exercise.

Answer: 3.

6. Calculate the length of an arch of the cycloid $f(t) = (t - \sin t, 1 - \cos t)$, $t \in [0, 2\pi]$.

Answer: 8.

7. A curve C in $\mathbb{R}^n$ is a (smooth) *simple closed curve* if C has a (smooth) C^1 parametrization of the form $f : [a, b] \subseteq \mathbb{R} \to \mathbb{R}^n$ such that $f(a) = f(b)$ and f is 1–1 on the half-open interval $[a, b[$. The length of C is then unambiguously defined by

$$l(C) = l(f) = \int_a^b \| f'(t) \|\,dt.$$

Sketch the following simple closed curves and find their length.
(a) The circle $x^2 + y^2 = 9$ (parametrize by $f(t) = (3\cos t, 3\sin t)$, $0 \leqslant t \leqslant 2\pi$);

(b)   the *cardioid* (a heart-shaped curve) parametrized by

$$f(t) = ((1 + \cos t)\cos t, (1 + \cos t)\sin t), \qquad 0 \leqslant t \leqslant 2\pi.$$

(c)   the curve (circle!) parametrized by

$$f(t) = (2 - 2\cos t, 2\sin t), \qquad 0 \leqslant t \leqslant 2\pi.$$

(d)   the curve (circle!) parametrized by

$$f(t) = (\sin t \cos t, \sin^2 t) \qquad 0 \leqslant t \leqslant \pi.$$

(e)   the four-pointed star (*hypocycloid* of four cusps) $x^{2/3} + y^{2/3} = 1$.

Answers: (a) 6;   (b) 8;   (c) 4;   (d) π;   (e) 6.

8.   Let $f : [a, b] \subseteq \mathbb{R} \to \mathbb{R}^2$ be a C^1 path in $\mathbb{R}^2$ defined by

$$f(t) = (r(t)\cos t, r(t)\sin t), \qquad t \in [a, b],$$

where $r(t) \geqslant 0$ for all $t \in [a, b]$.
Prove that the length of f is

$$l(f) = \int_a^b \sqrt{[r(t)^2 + r'(t)^2]}\, dt.$$

Hence find the lengths of the following curves of Exercise 7:
(a) the circle $r(t) = 3$;
(b) the cardioid $r(t) = 1 + \cos t$;
(c) the circle $r(t) = \sin t$.

(*Note*: the path f is said to be in *polar coordinate* form. The point $f(t)$ lies on the circle centre the origin, radius $r(t)$, at an angle t from the x-axis.)

9.   Let $h : E \subseteq \mathbb{R} \to \mathbb{R}^n$ be a C^1 function. Prove that if for all a, b in E

$$\int_a^b \|h'(s)\|\, ds = b - a,$$

then $\|h'(s)\| = 1$ for all $s \in E$.

(*Hint*: fix a, and treat b as variable. Differentiate with respect to b.)

10.   Find path-length parametrizations h that are properly equivalent to the given smooth parametrizations f of the following curves.
(a)   The unit circle $f(t) = (\cos 2t, \sin 2t)$, $t \in \mathbb{R}$;
(b)   the smooth simple arc in $\mathbb{R}^3$ parametrized by

$$f(t) = (e^t \cos t, e^t \sin t, e^t), \qquad t \in [0, \pi].$$

Answers: with base point 0
(a) $\lambda(t) = 2t$, $h(s) = f(\lambda^{-1}(s)) = (\cos s, \sin s)$;
(b) $\lambda(t) = 3(e^t - 1)$, $\lambda^{-1}(s) = \ln(1 + (s/\sqrt{3}))$, $s \in [0, \sqrt{3}(e^\pi - 1)]$,
$h = f \circ \lambda^{-1}$.

2.8 Differential geometry

In this section we shall show how the twisting and turning of a curve in $\mathbb{R}^n$ can be expressed in terms of the derivatives of a path-length parametrization. We shall then use Theorem 2.7.16 to extend the results to more general parametrizations.

Let $h : E \subseteq \mathbb{R} \to \mathbb{R}^n$ be a twice-differentiable path-length parametrization of the curve $C = h(E)$. Since $\|h'(s)\| = 1$ for all $s \in E$, the vector $h''(s)$ indicates the way in which the unit tangent vector $h'(s)$ is changing direction near s. The larger the value of $\|h''(s)\|$, the greater is the 'curving' of C at s.

By Theorem 2.5.14 $h''(s)$ is orthogonal to $h'(s)$.

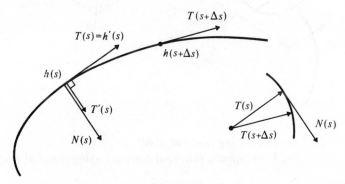

Fig. 2.16

2.8.1 Definition. *Let $h : E \subseteq \mathbb{R} \to \mathbb{R}^n$ be a twice-differentiable path-length parametrization of a curve $h(E)$ in $\mathbb{R}^n$.*

[i] *The unit tangent vector $h'(s)$ at $s \in E$ will also be denoted by $T(s)$.*

[ii] *The non-negative number*

$$\kappa(s) = \|T'(s)\| = \|h''(s)\|, \qquad s \in E,$$

is called the curvature *of h at s.*

[iii] *If $\kappa(s) \neq 0$, then the unit vector $N(s)$ such that*

$$T'(s) = \kappa(s)N(s)$$

is called the principal normal *to h at s. (If $\kappa(s) = 0$, the principal normal is not defined at s.)*

[iv] *The plane in $\mathbb{R}^n$ through $h(s)$ parallel to the subspace spanned by $T(s)$ and $N(s)$ is called the* osculating plane *of h at s.*

Since $\kappa(s) > 0$ in (iii), the principal normal $N(s)$ and the vector

$T'(s)$ point in the same direction. In fact, as shown in Fig. 2.16, that direction is towards the concave side of the curve.

The osculating plane is illustrated in Fig. 2.17(i). Note that the vectors $T(s)$ and $N(s)$ are orthogonal for all $s \in E$. This follows from the earlier remark that $h'(s)$ and $h''(s)$ are orthogonal.

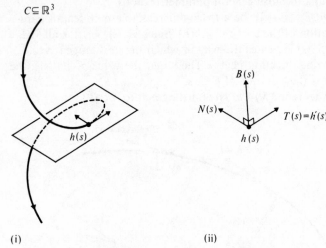

(i)   (ii)

Fig. 2.17 (i) Osculating plane at $h(s)$;
               (ii) Unit tangent, principal normal and binormal at $h(s)$

2.8.2 *Example*.   For the path-length parametrization of the helix given in Example 2.7.17,

$$T(s) = h'(s) = \frac{1}{c}\left(a, \, -b\omega\sin\frac{\omega s}{c}, \, b\omega\cos\frac{\omega s}{c}\right),$$

and

$$h''(s) = \frac{b\omega^2}{c^2}\left(0, \, -\cos\frac{\omega s}{c}, \, -\sin\frac{\omega s}{c}\right), \qquad s \in \mathbb{R}.$$

Hence the curvature $\kappa(s)$ is $b\omega^2/c^2$ and the principal normal is

$$N(s) = \left(0, \, -\cos\frac{\omega s}{c}, \, -\sin\frac{\omega s}{c}\right).$$

The subspace spanned by the orthogonal unit vectors $T(s)$ and $N(s)$ in $\mathbb{R}^3$ is the plane

$$b\omega x + a\left(\sin\frac{\omega s}{c}\right)y - a\left(\cos\frac{\omega s}{c}\right)z = 0.$$

The osculating plane to h at s is the plane parallel to this through $h(s)$, given by

2.8.3
$$b\omega x + a\left(\sin\frac{\omega s}{c}\right)y - a\left(\cos\frac{\omega s}{c}\right)z = \frac{ab\omega s}{c}.$$

Suppose now that $a = 0$. The image of h is then a circle of radius b in the y, z-plane. The curvature $b\omega^2/c^2$ is $1/b$, reflecting the fact that the curvature of a circle becomes greater as the radius becomes smaller. From 2.8.3 the osculating plane in this special case is $x = 0$, the y, z-plane itself.

Notice that Definition 2.8.1 essentially defines three functions $T : E \subseteq \mathbb{R} \to \mathbb{R}^n$, $N : E \subseteq \mathbb{R} \to \mathbb{R}^n$ and $\kappa : E \subseteq \mathbb{R} \to \mathbb{R}$ associated with the path-length parametrization h. When there is any risk of confusion we shall denote these three functions by T_h, N_h and κ_h.

2.8.4 Theorem. *Let $h : E \subseteq \mathbb{R} \to \mathbb{R}^n$ be a twice differentiable path-length parametrization. Then $\kappa(s) = 0$ for all $s \in E$ if and only if $h(E)$ is a subset of a straight line in $\mathbb{R}^n$.*

Proof. Exercise.

The following theorem is an example of how the functions κ, T and N can be used to study the geometry of curves in $\mathbb{R}^n$. Theorem 2.5.14 implies that the vector $T'(s) = \kappa(s)N(s)$ is orthogonal to $T(s)$ and similarly that $N(s)$ is orthogonal to $N'(s)$. It is therefore possible that $N'(s)$ and $T(s)$ are in the same direction.

2.8.5 Theorem. *Let $h : E \subseteq \mathbb{R} \to \mathbb{R}^n$ be a three times differentiable path-length parametrization of a curve C in $\mathbb{R}^n$ with $\kappa(s) \neq 0$ for all $s \in E$. The curve C lies in a plane in $\mathbb{R}^n$ if and only if $N'(s)$ is a multiple of $T(s)$ for all $s \in E$.*

Proof. Differentiating the identity $N(s) \cdot T(s) = 0$ gives

$$(N'(s) \cdot T(s)) + (N(s) \cdot T'(s)) = 0.$$

Hence

2.8.6
$$N'(s) \cdot T(s) = -\kappa(s), \qquad s \in E.$$

Suppose that $N'(s)$ is a multiple of $T(s)$. It follows from 2.8.6 that

2.8.7
$$N'(s) = -\kappa(s)T(s), \qquad s \in E.$$

Choose any $q \in E$. We shall prove that C lies in the osculating plane to h at q. It is enough to show that for all $s \in E$ the vector $h(q) - h(s)$ lies in that plane. This will follow if we can show that, for all $s \in E$,

2.8.8 $$(h(q) - h(s)) \cdot (T(s) \wedge N(s)) = 0.$$

Let

2.8.9 $$g(s) = (h(q) - h(s)) \cdot (T(s) \wedge N(s)), \qquad s \in E.$$

Bearing in mind that $h'(s) = T(s)$, that $T' = \kappa N$ and that $N' = -\kappa T$, a routine calculation establishes that $g'(s) = 0$. Therefore $g(s) = g(q) = 0$ for all $s \in E$, and 2.8.8 is proved.

The proof of the converse proposition, that if C lies in a plane then $N'(s)$ is a multiple of $T(s)$ for all $s \in D$ (in fact that $N'(s) = -\kappa(s)T(s)$), is left to the reader.

2.8.10 *Example.* Returning to the path-length parametrization of the helix considered in Example 2.8.2 we find that

$$N'(s) = \frac{\omega}{c}\left(0, \sin\frac{\omega s}{c}, -\cos\frac{\omega s}{c}\right), \qquad s \in E.$$

Hence $N'(s)$ is a multiple of $T(s)$ if and only if $a = 0$ (when the helix becomes a circle). In this case $N'(s) = (-1/b)T(s) = -\kappa(s)T(s)$ as asserted in the proof of Theorem 2.8.5.

It follows from Theorem 2.8.5 and in particular from 2.8.7 that the norm of the vector $N'(s) + \kappa(s)T(s)$ indicates whether or not the curve has any torsion – that is to say whether or not the curve twists out of its osculating planes.

2.8.11 *Theorem.* *With the hypothesis of Theorem* 2.8.5 *the vector* $N'(s) + \kappa(s)T(s)$ *is orthogonal to the osculating plane to* h *at* s.

Proof. It is enough to prove that $N'(s) + \kappa(s)T(s)$ is orthogonal to $T(s)$ and to $N(s)$. We have

$$(N'(s) + \kappa(s)T(s)) \cdot T(s) = (N'(s) \cdot T(s)) + \kappa(s) = 0 \qquad \text{by 2.8.6,}$$

$$(N'(s) + \kappa(s)T(s)) \cdot N(s) = (N'(s) \cdot N(s)) + 0 = 0 \qquad \text{by Theorem 2.5.14,}$$

and the proof is complete.

Our next result applies only to curves in $\mathbb{R}^3$.

2.8.12 *Definition.* *Suppose that the function* $h : E \subseteq \mathbb{R} \to \mathbb{R}^3$ *is a three* *times differentiable path-length parametrization of a curve in* $\mathbb{R}^3$ *with* $\kappa(s) \neq 0$ *for all* $s \in E$.

[i] *For each* $s \in E$ *the unit vector*

$$B(s) = T(s) \wedge N(s)$$

is called the binormal *to h at s* (see Fig. 2.17(ii)).

[ii] *By Theorem* 2.8.11 *there exists a number* $\tau(s)$ *such that*

2.8.13 $$N'(s) + \kappa(s)T(s) = \tau(s)B(s).$$

The number $\tau(s)$ *is called the* torsion *of h at s.*

2.8.14 Theorem (J.A. Serret, F-J. Frenet). *In the notation of Definition* 2.8.12, *the three vector-valued functions T, N, B on E and the two real-valued functions* κ *and* τ *on E satisfy the following formulae:*

[i] $T' = \kappa N$
[ii] $N' = -\kappa T + \tau B$
[iii] $B' = -\tau N$.

Proof. (i) and (ii) are matters of definition. Differentiating $B = T \wedge N$ we obtain

$$B' = (T' \wedge N) + (T \wedge N') = T \wedge (-\kappa T + \tau B) = \tau(T \wedge B) = -\tau N.$$

Notice that it is a consequence of (ii) and of Theorem 2.8.5 that $f(E)$ lies in a plane if and only if $\tau(s) = 0$ for all $s \in E$. Hence, from (iii), $h(E)$ is planar if and only if $B'(s) = 0$ for all $s \in E$. Therefore $h(E)$ is planar if and only if the binormal $B(s)$ is constant. See also Exercise 2.8.7.

The torsion is generally easier to compute from Theorem 2.8.14(iii) than from 2.8.13.

2.8.15 Example. Consider again the parametrization of the helix given in Example 2.7.17. It follows from Example 2.8.2 that for all $s \in \mathbb{R}$.

$$B(s) = T(s) \wedge N(s) = \left(-\frac{b\omega}{c}, \frac{a}{c}\sin\frac{\omega s}{c}, -\frac{a}{c}\cos\frac{\omega s}{c} \right).$$

Hence

$$B'(s) = -\frac{a\omega}{c^2}\left(0, -\frac{\cos\omega s}{c}, -\frac{\sin\omega s}{c} \right) = (-\tau(s))N(s).$$

Therefore $\tau(s) = a\omega/c^2 = a\omega/(a^2 + b^2\omega^2)$. Notice that, since $\omega \neq 0$, $\tau(s) = 0$ if and only if $a = 0$ (when the helix reduces to a circle in the y, z-plane).

In the helix example we found that the curvature and torsion were both constant. This is not generally true as we shall find in the exercises.

The following theorem shows that a curve in $\mathbb{R}^3$ is essentially characterized by its curvature and torsion.

2.8.16 Theorem. *Let* $g : E \subseteq \mathbb{R} \to \mathbb{R}^3$ *and* $h : E \subseteq \mathbb{R} \to \mathbb{R}^3$ *be two three times differentiable path-length parametrizations of curves* C_g *and* C_h *in* $\mathbb{R}^3$. *If* $\kappa_g(s) = \kappa_h(s) \neq 0$ *and* $\tau_g(s) = \tau_h(s)$ *for all* $s \in E$, *then the two curves are identical, except possibly in their positions in space.*

Proof. Pick any point $p \in E$. Hold C_g fixed and move C_h rigidly in $\mathbb{R}^3$ until $T_h(p) = T_g(p)$, $N_h(p) = N_g(p)$, $B_h(p) = B_g(p)$. Consider the function $\phi : E \subseteq \mathbb{R} \to \mathbb{R}$ defined by

$$\phi = T_g \cdot T_h + N_g \cdot N_h + B_g \cdot B_h$$

The Serret–Frénet formulae (Theorem 2.8.14) imply that $\phi' = 0$. Hence ϕ is a constant function and therefore $\phi(s) = \phi(p) = 3$ for all $s \in E$. By the Cauchy–Schwarz inequality, for each $s \in E$, $T_g(s) \cdot T_h(s) \leqslant \| T_g(s) \| \, \| T_h(s) \| = 1$, with equality if and only if $T_g(s) = T_h(s)$. A similar statement applies to the terms involving N and B. It follows that

$$T_g(s) \cdot T_h(s) = N_g(s) \cdot N_h(s) = B_g(s) \cdot B_h(s) = 1, \qquad s \in E.$$

Hence $T_g = T_h$, that is $g'(s) = h'(s)$ for all $s \in E$, and so $g(s) = h(s) + \mathbf{k}$ for some $\mathbf{k} \in \mathbb{R}^n$ and all $s \in E$. That is, C_h is a translation of C_g, and the proof is complete.

It is often convenient to study the differential geometry of a curve relative to a smooth parametrization which may not be a path-length parametrization. Suppose that $f : D \subseteq \mathbb{R} \to \mathbb{R}^n$ is a twice differentiable smooth parametrization of a curve $C = f(D)$ in $\mathbb{R}^n$, that a base point is chosen in D and that $\lambda : D \to E$ is the associated path-length function. We therefore have (By Theorem 2.7.16) a twice differentiable path-length parametrization $h = f \circ \lambda^{-1} : E \subseteq \mathbb{R} \to \mathbb{R}^n$ of the curve C. Provided $\kappa_h(s) > 0$ for all $s \in E$, the function h has its associated 'Frenet apparatus' T_h, N_h, κ_h and (if $n = 3$ and provided f is three times differentiable) B_h and τ_h.

2.8.17 Theorem. *With the above notation, and denoting* $\lambda'(t) = \| f'(t) \|$ *by* $v(t)$, *we have, for* $t \in D$

[i] $f'(t) = v(t)T_h(\lambda(t))$,

[ii] $f''(t) = v'(t)T_h(\lambda(t)) + (v(t))^2\kappa_h(\lambda(t))N_h(\lambda(t))$,   if $\kappa_h(\lambda(t)) > 0$,

[iii] $f''(t) = v'(t)T_h(\lambda(t))$,   if $\kappa_h(\lambda(t)) = 0$.

Proof. Exercises.

Theorem 2.8.17 motivates the following definition of the Frenet apparatus of the general smooth parametrization f.

2.8.18 Definition. *In the notation used in Theorem 2.8.17 define*

$$T_f(t) = T_h(\lambda(t)), \qquad N_f(t) = N_h(\lambda(t)), \qquad \kappa_f(t) = \kappa_h(\lambda(t))$$

and, provided $n = 3$,

$$B_f(t) = B_h(\lambda(t)) \qquad and \qquad \tau_f(t) = \tau_h(\lambda(t)).$$

The fact that this definition does not depend upon the base point chosen (and hence on λ) follows from Theorem 2.8.17 by expressing $T_f(t)$ and $\kappa_f(t)N_f(t)$ in terms of $v(t)$ and the derivatives of $f(t)$.

From Theorem 2.8.17 we now obtain expressions for the Frenet apparatus associated with a general smooth parametrization f of a curve C.

2.8.19 Theorem. *Let $f : D \subseteq \mathbb{R} \to \mathbb{R}^n$ be a twice-differentiable smooth parametrization of a curve $C = f(D)$ in $\mathbb{R}^n$, and let $v(t) = \|f'(t)\|$, $t \in D$. Then the unit tangent $T_f(t)$, the curvature $\kappa_f(t) \geqslant 0$, and if $\kappa_f(t) > 0$, the principal normal $N_f(t)$ to f at $t \in D$ are given by the relations*

2.8.20 $$f'(t) = v(t)T_f(t)$$

2.8.21 $$f''(t) = v'(t)T_f(t) + (v(t))^2\kappa_f(t)N_f(t).$$

Furthermore, for the case $n = 3$, if $\kappa_f(t) \neq 0$, the binomial $B_f(t)$ and torsion $\tau_f(t)$ to f at t are given by

2.8.22 $$B_f(t) = T_f(t) \wedge N_f(t)$$

2.8.23 $$B_f'(t) = -v(t)\tau_f(t)N_f(t).$$

Proof. Immediate from Theorem 2.8.17.

The reader will have noticed that the differential geometry of a smooth curve C has been developed relative to a particular smooth parametrization of C and not relative to the curve C itself. In general it is not possible to associate a unique Frenet apparatus with a point on a smooth curve. For example, there are four different unit tangent vectors at the point $(0, 0)$ on the figure 8 curve of Fig. 2.9, where the curve crosses itself. However, the differential geometry of an oriented smooth simple arc is independent of the choice of smooth parametrization. For such oriented curves C it is appropriate to refer to the unit tangent vector, the curvature and (if it exists) the principal normal of C at a point $q \in C$. These quantities can be calculated by applying Theorem 2.8.19 to any smooth parametrization that assigns the desired orientation to the curve. Expression 2.8.21 is awkward to use since it involves the derivative of $v(t)$. The calculation of $v'(t)$ can usually be avoided. (See the following example and Exercises 2.8.1 and 2.8.4.)

2.8.24 Example.   Find the unit tangent, the curvature and the principal normal at the point $\mathbf{q} = (-\frac{6}{5}, \frac{4}{5})$ on the semi-ellipse

$$\tfrac{1}{4}x^2 + y^2 = 1, \qquad\qquad y \geqslant 0,$$

oriented from $(-2, 0)$ to $(2, 0)$. See Fig. 2.18.

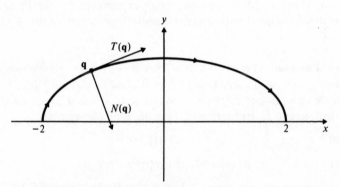

Fig. 2.18 Oriented semi-ellipse $\tfrac{1}{4}x^2 + y^2 = 1$, $y \geqslant 0$

The required orientation is afforded by the parametrization

$$f(t) = (-2\cos t, \sin t), \qquad\qquad t \in [0, \pi].$$

Then $\mathbf{q} = (-\frac{6}{5}, \frac{4}{5}) = f(\alpha)$, where $\alpha \in [0, \pi]$ is defined by $\cos\alpha = \frac{3}{5}$, $\sin\alpha = \frac{4}{5}$. We have

$$f'(t) = (2\sin t, \cos t) \quad \text{and} \quad f''(t) = (2\cos t, -\sin t).$$

Hence

$$f'(\alpha) = (\tfrac{8}{5}, \tfrac{3}{5}) \qquad \text{and} \qquad f''(\alpha) = (\tfrac{6}{5}, -\tfrac{4}{5}).$$

By 2.8.20, the unit tangent at **q** is the unit vector in the direction of $f'(\alpha)$:

$$T(\mathbf{q}) = \frac{1}{\sqrt{73}}(8, 3).$$

The principal normal $N(\mathbf{q})$ is orthogonal to $T(\mathbf{q})$ and points towards the concave side of the curve at **q**. Therefore (see Fig. 2.18).

$$N(\mathbf{q}) = \frac{1}{\sqrt{73}}(3, -8).$$

Finally, from 2.8.21, the curvature at **q** is given by

$$\kappa(\mathbf{q}) = \frac{f''(\alpha) \cdot N(\mathbf{q})}{\|f'(\alpha)\|^2} = \frac{250}{73^{3/2}}.$$

Expression 2.8.21 splits $f''(t)$ into two orthogonal components — one along the tangent $T_f(t)$ and the other along the principal normal $N_f(t)$. This is significant in the application of these results to dynamics, which we now undertake.

Exercises 2.8

1. Let C be a simple arc smoothly parametrized by $f : D \subseteq \mathbb{R} \to \mathbb{R}^3$. Show that at the point $\mathbf{q} \in C$, where $\mathbf{q} = f(\alpha)$, $\alpha \in D$, the curvature is given by

    $$\kappa(\mathbf{q}) = \frac{\|f'(\alpha) \wedge f''(\alpha)\|}{\|f'(\alpha)\|^3}.$$

Hint: apply 2.8.20 and 2.8.21.

2. Let the plane curve C be the graph $y = g(x)$ of a C^2 function $g : D \subseteq \mathbb{R} \to \mathbb{R}$. Prove that the curvature at $\mathbf{q} = (a, b) \in C$ is

    $$\kappa(\mathbf{q}) = \frac{|g''(a)|}{(1 + (g'(a))^2)^{3/2}}.$$

Hint: regard C as a space curve parametrized by $f(t) = (t, g(t), 0)$ and apply Exercise 1.

3. Sketch the semi-ellipse C defined by

    $$\frac{x^2}{9} + \frac{y^2}{4} = 1, \qquad x \leqslant 0.$$

    Assuming a 'clockwise' orientation of C (from $(0, -2)$ to $(0, 2)$), find the unit tangent, the principal normal and the curvature to C at $(-3/\sqrt{2}, 2/\sqrt{2}) \in C$.

4. Let C be an oriented simple arc in $\mathbb{R}^3$ smoothly parametrized by the C^3

function $f : D \subseteq \mathbb{R} \to \mathbb{R}^3$. Prove that at the point $\mathbf{q} \in C$ where $\mathbf{q} = f(\alpha)$, $\alpha \in D$, the unit vectors $T(\mathbf{q})$, $B(\mathbf{q})$, and $N(\mathbf{q})$ have the directions of $f'(\alpha)$, $f'(\alpha) \wedge f''(\alpha)$ and $(f'(\alpha) \wedge f''(\alpha)) \wedge f'(\alpha)$ respectively.

Show also that the torsion is given by

$$\tau(\mathbf{q}) = \frac{(f'(\alpha) \wedge f''(\alpha)) \cdot f'''(\alpha)}{\| f'(\alpha) \wedge f''(\alpha) \|^2}.$$

5. Let C be the curve (*twisted cubic*) in $\mathbb{R}^3$ with orientation determined by the parametrization

$$f(t) = (2t, t^2, t^3/3), \qquad t \in \mathbb{R}.$$

Find T, N, B, κ, τ and the equation of its osculating plane at $(2, 1, \tfrac{1}{3}) \in C$.

Hint: Apply Exercise 4.

Answer: $\tfrac{1}{3}(2, 2, 1)$, $\tfrac{1}{3}(-2, 1, 2)$, $\tfrac{1}{3}(1, -2, 2)$, $\tfrac{2}{9}$, $\tfrac{2}{9}$, $x - 2y + 2z = \tfrac{2}{3}$.

6. Calculate the (constant) curvature and torsion of the following circular helices.

(a) the right-handed helix

$$f(t) = (2t, \cos t, \sin t), \qquad t \in \mathbb{R};$$

(b) the left-handed helix

$$f(t) = (-2t, \cos t, \sin t), \qquad t \in \mathbb{R}.$$

Answer: (a) $\kappa = \tfrac{1}{5}$ $\tau = \tfrac{2}{5}$;   (b) $\kappa = \tfrac{1}{5}$, $\tau = -\tfrac{2}{5}$.

7. Prove that if all osculating planes of a curve are parallel, then the curve is planar.

8. Show that the curve parametrized by

$$f(t) = \left(t, \frac{1+t}{t}, \frac{1-t^2}{t} \right), \qquad t > 0$$

is planar.

9. Find the most general function g such that the curve parametrized by

$$f(t) = (a \cos t, a \sin t, g(t)), \qquad t \in \mathbb{R}$$

lies in a plane.

Hint: the binormal must be constant. Calculate $f'(t) \wedge f''(t)$ and apply Exercise 4.

Answer: $g(t) = b \cos t + c \sin t + d$.

2.9   Particle dynamics

In this section we consider the motion of a point or 'particle' in $\mathbb{R}^n$ over a 'time interval' $D \subseteq \mathbb{R}$. Such a motion is described by a function $f : D \subseteq \mathbb{R} \to \mathbb{R}^n$, where $f(t)$ specifies the position of the particle at time $t \in D$. The route traced by the particle lies on the curve $C = f(D)$. We shall assume that the function f is at least twice differentiable. The most important cases for practical applications are $n = 2$ and $n = 3$. We then have the machinery to obtain, relative to appropriate coordinate systems for space and time, a description of the motion of a physical particle in a plane ($n = 2$) or in space ($n = 3$).

The integral 2.7.14

$$s = \lambda(t) = \int_p^t \| f'(u) \| \, du$$

provides a formula for the distance travelled in $\mathbb{R}^n$ by the particle in the interval between $p \in D$ and $t \in D$. The derivative $f'(t)$ is called the *velocity* of f (or the velocity of the particle) at t. It is a tangent vector to f at t, which indicates the instantaneous magnitude and direction of the motion at t. By 2.7.15, $ds/dt = \| f'(t) \|$, and so $\| f'(t) \|$ measures at t the rate of increase of the distance s. Appropriately, $\| f'(t) \|$ is called the *scalar velocity* or the *speed* of f at t.

The second derivative $f''(t)$ is called the *acceleration* of f at t. Since $f'' = df'/dt$, the acceleration at t measures the rate of change of the velocity at t. We emphasize that this is a vectorial measure. The vector

$$f''(t) = \lim_{h \to 0} (f'(t + h) - f'(t))/h$$

is related to the rates of change of speed and of direction of velocity at t. See Fig. 2.19 and the following examples.

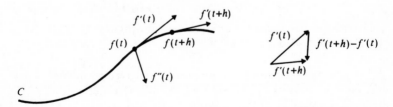

Fig. 2.19 Position $f(t)$, velocity $f'(t)$, acceleration $f''(t)$

2.9.1 *Example*.   Consider a particle moving in $\mathbb{R}^2$ such that its position at $t \in \mathbb{R}$ is $f(t) = (t^2, t^3) \in \mathbb{R}^2$.

The velocity at t is $f'(t) = (2t, 3t^2)$ and the acceleration at t is $f''(t) = (2, 6t)$. The particle traces the semi-cubical parabola $y^2 = x^3$ (see Fig. 2.14 and Example 2.7.5). The speed at t is $\| f'(t) \| = \sqrt{(4t^2 + 9t^4)}$.

The reader is invited to sketch the progress of the particle and to note the relationship between the velocity and the acceleration for various $t \in \mathbb{R}$. In particular, at $t = 0$ the particle is momentarily at rest and the acceleration is $(2, 0)$. Since at $t = 0$ the velocity changes from a 'westerly' to an 'easterly' direction, we would expect the acceleration to be 'easterly', and this is confirmed by our calculation.

2.9.2 *Example*.   A particle moves on a helix H in $\mathbb{R}^3$ such that its position at $t \in \mathbb{R}$ *is*

$$f(t) = (at, b\cos \omega t, b\sin \omega t),$$

where $b > 0$, and $\omega > 0$. (See Example 2.7.17. The case $a = 0$ corresponds to a circular motion in the y, z-plane.) At $t \in \mathbb{R}$ the particle has velocity

$$f'(t) = (a, -b\omega \sin \omega t, b\omega \cos \omega t)$$

and speed

$$\| f'(t) \| = (a^2 + b^2 \omega^2)^{1/2} = c.$$

It therefore moves at the uniform (constant) speed c. Its velocity is not constant, however, for its direction of motion changes continually. The acceleration at $t \in \mathbb{R}$ is

$$f''(t) = -b\omega^2 (0, \cos \omega t, \sin \omega t).$$

Therefore the acceleration is of constant magnitude $b\omega^2$ for all $t \in \mathbb{R}$. Since

$$\begin{aligned} f''(t) &= -\omega^2 (at, b\cos \omega t, b\sin \omega t) + \omega^2 at(1, 0, 0) \\ &= -\omega^2 f(t) + \omega^2 at(1, 0, 0), \end{aligned}$$

the acceleration $f''(t)$ lies in the plane spanned by $f(t)$ and the x-axis. Moreover,

$$f''(t) \cdot f'(t) = 0 \qquad \text{and} \qquad f''(t) \cdot (1, 0, 0) = 0,$$

and so the direction of the acceleration at t is at right angles to both the velocity at t and the x-axis.

The motion of a particle whose position is given by a twice-differentiable smooth function $f : D \subseteq \mathbb{R} \to \mathbb{R}^n$ is related to the differential geometry of the function f as follows. From Theorem 2.8.19 we have

2.9.3 $\qquad f'(t) = v(t)T(t)$

2.9.4 $\qquad f''(t) = v'(t)T(t) + (v(t))^2 \kappa(t)N(t) \qquad\qquad$ if $\kappa(t) > 0$

2.9.5 $\qquad f''(t) = v'(t)T(t) \qquad\qquad\qquad\qquad\qquad$ if $\kappa(t) = 0$.

where T, κ and N are the unit tangent, curvature and principal normal associated with f, and $v(t)$ is the speed of the particle at $t \in D$.

2.9.6 Remarks. [i] Expression 2.9.4 resolves the acceleration into two orthogonal components, one along the tangent and the other along the principal normal.

[ii] The acceleration is in the tangential direction at a point if and only if the curvature is zero there.

[iii] If a particle moves at constant speed (that is, $v'(t) = 0$) and if the acceleration is non-zero, then the curvature is non-zero and the acceleration is in the direction of the principal normal.

[iv] The normal component of acceleration depends on both the speed and the curvature. If $\kappa(t) \neq 0$ then the magnitude of the normal component, $(v(t))^2 \kappa(t)$, is often given in the form $(v(t))^2/\rho(t)$ where $\rho(t) = 1/\kappa(t)$. The number $\rho(t)$ is called the *radius of curvature* of f at t.

2.9.7 Example. Continuing Example 2.9.1, $f(t) = (t^2, t^3)$, $f'(t) = (2t, 3t^2)$ and $f''(t) = (2, 6t)$; we have

2.9.8 $\qquad v(t) = \sqrt{(4t^2 + 9t^4)} \qquad$ and $\qquad T(t) = \dfrac{1}{v(t)}(2t, 3t^2), \qquad t \neq 0.$

The tangential component of acceleration has magnitude

$$v'(t) = \frac{4 + 18t^2}{\sqrt{(4 + 9t^2)}}.$$

The principal normal $N(t)$ is orthogonal to $T(t)$ and points towards the concave side of the particle's trajectory, so

$$N(t) = \frac{1}{\sqrt{(4 + 9t^2)}}(-3|t|, 2), \qquad t \neq 0.$$

Hence by 2.9.4 the normal component of acceleration has magnitude

$$\frac{v^2(t)}{\rho(t)} = \frac{6|t|}{\sqrt{(4 + 9t^2)}}, \qquad t \neq 0.$$

Note that the point $t = 0$ must be excluded from stage 2.9.8 of our calculation, since the function f is not smooth at $t = 0$. Of course the acceleration at $t = 0$ is $f''(0) = (2, 0)$.

The motion of a particle in $\mathbb{R}^2$ is conveniently considered in terms of polar functions which we now described. We take the opportunity of introducing a notation which is common in the literature of planar particle dynamics.

A point P in $\mathbb{R}^2$ is uniquely specified by its position vector $\mathbf{r} = (x, y)$, $x \in \mathbb{R}$, $y \in \mathbb{R}$. Here x and y are called the *Cartesian coordinates* of P. Alternatively the point P is specified by a pair of numbers r, θ, where $r = \|\mathbf{r}\|$ and

2.9.9 $$x = r \cos \theta, \qquad y = r \sin \theta.$$

For example, if $\mathbf{r} = (1, -1)$, then $r = \sqrt{2}$ and we may choose $\theta = -\pi/4$. The choice of r in 2.9.9 is unique, but if $\theta = \theta_1$ is appropriate, then so is $\theta = \theta_1 + 2k\pi$ for any integer k. The numbers r, θ satisfying 2.9.9 are called *polar coordinates* of the point P.

Suppose now that a particle moves in $\mathbb{R}^2$ over a time interval $D \subseteq \mathbb{R}$. Then its position is given in polar coordinates by a rule

2.9.10 $$\mathbf{r}(t) = (x(t), y(t)), \qquad t \in D,$$

where

2.9.11 $$x(t) = r(t) \cos \theta(t), \qquad y(t) = r(t) \sin \theta(t), \qquad t \in D.$$

In 2.9.11, x, y, r, and θ are regarded as real-valued functions on $D \subseteq \mathbb{R}$. The functions r, θ are called *polar functions* corresponding to the Cartesian functions x, y. According to the notation in 2.9.10, we regard $\mathbf{r}$ as the vector-valued function on D that describes the motion of our particle. In the general case of motion in $\mathbb{R}^n$ we used the symbol f instead of $\mathbf{r}$. We now temporarily abandon this notation. We shall also change the notation for velocity and acceleration. Whereas f' and f'' were used to denote the derivatives df/dt and d^2f/dt^2, we now employ the more usual 'dot' notation and denote the derivatives $d\mathbf{r}/dt$ and $d^2\mathbf{r}/dt^2$ by $\dot{\mathbf{r}}$ and $\ddot{\mathbf{r}}$ respectively. The derivatives of other functions are expressed similarly.

The formulae 2.9.3 and 2.9.4 show how the velocity and the acceleration of a particle can be resolved into tangential and normal components. For planar motion given by polar functions there is another useful resolution—into radial and transverse components—which we now describe.

Suppose then that a particle moves in $\mathbb{R}^2$ according to a rule 2.9.10, 2.9.11, that is,

2.9.12 $$\mathbf{r}(t) = r(t)(\cos \theta(t), \sin \theta(t)), \qquad t \in D,$$

where $r : D \subseteq \mathbb{R} \to \mathbb{R}$ and $\theta : D \subseteq \mathbb{R} \to \mathbb{R}$ are twice-differentiable functions. Corresponding to this motion, we define two 'unit vector' functions $\hat{\mathbf{r}} : D \subseteq \mathbb{R} \to \mathbb{R}^2$ and $\hat{\mathbf{s}} : D \subseteq \mathbb{R} \to \mathbb{R}^2$ by

2.9.13

$$\hat{\mathbf{r}}(t) = (\cos \theta(t), \sin \theta(t))$$

$$\hat{\mathbf{s}}(t) = (-\sin \theta(t), \cos \theta(t)), \qquad t \in D.$$

Notice that $\hat{\mathbf{r}}(t)$ is the vector of unit length in the direction of $\mathbf{r}(t)$ and that $\hat{\mathbf{s}}(t)$ is a unit vector at right angles to $\mathbf{r}(t)$. (Calculate the dot product $\hat{\mathbf{r}}(t) \cdot \hat{\mathbf{s}}(t)$). See Fig. 2.20.

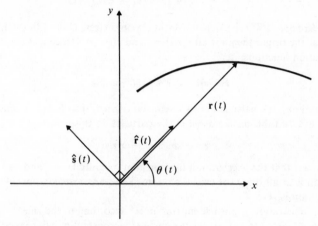

Fig. 2.20

Differentiating 2.9.13, we obtain, at $t \in D$,

2.9.14

$$\frac{d\hat{\mathbf{r}}}{dt}(t) = \dot{\theta}(t)(-\sin \theta(t), \cos \theta(t)) = \dot{\theta}(t)\hat{\mathbf{s}}(t)$$

$$\frac{d\hat{\mathbf{s}}}{dt}(t) = -\dot{\theta}(t)(\cos \theta(t), \sin \theta(t)) = -\dot{\theta}(t)\hat{\mathbf{r}}(t).$$

Let us now calculate the velocity and the acceleration of the particle at $t \in D$. From 2.9.12 and 2.9.13,

2.9.15 $$\mathbf{r}(t) = r(t)\hat{\mathbf{r}}(t), \qquad t \in D.$$

Differentiating 2.9.15 and applying 2.9.14, we obtain a formula for the velocity function $\dot{\mathbf{r}} : D \subseteq \mathbb{R} \to \mathbb{R}^2$:

2.9.16 $$\dot{\mathbf{r}} = \dot{r}\hat{\mathbf{r}} + r\dot{\theta}\hat{\mathbf{s}}.$$

A further differentiation, and applications of 2.9.14 give a formula for the acceleration function $\ddot{\mathbf{r}} : D \subseteq \mathbb{R} \to \mathbb{R}^2$:

2.9.17 $$\ddot{\mathbf{r}} = (\ddot{r} - r\dot{\theta}^2)\hat{\mathbf{r}} + (2\dot{r}\dot{\theta} + r\ddot{\theta})\hat{\mathbf{s}}.$$

The expressions 2.9.16 and 2.9.17 provide resolutions of the velocity and the acceleration at $t \in D$ into the *radial component* in the direction of $\hat{\mathbf{r}}(t)$ and the *transverse component* in the direction of $\hat{\mathbf{s}}(t)$. The transverse component is at right angles to the radial component.

From 2.9.16 we also find that the speed of the particle at $t \in D$ is

2.9.18 $$v(t) = \|\dot{\mathbf{r}}(t)\| = \sqrt{[(\dot{r}(t))^2 + (r(t)\dot{\theta}(t))^2]}.$$

2.9.19 Example. If a particle moves in $\mathbb{R}^2$ on a circle C of radius a and centre at the origin then, for all t, $r(t) = a$ and $\dot{r}(t) = 0$. Hence its velocity and acceleration functions are

$$\dot{\mathbf{r}} = a\dot{\theta}\hat{\mathbf{s}}, \qquad \ddot{\mathbf{r}} = -a\dot{\theta}^2\hat{\mathbf{r}} + a\ddot{\theta}\hat{\mathbf{s}}.$$

If, in addition, the particle moves at constant speed, then $\dot{\theta} = \omega$, a constant (which is called the *angular speed* of the particle). In this case

2.9.20 $$\ddot{\mathbf{r}} = -a\omega^2\hat{\mathbf{r}} = -\omega^2\mathbf{r}.$$

This means that the acceleration has constant magnitude $a\omega^2$ and its direction is at all times towards the origin. The transverse component of acceleration is zero.

As an illustration, a particle moving in $\mathbb{R}^2$ according to the rule $\mathbf{r} = (a\cos\omega t, a\sin\omega t)$, $t \in \mathbb{R}$ traces the circle C at constant angular speed ω. In contrast, the rule $\mathbf{r} = (a\cos(t^2), a\sin(t^2))$, $t \in \mathbb{R}$, also defines a motion on the circle C, but now the speed and the angular speed are not constant, and there is a non-trivial transverse component of acceleration. In both cases the radial component of acceleration is non-trivial.

2.9.21 Definition. *A particle moving in* $\mathbb{R}^2$ *is said to experience a* central acceleration *if the transverse component of acceleration is zero, that is, if its acceleration is a multiple of* $\mathbf{r}(t)$.

A central acceleration may be pictured as drawn from the particle towards or away from the origin.

2.9.22 Theorem. *If a twice-differentiable function* $\mathbf{r} : D \subseteq \mathbb{R} \to \mathbb{R}^2$ *describes a motion in* $\mathbb{R}^2$ *under a central acceleration, then there is a constant h such that*

$$(r^2\dot{\theta})(t) = h \qquad \text{for all } t \in D.$$

Proof. By 2.9.17, if the function **r** specifies a central acceleration, then $2\dot{r}\dot{\theta} + r\ddot{\theta}$ is the zero function on D. Since

$$r(2\dot{r}\dot{\theta} + r\ddot{\theta}) = \frac{\mathrm{d}}{\mathrm{d}t}(r^2\dot{\theta}),$$

the theorem follows.

2.9.23 Example. *Planetary motion. Central orbits.* In studying the motion of a planet around the sun it is usual to regard the sun and the planet as particles (points) in space with the sun fixed at an origin. Considering the enormous distances involved, this is a reasonable simplification. As the planet moves in space, the sun exerts on it a gravitational force of attraction according to the Inverse Square Law of gravitation. The law states that two particles in space attract each other with a force which is proportional to the product of their masses and inversely proportional to the square of the distance between them. All other forces on the planet are negligible in comparison. Consequently the planet moves under a central acceleration. Its orbit is called a central orbit. It can be shown that central orbits are planar orbits (Exercise 2.9.6).

From the Inverse Square Law Isaac Newton (1642–1727) deduced the three celebrated laws of planetary motion discovered experimentally by Johannes Kepler (1571–1630) (from a detailed study of the astronomer Tycho Brahe's observations of the planet Mars).

Kepler's First Law states that planets move in elliptical orbits with the

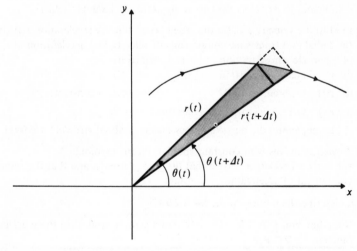

Fig. 2.21

sun at a focus of the ellipse. For a proof of this law from the Inverse Square Law see Smith & Smith, *Mechanics*, Chapter 9.

Kepler's Second Law states that a planet moves in its orbit in such a manner that a line drawn from the origin (sun) to the planet sweeps over equal areas in equal times. This is a general property enjoyed by particles moving under a central acceleration. We can prove this as follows. Consider a particle moving in $\mathbb{R}^2$ over a time interval D, and let its position be specified by the function $\mathbf{r} : D \subseteq \mathbb{R} \to \mathbb{R}^2$. With reference to Fig. 2.21, the area swept out by a line joining the origin and the particle in an interval $[t, t + \Delta t] \subseteq D$, where Δt is small, lies between the circle sector areas $\frac{1}{2}r^2(t)(\theta(t + \Delta t) - \theta(t))$ and $\frac{1}{2}r^2(t + \Delta t)(\theta(t + \Delta t) - \theta(t))$. Dividing by Δt and letting $\Delta t \to 0$, we deduce that the rate at which area is swept out at $t \in D$ is $|\frac{1}{2}(r^2\dot\theta)(t)|$. If the particle moves under a central acceleration, then, by Theorem 2.9.22, this rate is constant.

Exercises 2.9

1. Sketch the trajectory of a particle whose motion in $\mathbb{R}^2$ is described by $f(t) = (t^2, t^3)$, $t \in \mathbb{R}$. (See Example 2.9.1). Indicate the velocity and the acceleration at $t = 0$, $t = 1$ and $t = -1$.

2. Find (i) the velocity, and (ii) the tangential and normal components of acceleration at $t = 1$ of a particle whose motion in $\mathbb{R}^3$ is described by
    (a) $f(t) = (a\cos \pi t, a\sin \pi t, bt)$, $a > 0$, $b \neq 0$;
    (b) $f(t) = (t^2, \frac{2}{3}t^3, t)$.

Answer: (b) tangential acceleration 4, normal acceleration 2.

3. Prove that if a particle moves at constant speed, then its acceleration is orthogonal to its velocity. (This is illustrated in Example 2.9.2.)

4. Find (i) the velocity $\dot{\mathbf{r}}(t)$, (ii) the speed $\|\dot{\mathbf{r}}(t)\|$, (iii) the acceleration $\ddot{\mathbf{r}}(t)$, (iv) the radial and transverse components of velocity and acceleration at t, of a particle whose motion in $\mathbb{R}^2$ is described by
    (a) $\mathbf{r}(t) = (a\cos (t^2), a\sin (t^2))$, $t \in \mathbb{R}$;
    (b) $\mathbf{r}(t) = (a\cos \omega t, b\sin \omega t)$, $t \in \mathbb{R}$, ω constant;
    (c) $\mathbf{r}(t) = (a(1 + \cos t)\cos t, a(1 + \cos t)\sin t)$, $t \in \mathbb{R}$.
    (In Example 4(c) the particle moves on the cardioid $r(t) = a(1 + \cos t)$.)

5. A particle moves with constant speed V on the cardioid $r(t) = a(1 + \cos t)$, $t \in \mathbb{R}$. Prove that $\theta(t) = (V/2a)\sec\frac{1}{2}t$, and that the radial component of acceleration is constant.

Hint: describe the motion in the form 2.9.12.

6. If the function $\mathbf{r} : D \subseteq \mathbb{R} \to \mathbb{R}^3$ describes a central orbit, then there exists a function $F : D \subseteq \mathbb{R} \to \mathbb{R}$ such that
    $$\ddot{\mathbf{r}}(t) = F(t)\mathbf{r}(t), \qquad t \in D.$$

Deduce that the central orbit is planar as follows:

(a) Prove that $\ddot{\mathbf{r}}(t) \wedge \mathbf{r}(t) = \mathbf{0}$, $t \in D$.

(b) Show that there exists a constant vector $\mathbf{c} \in \mathbb{R}^3$ such that

$$\dot{\mathbf{r}}(t) \wedge \mathbf{r}(t) = \mathbf{c}, \ t \in D.$$

(c) Show that the dot product $\mathbf{c} \cdot \mathbf{r}(t) = 0$, $t \in D$.

(d) Conclude that the motion is planar. (The case $\mathbf{c} = \mathbf{0}$ needs separate consideration. In this case the motion is linear.)

2.10   Differentiability and linear approximation

We now look at the differentiability of a function $f : D \subseteq \mathbb{R} \to \mathbb{R}^n$ at a point $p \in D$ from a different point of view. This new approach will lead naturally to a definition of the differentiability of a function from a subset of $\mathbb{R}^m$ into $\mathbb{R}^n$.

We are concerned with the way in which the value of a function f changes as we move away from p (see Fig. 2.22(i)). Accordingly we consider the 'difference' function $\delta_{f,p} : D_p \subseteq \mathbb{R} \to \mathbb{R}^n$, where $D_p = \{h \in \mathbb{R} | p + h \in D\}$ and

2.10.1 $\delta_{f,p}(h) = f(p + h) - f(p),$ $h \in D_p.$

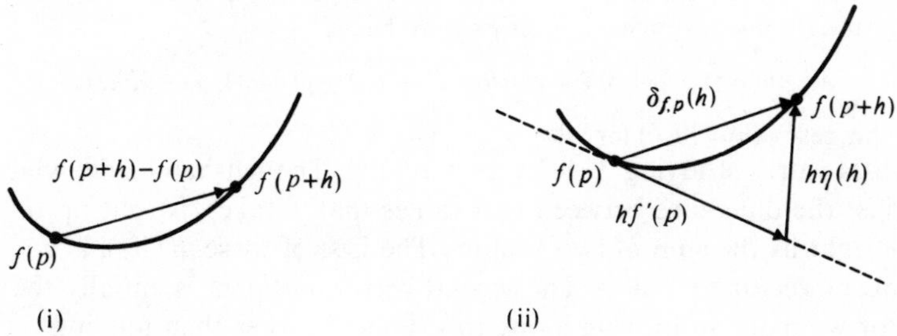

Fig. 2.22

2.10.2 *Example.*   Let $D =]0, 3[$ and let $f : D \subseteq \mathbb{R} \to \mathbb{R}$ be given by $f(x) = 1/x(x - 3)$. Then $D_1 =]-1, 2[$ and for $h \in D_1$,

$$\delta_{f,1}(h) = \frac{1}{(h + 1)(h - 2)} + \tfrac{1}{2}.$$

Suppose that the function $f : D \subseteq \mathbb{R} \to \mathbb{R}^n$ is differentiable at $p \in D$. Then

$$\lim_{h \to p} \frac{f(p + h) - f(p)}{h} = f'(p).$$

It follows that for each $h \in D_p$, $h \neq 0$, there exists a vector $\eta(h) \in \mathbb{R}^n$ such that

$$\frac{f(p+h)-f(p)}{h} = f'(p) + \eta(h) \qquad \text{and} \qquad \lim_{h \to 0} \eta(h) = \mathbf{0}.$$

Therefore, by defining $\eta(0) = \mathbf{0}$, we have a function $\eta : D_p \subseteq \mathbb{R} \to \mathbb{R}^n$ such that

2.10.3 $$\delta_{f,\,p}(h) = hf'(p) + h\eta(h),$$

and

2.10.4 $$\lim_{h \to 0} \eta(h) = \mathbf{0}.$$

2.10.5 *Example.* Define $f : \mathbb{R} \to \mathbb{R}^2$ by $f(t) = (t^3 + 1, t)$. For fixed $p \in \mathbb{R}$ we have $f'(p) = (3p^2, 1)$ and for all $h \in \mathbb{R}$,

$$\begin{aligned} \delta_{f,\,p}(h) &= ((p+h)^3 + 1, p + h) - (p^3 + 1, p) = (3p^2 h + 3ph^2 + h^3, h) \\ &= h(3p^2, 1) + h(3ph + h^2, 0). \end{aligned}$$

In this case $\eta(h) = (3ph + h^2, 0)$, $h \in \mathbb{R}$.

2.10.6 *Example.* Define $f : \mathbb{R} \to \mathbb{R}^2$ by $f(t) = (1, 2) + t(1, 1)$. The image of f is a straight line through $(1, 2)$. At $p \in \mathbb{R}$ we have

$$\delta_{f,\,p}(h) = (1 + p + h, 2 + p + h) - (1 + p, 2 + p) = h(1, 1) + h(0, 0).$$

In this case $\eta(h) = (0, 0)$ for all h.

It is worth studying 2.10.3 very carefully. The left-hand side, which is just the difference between two values that f takes, is split up on the right as the sum of two vectors. The first of these, $hf'(p)$, is a tangent vector to f at p. The second vector, $h\eta(h)$, is essentially the error we make in moving along this tangent rather than moving along the curve. This decomposition of $\delta_{f,\,p}$ is illustrated in Fig. 2.22(ii).

Expression 2.10.3 can be developed further by defining a *linear* function $L_{f,\,p} : \mathbb{R} \to \mathbb{R}^n$ by

2.10.7 $$L_{f,\,p}(t) = tf'(p), \qquad t \in \mathbb{R}.$$

We then have, from 2.10.3,

2.10.8 $$\delta_{f,\,p}(h) = L_{f,\,p}(h) + h\eta(h), \qquad h \in D_p.$$

$L_{f,\,p}$ is called the *linear approximation* to f at p or the *differential* of f at p.

2.10.9 Example.   Consider again the function $f : \mathbb{R} \to \mathbb{R}^2$, defined by $f(t) = (t^3 + 1, t)$. See Fig. 2.23. Then $f(0) = (1, 0)$ and $f(-1) = (0, -1)$, and we have

$$\delta_{f,\,0}(h) = (h^3, h), \qquad L_{f,\,0}(h) = hf'(0) = h(0, 1),$$
$$\eta(h) = (h^2, 0),$$

and

$$\delta_{f,\,-1}(h) = (3h - 3h^2 + h^3, h), \; L_{f,\,-1}(h) = hf'(-1) = h(3, 1),$$
$$\eta(h) = (-3h + h^2, 0).$$

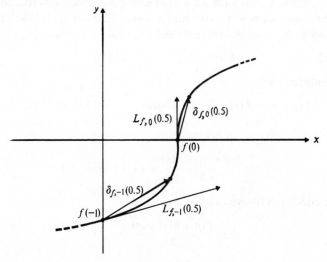

Fig. 2.23

2.10.10 Example.   The function $f : \mathbb{R} \to \mathbb{R}^2$ defined by $f(t) = (t|t|, t^2)$ has the image sketched in Fig. 2.9(ii). The function is differentiable at 0, where its image has a 'corner', and expression 2.10.8 takes the form

$$\delta_{f,\,0}(h) = h(0, 0) + h(|h|, h).$$

The differential $L_{f,\,0}$ is the zero function in this case. This is to be expected, since a non-zero vector $L_{f,\,0}(h)$ would produce a tangent line to f at 0, and no such line exists.

The following theorem shows that the existence of a linear function L satisfying 2.10.8, together with the requirement that $\lim_{h \to 0} \eta(h) = \mathbf{0}$, is also a sufficient condition for the differentiability of f at p.

2.10.11 *Theorem.* *A function* $f : D \subseteq \mathbb{R} \to \mathbb{R}^n$ *is differentiable at* $p \in D$ *if and only if there exists a linear function* $L : \mathbb{R} \to \mathbb{R}^n$ *and a function* $\eta : D_p \subseteq \mathbb{R} \to \mathbb{R}^n$ *such that*

[i] $\delta_{f,p}(h) = L(h) + h\eta(h)$, for all $h \in D_p$,

and

[ii] $\lim\limits_{h \to 0} \eta(h) = \mathbf{0}$.

If such a linear function exists then it is unique and equal to $L_{f,p}$.

Proof.   We have already shown that if f is differentiable, then such a linear function and such an η exist satisfying conditions (i) and (ii).

Conversely suppose we can find a linear function $L : \mathbb{R} \to \mathbb{R}^n$ and a function $\eta : D_p \to \mathbb{R}^n$ satisfying (i) and (ii). Since L is linear,

2.10.12 $\qquad\qquad L(t) = tL(1), \qquad\qquad t \in \mathbb{R}$.

By condition (i),

$$f(p + h) - f(p) = hL(1) + h\eta(h), \qquad\text{for all } h \in D_p.$$

Hence for $h \neq 0$,

$$\frac{f(p + h) - f(p)}{h} = L(1) + \eta(h).$$

Using condition (ii) we can see that

$$\lim_{h \to 0} \frac{f(p + h) - f(p)}{h} = L(1).$$

The function f is therefore differentiable at p and $f'(p) = L(1)$.

Finally, if such a linear function exists, then by the above argument f is differentiable and $L(1) = f'(p)$. Hence $L(t) = tf'(p)$, $t \in \mathbb{R}$, and therefore $L = L_{f,p}$.

The following definition puts the relationship between $\delta_{f,p}$ and $L_{f,p}$ into a more general setting.

2.10.13 *Definition.*   *Let* $g : N \subseteq \mathbb{R} \to \mathbb{R}^n$ *and* $g^* : M \subseteq \mathbb{R} \to \mathbb{R}^n$ *be two functions on intervals* N *and* M *where* $0 \in N$ *and* $N \subseteq M$. *We say that* g^* *closely approximates* g *near* 0 *if*

$$\lim_{h \to 0} \frac{g(h) - g^*(h)}{h} = \mathbf{0}, \qquad h \in N.$$

2.10.14 *Example*.   Let $g :]-1, \infty[\subseteq \mathbb{R} \to \mathbb{R}^2$ and $g^* : \mathbb{R} \to \mathbb{R}^2$ be defined by $g(t) = (\ln(1 + t), t^2)$ and $g^*(t) = (t + t^2, t^3)$. Then g^* is a close approximation to g near 0.

We now have the following restatement of Theorem 2.10.11.

2.10.15 *Corollary*.   *A function $f : D \subseteq \mathbb{R} \to \mathbb{R}^n$ is differentiable at $p \in D$ if and only if the difference function $\delta_{f, p} : D_p \subseteq \mathbb{R} \to \mathbb{R}^n$ can be closely approximated by a linear function near 0. If such a close linear approximation exists then it is unique and is $L_{f, p}$.*

Proof.   If $\delta_{f, p}$ is closely approximated by a linear function $L : \mathbb{R} \to \mathbb{R}^n$ near 0, then define a function $\eta : D_p \subseteq \mathbb{R} \to \mathbb{R}^n$ by

$$\eta(h) = \begin{cases} \dfrac{\delta_{f, p}(h) - L(h)}{h} & \text{when } h \in D_p \backslash \{0\} \\ 0 & \text{when } h = 0. \end{cases}$$

Then $\lim_{h \to 0} \eta(h) = 0$ and $\delta_{f, p}(h) = L(h) + h\eta(h)$. Hence, by Theorem 2.10.11, f is differentiable and $L = L_{f, p}$.

The converse is left as an exercise.

Our intention in this section has been to link the definition of the derivative of $f : D \subseteq \mathbb{R} \to \mathbb{R}^n$ given in Section 2.5 to the definition of the derivative of $f : D \subseteq \mathbb{R}^m \to \mathbb{R}^n$ given in later chapters. To do this we need to make a slight adjustment to the conditions for differentiability given in Theorem 2.10.11. For future reference this change is incorporated in the following new definition of differentiability.

2.10.16 *Definition*.   *The function $f : D \subseteq \mathbb{R} \to \mathbb{R}^n$ is* differentiable *at $p \in D$ if there is a linear function $L_{f, p} : \mathbb{R} \to \mathbb{R}^n$(called the* differential *of f at p) and a function $\eta : D_p \subseteq \mathbb{R} \to \mathbb{R}^n$ such that*

[i] $f(p + h) - f(p) = L_{f, p}(h) + |h|\eta(h), \text{ for all } h \in D_p.$
and

[ii] $\lim\limits_{h \to 0} \eta(h) = 0.$

The function η of Definition 2.10.16 is obtained from that of Theorem 2.10.11 by changing the sign of $\eta(h)$ for negative h. This change does not alter the limit in (ii).

We now illustrate the new approach to differentiability contained in the above definition by rephrasing the Chain Rule in a form which leads to a natural generalization in later chapters.

2.10.17 Definition.   *If the function* $f : D \subseteq \mathbb{R} \to \mathbb{R}^n$ *is differentiable at* $p \in D$. *then the* $n \times 1$ *matrix* $J_{f, p}$ *which represents the linear transformation* $L_{f, p} : \mathbb{R} \to \mathbb{R}^n$ *with respect to standard bases is called the* Jacobian *of* f *at* p.

Since $L_{f, p}(1) = f'(p)$ (see 2.10.7), the Jacobian of f at p is the $n \times 1$ matrix

2.10.18
$$J_{f, p} = \begin{bmatrix} f'_1(p) \\ \vdots \\ f'_n(p) \end{bmatrix}.$$

2.10.19 Theorem. (Chain Rule)   *Let* $\phi : E \subseteq \mathbb{R} \to \mathbb{R}$ *and* $f : D \subseteq \mathbb{R} \to \mathbb{R}^n$ *be differentiable functions and let* $\phi(E) \subseteq D$. *Then* $f \circ \phi : E \subseteq \mathbb{R} \to \mathbb{R}^n$ *is differentiable, and*

2.10.20
$$L_{f \circ \phi, p} = L_{f, \phi(p)} \circ L_{\phi, p}, \qquad p \in E$$

with the corresponding Jacobian relation

2.10.21
$$J_{f \circ \phi, p} = J_{f, \phi(p)} J_{\phi, p}, \qquad p \in E.$$

Proof.   The fact that $f \circ \phi$ is differentiable is part of Theorem 2.6.11. Expression 2.10.21 follows immediately from 2.6.12. (This gives further justification for writing the scalar on the right in that expression.)

Expression 2.10.20 follows directly from 2.10.21. Alternatively it can be proved by noting that, for all $t \in \mathbb{R}$,

$$L_{f \circ \phi, p}(t) = t(f \circ \phi)'(p) = t f'(\phi(p)) \phi'(p) = L_{f, \phi(p)}(t \phi'(p))$$
$$= L_{f, \phi(p)}(L_{\phi, p}(t)),$$

the identities following from 2.10.7.

2.10.22 Example.   As in Example 2.6.14, let $\phi : \mathbb{R} \to \mathbb{R}$ and $f : \mathbb{R} \to \mathbb{R}^3$ be defined by $\phi(t) = \sin t$, $t \in \mathbb{R}$ and $f(u) = (2u, u^3, 1)$, $u \in \mathbb{R}$. Then, for any $p \in \mathbb{R}$,

$$L_{f \circ \phi, p}(t) = t(f \circ \phi)'(p) = t(2 \cos p, 3 \sin^2 p \cos p, 0),$$
$$L_{f, \phi(p)}(u) = u f'(\phi(p)) = u(2, 3 \sin^2 p, 0),$$
$$L_{\phi, p}(t) = t \phi'(p) = t \cos p,$$

and the expression 2.10.20 is satisfied.

The related Jacobians are as follows:

$$J_{f \circ \phi, p} = \begin{bmatrix} 2\cos p \\ 3\sin^2 p \cos p \\ 0 \end{bmatrix}, \qquad J_{f, \phi(p)} = \begin{bmatrix} 2 \\ 3\sin^2 p \\ 0 \end{bmatrix}, \qquad J_{\phi, p} = [\cos p].$$

Clearly 2.10.21 is satisfied.

Exercises 2.10

1. Calculate the difference function $\delta_{f, p}$ and the differential $L_{f, p}$ (i) at $p = 0$, (ii) at $p = 1$, (iii) at $p = -1$ for the following functions $f : \mathbb{R} \to \mathbb{R}^2$, and in each case obtain the relation of Theorem 2.10.11.

    (a) $f(t) = (t, t^2)$, $t \in \mathbb{R}$;
    (b) $f(t) = (t, t^3)$, $t \in \mathbb{R}$;
    (c) $f(t) = (t^2, t^3)$, $t \in \mathbb{R}$.

2. Prove that the function $f : \mathbb{R} \to \mathbb{R}^2$ defined by $f(t) = (|t|, t)$ is not differentiable at 0, by calculating $\delta_{f, 0}(h)$ and showing that the condition for differentiability in Theorem 2.10.11 fails.

3. Define $g : \mathbb{R} \to \mathbb{R}^2$ and $g^* : \mathbb{R} \to \mathbb{R}^2$ by

    $$g(t) = (e^t, \sin t), \qquad g^*(t) = (1 + t - t^2, t), \qquad\qquad t \in \mathbb{R}.$$

    Prove that g^* closely approximates g near 0.

4. Verify the expression $L_{f \circ \phi, p} = L_{f, \phi(p)} \circ L_{\phi, p}$, $p \in \mathbb{R}$ for the following functions $f : \mathbb{R} \to \mathbb{R}^3$, $\phi : \mathbb{R} \to \mathbb{R}$:
    (a) $f(t) = (e^t, t, 1)$, $\phi(t) = t^2$;
    (b) $f(t) = (0, -t, t^2 + 1)$, $\phi(t) = \sin t$.
    Verify also the expression 2.10.21 for the corresponding Jacobians.

3

Real-valued functions of $\mathbb{R}^m$

3.1 Introduction. Level sets and graphs

We now come to the study of what are often called real-valued functions of many variables. Such functions $f : D \subseteq \mathbb{R}^m \to \mathbb{R}$, for various dimensions m, frequently occur in physical problems.

3.1.1 Example. In the study of changing weather conditions the temperature is measured at various points in space at different times. By choosing frames of reference for time and space we can define an underlying 'temperature function' $\theta : \mathbb{R}^4 \to \mathbb{R}$ by the rule that $\theta(x, y, z, t)$ is the temperature in degrees centigrade at the point in space with position vector (x, y, z) at time t units.

3.1.2 Example. The volume V of a cylinder is given by the formula $V = \pi r^2 h$ in terms of its radius r and its height h. The underlying volume function $f : D \subseteq \mathbb{R}^2 \to \mathbb{R}$ is defined by $f(r, h) = \pi r^2 h$, where D is the first quadrant $\{(r, h) \in \mathbb{R}^2 | r > 0, h > 0\}$ in $\mathbb{R}^2$.

A function $f : D \subseteq \mathbb{R}^m \to \mathbb{R}$ is sometimes called a *scalar field* on D. It is a rule associating a real number $f(\mathbf{p})$ with each point $\mathbf{p} \in D$. For any real number c, the set of all points in D at which the function takes the value c will be called a level set of the function. More formally, the *level set corresponding to c* is

3.1.3 $\qquad\qquad \{\mathbf{x} \in D | f(\mathbf{x}) = c\}.$

3.1.4 Example. The surface of the earth corresponds to a subset D of $\mathbb{R}^3$ with respect to a frame of reference in space. The pressure at each point at a certain time, the mean annual temperature at each point, the height of each point above sea level all lead to scalar fields on D. The level sets of these scalar fields correspond to isobars, isotherms and contours respectively.

3.1.5 Example. Consider the function defined in Example 3.1.2. The level sets corresponding to $c \leqslant 0$ are all empty. For $c > 0$ the level sets are graphs $h = c/\pi r^2$ in the (r, h)-plane. See Fig. 3.1(i).

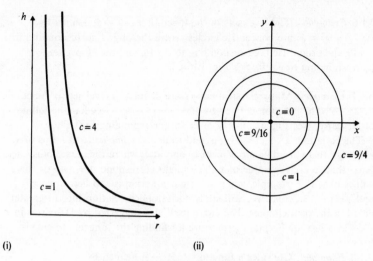

Fig. 3.1 (i) Level sets of $f(r, h) = \pi r^2 h$;
(ii) Level sets of $f(x, y) = x^2 + y^2$

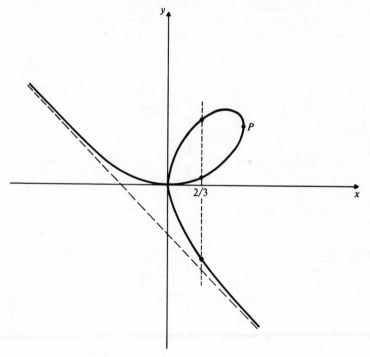

Fig. 3.2 Folium of Descartes $x^3 + y^3 - 3xy = 0$

3.1.6 Example. The level sets of the function $f : \mathbb{R}^2 \to \mathbb{R}$ defined by $f(x, y) = x^2 + y^2$ are concentric circles centre the origin (corresponding to $c > 0$), the origin itself (corresponding to $c = 0$), and the empty set (corresponding to $c < 0$). See Fig. 3.1(ii).

3.1.7 Example. Many classical curves are defined as level sets of functions $f : \mathbb{R}^2 \to \mathbb{R}$. The function defined by $f(x, y) = x^3 + y^3 - 3xy$ has the folium of Descartes (see Fig. 3.2) as the level set corresponding to 0.

The equation, $x^3 + y^3 = 3xy$, is said to define y *implicitly* in terms of x, although there are difficulties at $(0, 0)$ and at P where the curve folds back. Note that to a given value of x there might correspond one, two or three values of y. For example, when $x = \frac{2}{3}$ the equation is satisfied when $y = \frac{4}{3}$ and $y = (-2 \pm \sqrt{6})/3$. We will study such implicit relationships in greater detail in the next chapter. The curve itself was suggested by Descartes in 1638 as a test for Fermat's procedure for finding the tangents to curves.

3.1.8 Example. Consider a function $f : \mathbb{R}^2 \to \mathbb{R}$ defined by

$$f(x, y) = \begin{cases} -|y| & \text{if } |y| \le |x|, \\ -|x| & \text{if } |x| \le |y|. \end{cases}$$

The level set corresponding to 0 is the union of the x and y axes. The level set corresponding to -2 (and indeed to all negative values of c) consists of four components (the case $c = -2$ is shown in Fig. 3.3).

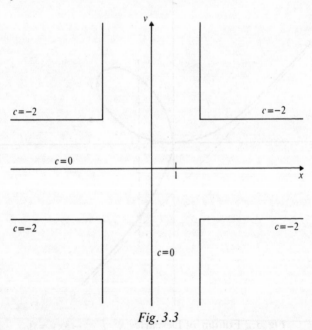

Fig. 3.3

In the previous chapter we found it helpful to picture functions $f : \mathbb{R} \to \mathbb{R}^n$, $n > 2$, by drawing their images as subsets of $\mathbb{R}^n$. There was usually no need to consider the graph. In the case of a function $f : D \subseteq \mathbb{R}^m \to \mathbb{R}$, however, the image of f is squashed up within $\mathbb{R}$ and the subtleties of the function are lost. In this case, as is usual in particular when $m = 1$, we can picture the function by considering its graph.

3.1.9 Definition. *The graph of $f : D \subseteq \mathbb{R}^m \to \mathbb{R}$ is the subset of $\mathbb{R}^{m+1}$ given by*

$$\{(x_1, \ldots, x_m, x_{m+1}) \in \mathbb{R}^{m+1} \,|\, x_{m+1} = f(x_1, \ldots, x_m)\}.$$

Equivalently the graph is $\{(\mathbf{x}, f(\mathbf{x})) \in \mathbb{R}^{m+1} \,|\, \mathbf{x} \in D\}$. The expression $x_{m+1} = f(\mathbf{x})$ is called the equation *of the graph.*

In sketching the graph (when $m = 2$) knowledge of the level sets of f is useful since the intersection of the plane $z = c$ and the graph $z = f(x, y)$ is a copy in the plane $z = c$ of the level set $f(x, y) = c$.

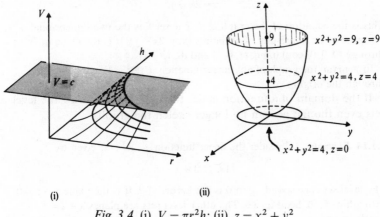

$$\text{Fig. 3.4} \quad \text{(i)} \ V = \pi r^2 h; \ \text{(ii)} \ z = x^2 + y^2$$

3.1.10 Example.   The graph of the function $f(r, h) = \pi r^2 h$ has equation $V = \pi r^2 h$ in an r, h, V co-ordinate system. The plane $V = c$ intersects the graph at points at which $\pi r^2 h = c$. This set lies above the level set corresponding to c in the (r, h)-plane. See Fig. 3.4 (i).

3.1.11 Example.   The graph of the function $f(x, y) = x^2 + y^2$ has equation $z = x^2 + y^2$. For $c > 0$ the plane $z = c$ intersects the graph in a circle lying above the level set $x^2 + y^2 = c$ in the (x, y)-plane. The graph is a parabolic bowl with circular horizontal cross sections. See Fig. 3.4(ii).

3.1.12 *Example.* The graph of the function defined in Example 3.1.8 is shown in Fig. 3.5. It is worth looking at this graph carefully to see how the level sets illustrated in Fig. 3.3 are related to it.

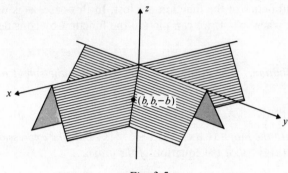

Fig. 3.5

3.1.13 *Example.* The graph of the linear function $f : \mathbb{R}^2 \to \mathbb{R}$ given by $f(x, y) = 2x - y$ is the subset S of points $(x, y, z) \in \mathbb{R}^3$ such that

$$z = 2x - y.$$

This is the equation of the graph of f. The set S is the two-dimensional subspace of $\mathbb{R}^3$ consisting of all points $(x, y, 2x - y)$. It is the plane in $\mathbb{R}^3$ through $(0, 0, 0)$ containing $(1, 0, 2)$ and $(0, 1, -1)$.

In general, the graph of any linear function $f : \mathbb{R}^2 \to \mathbb{R}$ is a plane in $\mathbb{R}^3$ through the origin.

If the domain of a function is $\mathbb{R}^3$, then we can still draw the level sets even though we can no longer sketch the graph.

3.1.14 *Example.* Consider the linear function $f : \mathbb{R}^3 \to \mathbb{R}$ given by

$$f(x, y, z) = x + z.$$

The level set corresponding to 0 is the kernel of f. It is the plane $x + z = 0$ through $(0, 0, 0)$. See Fig. 3.6. The other level sets are planes $x + z = c$ parallel to ker f.

Exercises 3.1

1. Sketch the level sets $f(x, y) = c$ of the function $f : \mathbb{R}^2 \to \mathbb{R}$ defined by
   (a) $f(x, y) = x^2 - y^2$ (consider separately the case $c > 0$, $c = 0$, $c < 0$),
   (b) $f(x, y) = (x - 1)^2 + (y + 2)^2$,
   (c) $f(x, y) = x^2 - y$,
   (d) $f(x, y) = x + 3y$,
   (e) $f(x, y) = xy$.

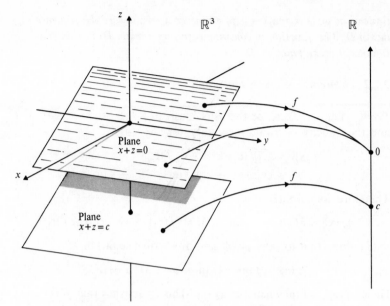

Fig. 3.6 Level sets of $f(x, y, z) = x + z$

2. Attempt a sketch (in $\mathbb{R}^3$) of the graphs of the functions f of Exercise 1.

3. Let $f : \mathbb{R}^m \to \mathbb{R}$ be a non-trivial linear function. Prove that (a) the level set of f corresponding to 0 is ker f, an $(m - 1)$-dimensional subspace of $\mathbb{R}^m$, (b) if $f(\mathbf{p}) = c$, then the level set corresponding to c is the subset $\mathbf{p} + \ker f \subseteq \mathbb{R}^m$, the translation of ker f through $\mathbf{p}$.

Hint: for part (b): if $f(\mathbf{p}) = c$ and $f(\mathbf{q}) = c$, then $0 = f(\mathbf{q}) - f(\mathbf{p}) = f(\mathbf{q} - \mathbf{p})$.

4. Prove that the graph of a linear function $f : \mathbb{R}^m \to \mathbb{R}$ is an m-dimensional subspace of $\mathbb{R}^{m+1}$.

Hint: show that the graph of f is the set spanned by the vectors $(\mathbf{e}_i, f(\mathbf{e}_i)) \in \mathbb{R}^{m+1}$, $i = 1, \ldots, m$.

3.2 Continuity and limits

The definition of the continuity of a function $f : D \subseteq \mathbb{R}^m \to \mathbb{R}$ will present little difficulty if the work on sequences, continuity and limits in the last chapter has been understood. We need only make minor changes to Definition 2.3.1 as follows.

3.2.1 Definition. *The function $f : D \subseteq \mathbb{R}^m \to \mathbb{R}$ is said to be con-*

tinuous *at* $\mathbf{p} \in D$ *if* $f(\mathbf{a}_k) \to f(\mathbf{p})$ *whenever* $\mathbf{a}_k \to \mathbf{p}$, *where the sequence* $(\mathbf{a}_k)$ *lies in* D. *The function is continuous* (*on its domain* D) *if it is continuous at every point of* D.

3.2.2 Theorem.   *A linear function* $f : \mathbb{R}^m \to \mathbb{R}$ *is continuous.*

Proof.   Let $\mathbf{e}_1, \ldots, \mathbf{e}_m$ be the usual basis of $\mathbb{R}^m$. By the linearity of f and the Cauchy–Schwarz inequality, for any $\mathbf{x} \in \mathbb{R}^m$,

$$|f(\mathbf{x})|^2 = |x_1 f(\mathbf{e}_1) + \cdots + x_m f(\mathbf{e}_m)|^2$$
$$\leqslant (x_1^2 + \cdots + x_m^2)(f(\mathbf{e}_1)^2 + \cdots + f(\mathbf{e}_m)^2).$$

Therefore, for all $\mathbf{x} \in D$

$$|f(\mathbf{x})| \leqslant M \|\mathbf{x}\|, \qquad \text{where } M = (f(\mathbf{e}_1)^2 + \cdots + f(\mathbf{e}_m)^2)^{1/2}.$$

It follows that for any $\mathbf{p} \in \mathbb{R}^m$ and any sequence $(\mathbf{a}_k)$ in $\mathbb{R}^m$

$$|f(\mathbf{a}_k) - f(\mathbf{p})| = |f(\mathbf{a}_k - \mathbf{p})| \leqslant M \|\mathbf{a}_k - \mathbf{p}\|.$$

Hence $f(\mathbf{a}_k) \to f(\mathbf{p})$ whenever $\mathbf{a}_k \to \mathbf{p}$. This establishes that f is continuous at each $\mathbf{p} \in \mathbb{R}^m$.

3.2.3 Theorem

[i]   *All constant functions on* $D \subseteq \mathbb{R}^m$ *are continuous.*

[ii]   *If* f *and* g *are real-valued functions on* $D \subseteq \mathbb{R}^m$ *and if they are both continuous at* $\mathbf{p} \in D$, *then so are* $f + g$ *and* fg, *and* (*provided* $g(\mathbf{p}) \neq 0$) *so is* f/g.

[iii]   *If* f *is a real-valued function on* $D \subseteq \mathbb{R}^m$ *which is continuous at* $\mathbf{p} \in D$ *and if the function* $\phi : \mathbb{R} \to \mathbb{R}$ *is continuous at* $f(\mathbf{p})$, *then the composition* $\phi \circ f : D \subset \mathbb{R}^m \to \mathbb{R}$ *is continuous at* $\mathbf{p}$.

Proof.   Exercise.

3.2.4 Example.   The function $f : \mathbb{R}^2 \to \mathbb{R}$ defined by

$$f(x_1, x_2) = \begin{cases} x_1 + 2x_2 & \text{when } (x_1, x_2) \neq (0, 0), \\ 1 & \text{when } (x_1, x_2) = (0, 0), \end{cases}$$

is continuous everywhere except at the origin. To see this we relate f to the linear function $g : \mathbb{R}^2 \to \mathbb{R}$ given by $g(x_1, x_2) = x_1 + 2x_2$. Let $\mathbf{p} \in \mathbb{R}^2$, where $\mathbf{p} \neq (0, 0)$. If $\mathbf{a}_k \to \mathbf{p}$, then for large enough $k \in \mathbb{N}$, $\mathbf{a}_k \neq \mathbf{0}$. Hence for large enough k, $f(\mathbf{a}_k) = g(\mathbf{a}_k)$. But g is continuous at $\mathbf{p}$ (Theorem 3.2.2) and therefore

$$\lim_{k \to \infty} f(\mathbf{a}_k) = \lim_{k \to \infty} g(\mathbf{a}_k) = g(\mathbf{p}) = f(\mathbf{p}).$$

This establishes that f is continuous at $\mathbf{p} \neq (0, 0)$. To show that f is not continuous at $\mathbf{0}$ it is enough to find one sequence which does not satisfy the conditions of Definition 3.2.1. Consider the sequence $\mathbf{b}_k = (1/k, 1/k)$, $k \in \mathbb{N}$. Then $\mathbf{b}_k \to \mathbf{0}$ but $f(\mathbf{b}_k) \not\to f(\mathbf{0})$ since $f(\mathbf{b}_k) = 3/k$, whereas $f(\mathbf{0}) = 1$.

The graph of the above example is the plane $x_3 = x_1 + 2x_2$ in $\mathbb{R}^3$ with the point $(0, 0, 0)$ replaced by $(0, 0, 1)$. In general if there is such a jump or tear in the graph then the function has discontinuities.

3.2.5 Example. Let $f : \mathbb{R}^2 \to \mathbb{R}$ be defined by

$$f(x_1, x_2) = \begin{cases} -\frac{1}{2}x_2 + 2 & \text{when } x_1 \geqslant 0 \text{ and } x_2 \geqslant 0, \\ 2 & \text{otherwise.} \end{cases}$$

The discontinuities of f are revealed by sketching its graph (Fig. 3.7). The function is not continuous at $(0, 1)$, for example. It is enough to find just one sequence $(\mathbf{b}_k)$ in $\mathbb{R}^2$ such that $\mathbf{b}_k \to (0, 1)$ but $f(\mathbf{b}_k) \not\to f(0, 1) = \frac{3}{2}$. Consideration of the graph suggests the choice $\mathbf{b}_k = (-1/k, 1)$, $k \in \mathbb{N}$. Then $f(\mathbf{b}_k) = 2$ for all k and we have the required counter example. A similar argument can be used to show that f is discontinuous at all points of the form $(0, x_2)$, $x_2 > 0$. The function is however continuous at every other point, as we now show. Let $\mathbf{a}_k = (a_{1k}, a_{2k})$.

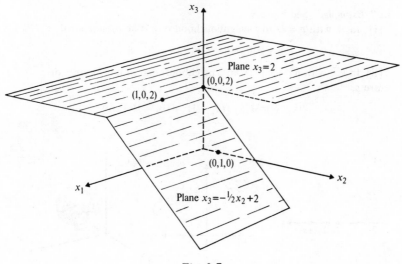

Fig. 3.7

[i] If $\mathbf{a}_k \to \mathbf{0}$ then $a_{2k} \to 0$ and it is clear from the definition that $f(\mathbf{a}_k) \to 2 = f(\mathbf{0})$. So f is continuous at $\mathbf{0}$.

[ii] If $\mathbf{a}_k \to \mathbf{p}$ where $p_1 > 0$ and $p_2 > 0$, then for large enough $k \in \mathbb{N}$, $a_{1k} > 0$

and $a_{2k} > 0$. Hence the function f on $\mathbf{a}_k$ is, for large k, the same as the function g given by $g(x_1, x_2) = -\frac{1}{2}x_2 + 2$. Now g, being the sum of a linear function and a constant function, is continuous at $\mathbf{p}$. Therefore

$$\lim_{k \to \infty} f(\mathbf{a}_k) = \lim_{k \to \infty} g(\mathbf{a}_k) = g(\mathbf{p}) = f(\mathbf{p}).$$

So f is continuous at $\mathbf{p}$.

[iii] Similarly if either $p_1 < 0$ or $p_2 < 0$ (or both) then the function f is the same as the constant function $h(x_1, x_2) = 2$ near $\mathbf{p}$. Again we have that f is continuous at $\mathbf{p}$.

[iv] The remaining cases where $\mathbf{p} = (p_1, 0)$, $p_1 > 0$, will be considered later in this section. See Example 3.2.24.

The domains which are particularly appropriate for the calculus of real valued functions on $\mathbb{R}^m$ are the open subsets of $\mathbb{R}^m$. They are generalizations of open intervals $]a, b[$ in $\mathbb{R}$. Roughly speaking they are subsets of $\mathbb{R}^m$ which 'entirely surround' each of their points. In order to make this precise we need two preparatory definitions.

3.2.6 Definition.   *Given* $\varepsilon > 0$ *and* $\mathbf{p} \in \mathbb{R}^m$, *the set* $\{\mathbf{x} \in \mathbb{R}^m \mid \|\mathbf{x} - \mathbf{p}\| < \varepsilon\}$ *is called the* ε-neighbourhood *of* $\mathbf{p}$ *and will be denoted by* $N(\mathbf{p}, \varepsilon)$.

3.2.7 Example.   See Fig. 3.8.

[i] In $\mathbb{R}$, with $p = 2$, an ε-neighbourhood of p is an *open interval*

$$\{t \in \mathbb{R} \mid |t - 2| < \varepsilon\} =]2 - \varepsilon, 2 + \varepsilon[.$$

[ii] In $\mathbb{R}^2$, with $\mathbf{p} = (-1, 1)$, an ε-neighbourhood of $\mathbf{p}$ is an *open disc* centre $\mathbf{p}$,

$$\{(x_1, x_2) \in \mathbb{R}^2 \mid \sqrt{[(x_1 + 1)^2 + (x_2 - 1)^2]} < \varepsilon\}.$$

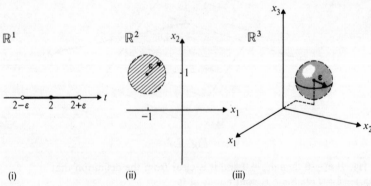

Fig. 3.8 (i) open interval in $\mathbb{R}$; (ii) open disc in $\mathbb{R}^2$; (iii) open ball in $\mathbb{R}^3$

[iii] In $\mathbb{R}^3$, with $\mathbf{p} = (-1, 1, 2)$, an ε-neighbourhood of $\mathbf{p}$ is an *open ball* centre $\mathbf{p}$,

$$\{(x_1, x_2, x_3) \in \mathbb{R}^3 \,|\, \sqrt{[(x_1 + 1)^2 + (x_2 - 1)^2 + (x_3 - 2)^2]} < \varepsilon\}.$$

3.2.8 Definition. *Let D be a subset of $\mathbb{R}^m$ and let $\mathbf{p} \in D$. We say that $\mathbf{p}$ is an* interior point *of D if there is a real number $\varepsilon > 0$ such that* $N(\mathbf{p}, \varepsilon) \subseteq D$.

3.2.9 Example. **[i]** Let $A =]1, 2[\subseteq \mathbb{R}$ and let $p = 1.8$. Then p is an interior point of A since $N(p, 0.1) \subseteq A$. See Fig. 3.9(i). One could show similarly that every point of A is an interior point of A.
[ii] Let $B = \{(x, y) \in \mathbb{R}^2 \,|\, 1 < x < 2, y = 0\} \subseteq \mathbb{R}^2$ and let $\mathbf{p} = (1.8, 0)$. Then $\mathbf{p}$ is not an interior point of B since for all $\varepsilon > 0$, $(1.8, \tfrac{1}{2}\varepsilon) \in N(\mathbf{p}, \varepsilon)$ but $(1.8, \tfrac{1}{2}\varepsilon) \notin B$. See Fig. 3.9(b).

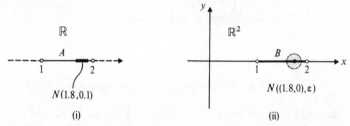

$N(1.8, 0.1)$

$N((1.8, 0), \varepsilon)$

(i) (ii)

Fig. 3.9 (i) $A \subseteq \mathbb{R}$ has interior points; (ii) $B \subseteq \mathbb{R}^2$ has no interior points

3.2.10 Definition. *A subset D of $\mathbb{R}^m$ is* open *in $\mathbb{R}^m$ if every point of D is an interior point of D.*

In Example 3.2.9(i) the set A is open in $\mathbb{R}$, and indeed one can use a similar argument to show that all open intervals are open in $\mathbb{R}$. In Example 3.2.9(ii) the set B is not open in $\mathbb{R}^2$ since the point $(1.8, 0)$ is not an interior point.

3.2.11 Example. For any $\mathbf{p} \in \mathbb{R}^m$ and any $\varepsilon > 0$, the ε-neighbourhood $N(\mathbf{p}, \varepsilon)$ is an open subset of $\mathbb{R}^m$. For if $\mathbf{q} \in N(\mathbf{p}, \varepsilon)$ and if $\|\mathbf{q} - \mathbf{p}\| = \gamma < \varepsilon$, then $N(\mathbf{q}, \varepsilon - \gamma) \subseteq N(\mathbf{p}, \varepsilon)$ (use the triangle inequality and the identity $\mathbf{x} - \mathbf{p} = \mathbf{x} - \mathbf{q} + \mathbf{q} - \mathbf{p}$).

3.2.12 Example. The rectangle $R = \{(x, y) \in \mathbb{R}^2 \,|\, 0 < x < 1, 0 < y < 3\}$ is an open subset of $\mathbb{R}^2$ since for any point $\mathbf{p} \in R$ there exists an $\varepsilon > 0$ such that $N(\mathbf{p}, \varepsilon) \subseteq R$. See Fig. 3.10.

Notice that in Example 3.2.12 for each $\mathbf{p} \in R$ there is a sequence

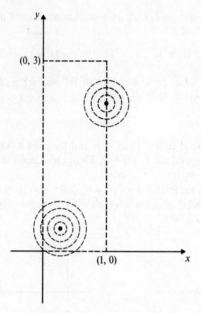

Fig. 3.10 Cluster points of open rectangle

$(\mathbf{a}_k)$ such that (i) $\mathbf{a}_k \in R$ for all $k \in \mathbb{N}$, (ii) $\mathbf{a}_k \neq \mathbf{p}$ for all $k \in \mathbb{N}$, and
(iii) $\mathbf{a}_k \to \mathbf{p}$. There are also other points $\mathbf{p}$ of the plane for which such
a sequence exists. Each point $\mathbf{p}$ on the edge of the rectangle is so
'close' to R that every neighbourhood $N(\mathbf{p}, 1/k), k \in \mathbb{N}$, intersects R.
By choosing $\mathbf{a}_k \in N(\mathbf{p}, 1/k) \cap R$, we can generate a sequence satisfying
the above three properties. See Fig. 3.10. We are led to the following
definition.

3.2.13 Definition.   *Let D be a subset of $\mathbb{R}^m$. A point $\mathbf{c}$ is called a*
cluster point (or a limit point) of D if there is a sequence of points
$(\mathbf{x}_k)$ *in D such that $\mathbf{x}_k \neq \mathbf{c}$ for all $k \in \mathbb{N}$, but $\mathbf{x}_k \to \mathbf{c}$.*

3.2.14 Example.   [i] The cluster points of the set A of Example 3.2.9(i)
form the closed interval $[1, 2]$. In general the set of cluster points of any
interval in $\mathbb{R}$ is the union of the interval and its end points. (Compare
Definition 2.4.1.)

   [ii] In Example 3.2.9(ii) the cluster points of B are the points of B
together with the points $(1, 0)$ and $(2, 0)$. Every point of B is also a cluster
point of $\mathbb{R}^2 \backslash B$, the complement of B in $\mathbb{R}^2$.

   [iii] The cluster points of $N(\mathbf{p}, \varepsilon)$ in $\mathbb{R}^m$ form the *closed ball*
$\{\mathbf{x} \in \mathbb{R}^m | \, \|\mathbf{x} - \mathbf{p}\| \leq \varepsilon\}$.

[iv] The cluster points of the rectangle R in Example 3.2.12 form the *closed rectangle* $[(x, y) \in \mathbb{R}^2 | 0 \leqslant x \leqslant 1, 0 \leqslant y \leqslant 3\}$.

3.2.15 Definition. *A subset D of $\mathbb{R}^m$ is* closed *in $\mathbb{R}^m$ if it contains all its cluster points.*

3.2.16 Example. A closed interval in $\mathbb{R}$, a closed ball in $\mathbb{R}^m$, a closed rectangle in $\mathbb{R}^2$ are all closed sets in their respective Euclidean spaces.

Notice that there are sets which are neither open nor closed – in this sense the terms are unfortunate. In Example 3.2.9(ii) for instance, the set B is not open in $\mathbb{R}^2$ since $(1.8, 0)$ is not an interior point, and it is not closed in $\mathbb{R}^2$ since it does not contain its cluster point $(1, 0)$. We do however have the following important result.

3.2.17 Theorem. *A subset D of $\mathbb{R}^m$ is open if and only if its complement in $\mathbb{R}^m$ is closed.*

Proof. Exercise.

We are now in a position to adapt Definition 2.4.5 and the theorems which follow to our present situation.

3.2.18 Definition. *Given a cluster point $\mathbf{p}$ of $D \subseteq \mathbb{R}^m$, a point q in $\mathbb{R}$ and a function $f : D \to \mathbb{R}$, we write $\lim_{\mathbf{x} \to \mathbf{p}} f(\mathbf{x}) = q$ if $f(\mathbf{a}_k) \to q$ whenever $\mathbf{a}_k \to \mathbf{p}$ where the sequence $(\mathbf{a}_k)$ lies in D and $\mathbf{a}_k \neq \mathbf{p}$ for all $k \in \mathbb{N}$.*

3.2.19 Example. **[i]** In the case of the function of Example 3.2.4, $\lim_{\mathbf{x} \to \mathbf{0}} f(\mathbf{x}) = 0$.
[ii] In the case of the function of Example 3.2.5, $\lim_{\mathbf{x} \to \mathbf{0}} f(\mathbf{x}) = 2$.

3.2.20 Theorem. *The function $f : D \subseteq \mathbb{R}^m \to \mathbb{R}$ is continuous at a cluster point $\mathbf{p} \in D$ if and only if $\lim_{\mathbf{x} \to \mathbf{p}} f(\mathbf{x}) = f(\mathbf{p})$.*

Proof. Exercise (compare Theorem 2.4.9).

3.2.21 Theorem. *Given a function $f : D \subseteq \mathbb{R}^m \to \mathbb{R}$ and $\mathbf{p}$ a cluster point of D, then $\lim_{\mathbf{x} \to \mathbf{p}} f(\mathbf{x}) = q$ if and only if to each $\varepsilon > 0$ (however small) there corresponds a real number $\delta > 0$ such that $|f(\mathbf{x}) - q| < \varepsilon$ whenever $\mathbf{x} \in D$ and $0 < \|\mathbf{x} - \mathbf{p}\| < \delta$.*

Proof. Exercise (compare Theorem 2.4.11).

We note again that the limiting process is not concerned with the value that f takes at $\mathbf{p}$, nor even whether f is defined at $\mathbf{p}$.

We can combine Theorems 3.2.20 and 3.2.21 to provide a manipulative test for continuity.

3.2.22 Theorem.   *The function* $f : D \subseteq \mathbb{R}^m \to \mathbb{R}$ *is continuous at* $\mathbf{p} \in D$ *if and only if to each* $\varepsilon > 0$ *there corresponds* $\delta > 0$ *such that* $f(\mathbf{x}) \in N(f(\mathbf{p}), \varepsilon)$ *whenever* $\mathbf{x} \in D$ *and* $\mathbf{x} \in N(p, \delta)$.

Proof.   Exercise (compare Corollary 2.4.16).

Theorem 3.2.22 is useful for proving the continuity of a function f at a point $\mathbf{p}$ in its domain. There is some risk of becoming lost in the calculations, and it is as well to establish a systematic procedure. We recommend the following.

1.   Consider a δ-neighbourhood $N(\mathbf{p}, \delta)$ of $\mathbf{p}$ for small δ. Locate the image $f(N(\mathbf{p}, \delta))$ as a subset of $\mathbb{R}$.
2.   Consider the possible values of ε such that $f(N(\mathbf{p}, \delta))$ is a subset of the ε-neighbourhood of $f(\mathbf{p})$; that is, find values of ε such that

3.2.23 $f(N(\mathbf{p}, \delta)) \subseteq N(f(\mathbf{p}), \varepsilon)$.

3.   Finally, prove continuity by showing that to each choice of ε, however small, there corresponds a δ (which will depend on ε) for which the inclusion 3.2.23 is true.

3.2.24 Example.   Let us apply the above procedure to prove the continuity of the function $f : \mathbb{R}^2 \to \mathbb{R}$ of Example 3.2.5 at the point $\mathbf{p} = (1, 0)$. We repeat the definition

$$f(x_1, x_2) = \begin{cases} -\tfrac{1}{2}x_2 + 2 & \text{when } x_1 \geqslant 0 \text{ and } x_2 \geqslant 0, \\ 2 & \text{otherwise.} \end{cases}$$

We have $f(\mathbf{p}) = f(1, 0) = 2$. (The point $(\mathbf{p}, f(\mathbf{p}))$ on the graph of f marked as $(1, 0, 2)$ in Fig. 3.7.)

1.   Consider a small $\delta > 0$. Now $N(\mathbf{p}, \delta)$ is a disc in $\mathbb{R}^2$ centred at $\mathbf{p}$ (Fig. 3.11). We wish to locate its image under f as a subset of $\mathbb{R}$.

Note that $N(\mathbf{p}, \delta)$ is a subset of the open square $S(\mathbf{p}, \delta)$ centred at $\mathbf{p}$ of edge 2δ. It is clear from the definition of f that

$$f(N(\mathbf{p}, \delta)) \subseteq f(S(\mathbf{p}, \delta)) = \{t \in \mathbb{R} \mid 2 - \tfrac{1}{2}\delta < t < 2\}.$$

2.   We deduce that

$$f(N(\mathbf{p}, \delta)) \subseteq N(2, \tfrac{1}{2}\delta),$$

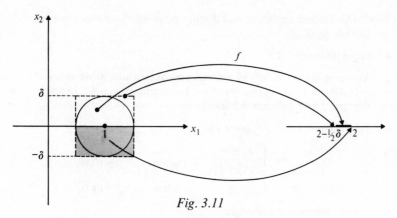

Fig. 3.11

and hence that

$$f(N(\mathbf{p}, \delta)) \subseteq N(f(\mathbf{p}), \varepsilon) = N(2, \varepsilon)$$

whenever $\varepsilon \geqslant \frac{1}{2}\delta$.

3. We conclude that to each $\varepsilon > 0$ there corresponds a δ such that condition 3.2.23 is satisfied. We need only choose δ such that $\delta \leqslant 2\varepsilon$. This proves that f is continuous at $\mathbf{p}$.

Exercises 3.2

1. Which of the following subsets of $\mathbb{R}^2$ are (i) open, (ii) closed, (iii) both open and closed, (iv) neither open nor closed?
    (a) $1 < x_1 < 2$ and $-1 < x_2 < 2$;
    (b) $1 < x_1 < 2$ and $-1 \leqslant x_2 < 2$;
    (c) $x_1^2 + x_2^2 > 0$;
    (d) $x_1^2 + \frac{1}{2}x_2^2 \leqslant 1$;
    (e) $\|\mathbf{x} - (1, 3)\| < 1$;
    (f) $x_1 > x_2$;
    (g) $\mathbb{R}^2$
    In each case determine the cluster points of the set.

Answers: (a), (c), (e), (f), (g) open;   (d), (g) closed.

2. Prove that the function of Example 3.2.5 is (a) continuous at $(2, 0)$;
    (b) discontinuous at $(0, 2)$. (In (a) apply the procedure of Example 3.2.24. In (b) construct a sequence demonstrating the failure of Definition 3.2.1.)

3. Apply the method of Example 3.2.24 to prove that the function $f : \mathbb{R}^2 \to \mathbb{R}$ defined by $f(x, y) = x^2 + y^2$ is continuous at $\mathbf{p} = (1, 2)$.

Hint: Show that, provided $0 < \delta < 1$, $f(N(p, \delta)) \subseteq N(5, 8\delta)$. Hence for a given small $\varepsilon > 0$, we can choose $\delta \leqslant \varepsilon/8$ in Theorem 3.2.22.

Note: The method applies to an arbitrary point $\mathbf{p} \in \mathbb{R}^2$, and so f is continuous on $\mathbb{R}^2$.

4. Prove Theorem 3.2.3.

5. Assuming the continuity of the exponential function, prove that $g : \mathbb{R}^2 \to \mathbb{R}$ defined by $g(x, y) = \exp(x^2 + y^2)$ is continuous on $\mathbb{R}^2$. (Apply Exercise 3 and Theorem 3.2.3(iii).)

6. The function $f : \mathbb{R}^2 \to \mathbb{R}$ given by

$$f(x_1, x_2) = \begin{cases} \dfrac{x_1 + x_2}{\sqrt{(x_1^2 + x_2^2)}} & \text{when } (x_1, x_2) \neq (0, 0), \\ 0 & \text{when } (x_1, x_2) = (0, 0) \end{cases}$$

is discontinuous at the origin.

Hint: consider the sequence $\mathbf{a}_k = \frac{1}{k}(\cos \alpha, \sin \alpha)$, $k \in \mathbb{N}$, α fixed.

7. Prove that the function $f : \mathbb{R}^2 \to \mathbb{R}$ given by

$$f(x, y) = \begin{cases} \dfrac{2xy}{x^2 + y^2} & \text{when } (x, y) \neq (0, 0), \\ 0 & \text{when } (x, y) = (0, 0) \end{cases}$$

is discontinuous at the origin.

8. Prove that the functions $f : \mathbb{R}^2 \to \mathbb{R}$ and $g : \mathbb{R}^2 \to \mathbb{R}$ given by

$$f(x, y) = \begin{cases} \dfrac{x^2 y}{x^2 + y^2} & \text{when } (x, y) \neq (0, 0) \\ 0 & \text{when } (x, y) = (0, 0), \end{cases}$$

$$g(x, y) = \begin{cases} \dfrac{2xy}{\sqrt{(x^2 + y^2)}} & \text{when } (x, y) \neq (0, 0) \\ 0 & \text{when } (x, y) = (0, 0) \end{cases}$$

are everywhere continuous.

Hint: to prove continuity at $\mathbf{p} \neq \mathbf{0}$ apply Theorem 3.2.3; to prove continuity at $\mathbf{p} = \mathbf{0}$, put $(x, y) = (r\cos \theta, r\sin \theta)$, $r \geq 0$.

9. Let $f : D \subseteq \mathbb{R}^m \to \mathbb{R}$ be continuous. Prove that the level sets of f are closed subsets in D.

3.3   Linear approximation and differentiability

Our aim in this section is to formulate a definition of the differentiability of a function $f : D \subseteq \mathbb{R}^m \to \mathbb{R}$ at a point in its domain. When

$m = 1$ the new definition must agree with that given (in Section 2.5) of the differentiability of function $f : D \subseteq \mathbb{R} \to \mathbb{R}^n$ when $n = 1$. To avoid becoming tangled in special cases we consider only those functions whose domain D is an open subset of $\mathbb{R}^m$.

It is more appropriate to take the approach of Section 2.10 than that of Section 2.5 (see Exercise 3.3.1) and accordingly we introduce the relevant ideas.

3.3.1 Definition. *For an open set D in $\mathbb{R}^m$ with $\mathbf{p} \in D$, let*
$D_{\mathbf{p}} = \{\mathbf{h} | \mathbf{p} + \mathbf{h} \in D\}.$

Notice that $D_{\mathbf{p}}$, which is merely the translation of D through $-\mathbf{p}$, contains $\mathbf{0}$ and is itself an open set. See Fig. 3.12(i).

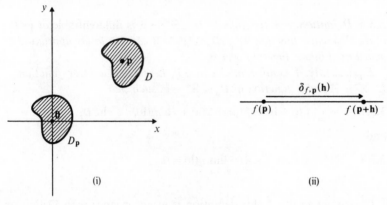

Fig. 3.12

3.3.2 Example. Let $D = \{(x, y) | x \in]1, 3[, \ y \in]2, 6[\}$. Then
$$D_{(2, 5)} = \{(x, y) | x \in]-1, 1[, \ y \in]-3, 1[\}.$$

3.3.3 Definition. *Consider a function $f : D \subseteq \mathbb{R}^m \to \mathbb{R}$ and let $\mathbf{p} \in D$. The difference function $\delta_{f, \mathbf{p}} : D_{\mathbf{p}} \subset \mathbb{R}^m \to \mathbb{R}$ is defined by*
$$\delta_{f, \mathbf{p}}(\mathbf{h}) = f(\mathbf{p} + \mathbf{h}) - f(\mathbf{p}), \qquad \mathbf{h} \in D_{\mathbf{p}}.$$

The difference function expresses the change in $f(\mathbf{x})$ as $\mathbf{x}$ moves away from $\mathbf{p}$. See Fig. 3.12(ii).

3.3.4 Example. If $f : \mathbb{R}^2 \to \mathbb{R}$ is defined by $f(x_1, x_2) = x_1^2 + x_2^2$, then
$$\delta_{f, \mathbf{p}}(\mathbf{h}) = 2h_1 p_1 + 2h_2 p_2 + h_1^2 + h_2^2.$$

3.3.5 Definition.   Let $g : N \subseteq \mathbb{R}^m \to \mathbb{R}$ and $g^* : M \subseteq \mathbb{R}^m \to \mathbb{R}$ be two functions defined on open domains N and M such that $\mathbf{0} \in N \cap M$. We say that g and g^* closely approximate each other near $\mathbf{0} \in \mathbb{R}^m$ if

$$g(\mathbf{0}) = g^*(\mathbf{0}) \quad and \quad \lim_{\mathbf{h} \to \mathbf{0}} \frac{g(\mathbf{h}) - g^*(\mathbf{h})}{\|\mathbf{h}\|} = 0.$$

Equivalently, g and g^* closely approximate each other near $\mathbf{0}$ if there exists a function $\eta : N \cap M \subseteq \mathbb{R}^m \to \mathbb{R}$ *such that*

[i] $g(\mathbf{h}) = g^*(\mathbf{h}) + \|\mathbf{h}\| \eta(\mathbf{h})$ *for all* $\mathbf{h} \in N \cap M$ *and*

[ii] $\displaystyle\lim_{\mathbf{h} \to \mathbf{0}} \eta(\mathbf{h}) = 0.$

The definition expresses the order of the difference between g and g^* near $\mathbf{0}$.

3.3.6 Definition.   *A function* $f : D \subseteq \mathbb{R}^m \to \mathbb{R}$ *is* differentiable *at* $\mathbf{p} \in D$ *if the difference function* $\delta_{f, \mathbf{p}} : D_{\mathbf{p}} \subseteq \mathbb{R}^m \to \mathbb{R}$ *can be closely approximated by a linear function near* $\mathbf{0}$.

Equivalently, f is differentiable at $\mathbf{p}$ *if there exists a linear function* $L : \mathbb{R}^m \to \mathbb{R}$ *and a function* $\eta : D_{\mathbf{p}} \subseteq \mathbb{R}^m \to \mathbb{R}$ *such that*

3.3.7 $f(\mathbf{p} + \mathbf{h}) - f(\mathbf{p}) = L(\mathbf{h}) + \|\mathbf{h}\| \eta(\mathbf{h}), \qquad \mathbf{h} \in D_{\mathbf{p}}$

and

3.3.8 $\displaystyle\lim_{\mathbf{h} \to \mathbf{0}} \eta(\mathbf{h}) = 0.$

Clearly when $m = 1$ this definition is in accordance with Definition 2.10.16 as applied to the case $n = 1$, since if $h \in \mathbb{R}$, then $\|h\| = |h|$.

3.3.9 Example.   A linear function $L : \mathbb{R}^m \to \mathbb{R}$ is differentiable everywhere.

3.3.10 Example.   Let $f(x_1, x_2) = x_1^2 + x_2^2$, as in Example 3.3.4. For each $\mathbf{p} \in \mathbb{R}^2$ the condition 3.3.7 is satisfied if we take $L(\mathbf{h}) = 2p_1 h_1 + 2p_2 h_2$ and $\eta(\mathbf{h}) = \|\mathbf{h}\| = \sqrt{(h_1^2 + h_2^2)}$. Since $\lim_{\mathbf{h} \to \mathbf{0}} \|\mathbf{h}\| = 0$, the function f is differentiable at $\mathbf{p}$.

3.3.11 Theorem.   *A function* $f : D \subseteq \mathbb{R}^m \to \mathbb{R}$ *which is differentiable at* $\mathbf{p} \in D$ *is also continuous there.*

Proof.   Let $(\mathbf{a}_k)$ be a sequence in D such that $\mathbf{a}_k \to \mathbf{p}$. For each $k \in \mathbb{N}$, let $\mathbf{h}_k = \mathbf{a}_k - \mathbf{p}$. If f is differentiable at $\mathbf{p}$, then there exists a linear function L and a function η satisfying 3.3.7 and 3.3.8. Hence

3.3.12 $f(\mathbf{a}_k) = f(\mathbf{p}) + L(\mathbf{h}_k) + \|\mathbf{h}_k\| \eta(\mathbf{h}_k),$ $k \in \mathbb{N}.$

But $\mathbf{h}_k \to \mathbf{0}$ and so (by Theorem 3.2.2) $L(\mathbf{h}_k) \to 0$ and (from 3.3.8) $\|\mathbf{h}_k\| \eta(\mathbf{h}_k) \to 0$. It follows from 3.3.12 that $f(\mathbf{a}_k) \to f(\mathbf{p})$ and the proof is complete.

We shall describe some continuous functions which are not differentiable later in this section.

3.3.13 Theorem.   *Let* $f \cdot : D \subseteq \mathbb{R}^m \to \mathbb{R}$ *be differentiable at* $\mathbf{p} \in D$. *Then there is only one close linear approximation to* $\delta_{f,\mathbf{p}}$ *near* $\mathbf{0}$.

Proof. Let $\mathbf{e}_1, \ldots, \mathbf{e}_m$ be the usual basis of $\mathbb{R}^m$, let $L : \mathbb{R}^m \to \mathbb{R}$ be a close linear approximation to $\delta_{f,\mathbf{p}}$ near $\mathbf{0}$ and let $\eta : D_\mathbf{p} \to \mathbb{R}$ be a function satisfying 3.3.7 and 3.3.8. Since f is differentiable at $\mathbf{p}$ we have for each j, $1 \leqslant j \leqslant m$,

[i] $f(\mathbf{p} + t\mathbf{e}_j) - f(\mathbf{p}) = L(t\mathbf{e}_j) + \|t\mathbf{e}_j\| \eta(t\mathbf{e}_j),$ $t\mathbf{e}_j \in D_\mathbf{p}$

[ii] $\lim\limits_{t \to 0} \eta(t\mathbf{e}_j) = 0.$

It follows that

$$f(\mathbf{p} + t\mathbf{e}_j) - f(\mathbf{p}) = tL(\mathbf{e}_j) + |t|\eta(t\mathbf{e}_j),$$

and therefore, for $t \neq 0$,

$$\frac{f(\mathbf{p} + t\mathbf{e}_j) - f(\mathbf{p})}{t} = L(\mathbf{e}_j) + \frac{|t|}{t}\eta(t\mathbf{e}_j).$$

Using (ii) above, we obtain

3.3.14 $$\lim\limits_{t \to 0} \frac{f(\mathbf{p} + t\mathbf{e}_j) - f(\mathbf{p})}{t} = L(\mathbf{e}_j).$$

Now if $L^* : \mathbb{R}^m \to \mathbb{R}$ were another close linear approximation to f near $\mathbf{p}$, the above argument would also show that

$$\lim\limits_{t \to 0} \frac{f(\mathbf{p} + t\mathbf{e}_j) - f(\mathbf{p})}{t} = L^*(\mathbf{e}_j).$$

Hence $L(\mathbf{e}_j) = L^*(\mathbf{e}_j)$ for each j, $1 \leqslant j \leqslant m$. But a linear function on $\mathbb{R}^m$ is uniquely determined by its effect on $\mathbf{e}_1, \ldots, \mathbf{e}_m$. We have therefore proved that $L = L^*$.

3.3.15 Definition. *If $f : D \subseteq \mathbb{R}^m \to \mathbb{R}$ is differentiable at $\mathbf{p} \in D$, then the (unique) close linear approximation to $\delta_{f,\mathbf{p}}$ at $\mathbf{0}$ is denoted by $L_{f,\mathbf{p}}$ and is called the* differential *of f at* $\mathbf{p}$.

The differentiability of $f : D \subseteq \mathbb{R}^m \to \mathbb{R}$ at $\mathbf{p} \in D$ implies that there exists a function $\eta : D_{\mathbf{p}} \subseteq \mathbb{R}^m \to \mathbb{R}$ and a linear function $L_{f,\mathbf{p}} : \mathbb{R}^m \to \mathbb{R}^m$ such that for all $\mathbf{h} \in D_{\mathbf{p}}$,

$$f(\mathbf{p} + \mathbf{h}) - f(\mathbf{p}) = L_{f,\mathbf{p}}(h_1\mathbf{e}_1 + \cdots + h_m\mathbf{e}_m) + \|\mathbf{h}\|\eta(\mathbf{h})$$
$$= h_1 L_{f,\mathbf{p}}(\mathbf{e}_1) + \cdots + h_m L_{f,\mathbf{p}}(\mathbf{e}_m) + \|\mathbf{h}\|\eta(\mathbf{h}),$$

where $\lim_{\mathbf{h} \to \mathbf{0}} \eta(\mathbf{h}) = 0$.

It is important to know how to find $L_{f,\mathbf{p}}(\mathbf{e}_j)$ for each $j = 1, \ldots, m$. We have seen in the proof of Theorem 3.3.13 (see in particular 3.3.14) that

3.3.16 $$L_{f,\mathbf{p}}(\mathbf{e}_j) = \lim_{t \to 0} \frac{f(\mathbf{p} + t\mathbf{e}_j) - f(\mathbf{p})}{t}, \qquad j = 1, \ldots, m.$$

The limit on the right-hand side of 3.3.16 may exist even if the function f is not differentiable at $\mathbf{p}$. If it does exist, then it is called the *partial derivative* of f with respect to the jth coordinate x_j and is denoted by

$$\frac{\partial f}{\partial x_j}(\mathbf{p}) = \lim_{t \to 0} \frac{f(\mathbf{p} + t\mathbf{e}_j) - f(\mathbf{p})}{t}$$

3.3.17

$$= \lim_{t \to 0} \frac{f(p_1, \ldots, p_{j-1}, p_j + t, p_{j+1}, \ldots, p_m) - f(p_1, \ldots, p_m)}{t}$$

The techniques of elementary calculus are all that is required to evaluate partial derivatives. In order to determine $(\partial f / \partial x_j)(\mathbf{p})$ we simply have to differentiate $f(p_1, \ldots, p_{j-1}, x_j, p_{j+1}, \ldots, p_m)$ with respect to x_j and evaluate the derivative at $x_j = p_j$.

3.3.18 Example. Let $f : \mathbb{R}^3 \to \mathbb{R}$ be defined by

$$f(x_1, x_2, x_3) = x_1^2 x_2 + 2x_3.$$

Then

$$\frac{\partial f}{\partial x_1}(\mathbf{p}) = 2p_1 p_2, \quad \frac{\partial f}{\partial x_2}(\mathbf{p}) = p_1^2, \quad \frac{\partial f}{\partial x_3}(\mathbf{p}) = 2.$$

Provided partial derivatives of $f : D \subseteq \mathbb{R}^m \to \mathbb{R}$ exist at every point $\mathbf{p}$

of the (open) domain D we can regard $\partial f/\partial x_1$, $\partial f/\partial x_2, \ldots$ themselves as functions from D into $\mathbb{R}$. We find $(\partial f/\partial x_j)(\mathbf{x})$ by differentiating the expression for $f(x_1, \ldots, x_m)$ with respect to x_j, regarding the other variables as constants. In Example 3.3.18 we have $(\partial f/\partial x_1)(\mathbf{x}) = 2x_1x_2$, for example.

3.3.19 Remark. The notation is adjusted to suit the problem. For example, in Example 3.1.2 we considered the relationship, $V = \pi r^2 h$, between the volume V, the radius r and the height h of the cylinder. We find that $(\partial V/\partial r)(r, h) = 2\pi rh$ and that $(\partial V/\partial h)(r, h) = \pi r^2$.

Our notation for partial derivatives, which is the one most commonly used, is meaningful only with reference to the notation used for the vectors in the domain. For example, if a function $f : \mathbb{R}^3 \to \mathbb{R}$ is defined by its action on vectors (x_1, x_2, x_3) then it makes no sense to speak of $\partial f/\partial y$. An alternative notation is to let $f_j(\mathbf{p})$ stand for the partial derivative of f at $\mathbf{p}$ with respect to the jth coordinate. Thus $f_2(x_1, x_2, x_3)$ stands for $(\partial f/\partial x_2)(x_1, x_2, x_3)$ and $f_2(x, y, z)$ stands for $(\partial f/\partial y)(x, y, z)$. This notation has much to recommend it, but we refrain from using it to avoid confusion with our notation (adopted in Chapter 2) for coordinate functions. Coordinate functions and partial derivatives play a very important role in vector calculus. There are many theorems which involve both at the same time and they must be clearly distinguished in the notation.

Now that we have a notation for the limit in 3.3.16 we can state the following important corollary of Theorem 3.3.13.

3.3.20 Theorem. *Let $f : D \subseteq \mathbb{R}^m \to \mathbb{R}$ be differentiable at $\mathbf{p} \in \mathbb{R}^m$. Then*
[i] *the partial derivative $(\partial f/\partial x_j)(\mathbf{p})$ exists and is equal to $L_{f,\mathbf{p}}(\mathbf{e}_j)$ for each $1 \leqslant j \leqslant m$,*
[ii] *for all $\mathbf{h} \in \mathbb{R}^m$,*

$$L_{f,\mathbf{p}}(\mathbf{h}) = h_1 \frac{\partial f}{\partial x_1}(\mathbf{p}) + \cdots + h_m \frac{\partial f}{\partial x_m}(\mathbf{p}),$$

[iii] *the $1 \times m$ matrix representing $L_{f,\mathbf{p}}$ (with respect to the usual bases) is*

$$J_{f,\mathbf{p}} = \left[\frac{\partial f}{\partial x_1}(\mathbf{p}) \quad \cdots \quad \frac{\partial f}{\partial x_m}(\mathbf{p}) \right].$$

Proof. Exercise. The matrix representing $L_{f,\mathbf{p}}$ is
$[L_{f,\mathbf{p}}(\mathbf{e}_1) \quad \cdots \quad L_{f,\mathbf{p}}(\mathbf{e}_m)]$.

3.3.21 Definition.   *The above matrix $J_{f,\mathbf{p}}$ representing the differential $L_{f,\mathbf{p}}$ is called the* Jacobian *matrix of f at $\mathbf{p}$.*

We can also rephrase the definition of differentiability in terms of partial derivatives.

3.3.22 Theorem.   *The function $f : D \subseteq \mathbb{R}^m \to \mathbb{R}$ is differentiable at $\mathbf{p} \in D$ if and only if*
 [i] *all the partial derivatives of f exist at $\mathbf{p}$, and*
 [ii] *there exists a function $\eta : D_\mathbf{p} \subseteq \mathbb{R}^m \to \mathbb{R}$ such that for all $\mathbf{h} \in D_\mathbf{p}$*

3.3.23 $$f(\mathbf{p} + \mathbf{h}) - f(\mathbf{p}) = h_1 \frac{\partial f}{\partial x_1}(\mathbf{p}) + \cdots + h_m \frac{\partial f}{\partial x_m}(\mathbf{p}) + \|\mathbf{h}\| \eta(\mathbf{h}),$$

where

3.3.24 $$\lim_{\mathbf{h} \to 0} \eta(\mathbf{h}) = 0.$$

Proof.   Exercise.

3.3.25 Example.   Consider again (see Examples 3.3.4 and 3.3.10) the function $f : \mathbb{R}^2 \to \mathbb{R}$ given by

$$f(x_1, x_2) = x_1^2 + x_2^2.$$

We have seen that

$$f(\mathbf{x} + \mathbf{h}) - f(\mathbf{x}) = 2x_1 h_1 + 2x_2 h_2 + \|\mathbf{h}\| \|\mathbf{h}\|.$$

Since $(\partial f / \partial x_1)(\mathbf{x}) = 2x_1$ and $(\partial f / \partial x_2)(\mathbf{x}) = 2x_2$, the Jacobian matrix of f at $\mathbf{x}$ is $J_{f,\mathbf{x}} = [2x_1 \quad 2x_2]$. Hence $L_{f,\mathbf{x}}(\mathbf{h}) = 2x_1 h_1 + 2x_2 h_2$. By taking $\eta(\mathbf{h}) = \|\mathbf{h}\|$ we have explained the presence of the various components in the above expression.

Theorem 3.3.20 tells us that if any one of the partial derivatives of a function $f : D \subseteq \mathbb{R}^n \to \mathbb{R}$ does not exist at $\mathbf{p} \in D$, then f is not differentiable at $\mathbf{p}$.

3.3.26 Example.   Let $f : \mathbb{R}^m \to \mathbb{R}$ be the function defined by $f(\mathbf{x}) = \|\mathbf{x}\|$. The partial derivative $(\partial f / \partial x_1)(\mathbf{0})$, if it exists, is found by considering

$$\frac{f(\mathbf{0} + t\mathbf{e}_1) - f(\mathbf{0})}{t} = \frac{|t|}{t}.$$

But $\lim_{t \to 0} |t|/t$ does not exist, and so f is not differentiable at $\mathbf{0}$.

The converse of Theorem 3.3.20(i) is not true: the existence of the partial derivatives of a function $f : D \subseteq \mathbb{R}^m \to \mathbb{R}$ at $\mathbf{p} \in D$ is not enough to guarantee that f is differentiable at $\mathbf{p}$. We show this in the following example by using Theorem 3.3.22.

3.3.27 Example. Refer again to the function f defined in Example 3.1.8. Since $f(t, 0) = f(0, t) = f(0, 0)$ for all $t \in \mathbb{R}$, the partial derivatives of f both exist at $\mathbf{0}$ and are both 0. However, f is not differentiable at $\mathbf{0}$, for if it were, then the close linear approximation L to $\delta_{f,\mathbf{0}}$ at $\mathbf{0}$ would have to be given by

$$L(h_1, h_2) = 0h_1 + 0h_2, \qquad (h_1, h_2) \in \mathbb{R}^2.$$

The corresponding function $\eta : \mathbb{R}^2 \to \mathbb{R}$ would have to satisfy (compare Theorem 3.3.22)

$$f(h_1, h_2) = f(0, 0) + 0h_1 + 0h_2 + \sqrt{(h_1^2 + h_2^2)}\eta(h_1, h_2), \text{ for all } (h_1, h_2) \in \mathbb{R}^2.$$

Hence, for $(h_1, h_2) \neq (0, 0)$,

$$\eta(h_1, h_2) = \frac{f(h_1, h_2)}{\sqrt{(h_1^2 + h_2^2)}}.$$

In particular,

$$f(h_1, h_2) = -|h| \qquad \text{when } h_1 = h_2 = h,$$

and so

$$\eta(h, h) = \frac{-|h|}{|h|\sqrt{2}} = -\frac{1}{\sqrt{2}}, \qquad \text{when } h \neq 0.$$

Hence $\lim_{\mathbf{h} \to \mathbf{0}} \eta(\mathbf{h}) \neq 0$. This establishes that f is not differentiable at $\mathbf{0}$.

3.3.28 Example. In Example 3.3.18 we considered a function $f : \mathbb{R}^3 \to \mathbb{R}$ defined by $f(x_1, x_2, x_3) = x_1^2 x_2 + 2x_3$. The partial derivatives of f are given by

$$\frac{\partial f}{\partial x_1}(\mathbf{x}) = 2x_1 x_2, \qquad \frac{\partial f}{\partial x_2}(\mathbf{x}) = x_1^2, \qquad \frac{\partial f}{\partial x_3}(\mathbf{x}) = 2.$$

To determine whether f is differentiable at $\mathbf{x} \in \mathbb{R}^3$ we must ask whether the linear function $L : \mathbb{R}^3 \to \mathbb{R}$ given by

$$L(\mathbf{h}) = 2x_1 x_2 h_1 + x_1^2 h_2 + 2h_3, \qquad \mathbf{h} \in \mathbb{R}^3$$

is a close linear approximation to $\delta_{f,\mathbf{x}}$ near $\mathbf{0}$. Now

$$f(\mathbf{x} + \mathbf{h}) - f(\mathbf{x}) = 2x_1 x_2 h_1 + x_1^2 h_2 + 2h_3 + 2x_1 h_1 h_2 + h_1^2 x_2 + h_1^2 h_2.$$

and so

$$\delta_{f,\mathbf{x}}(\mathbf{h}) = L(\mathbf{h}) + \|\mathbf{h}\|\eta(\mathbf{h}),$$

where

$$\eta(\mathbf{h}) = \begin{array}{ll} \dfrac{2x_1 h_1 h_2 + h_1^2 x_2 + h_1^2 h_2}{\|\mathbf{h}\|} & \text{if } \mathbf{h} \neq \mathbf{0} \\[2ex] 0 & \text{if } \mathbf{h} = \mathbf{0}. \end{array}$$

It is not difficult to see (since $|h_i| \leqslant \|\mathbf{h}\|$ for $i = 1, 2, 3$) that $\lim_{\mathbf{h} \to \mathbf{0}} \eta(\mathbf{h}) = 0$. Therefore by Theorem 3.3.22 f is differentiable at $\mathbf{x}$. Notice that different points $\mathbf{x}$ lead to different functions η, but in each case our conclusion is valid.

In the last example partial differentiation leads to three *continuous* functions $\partial f/\partial x_1$, $\partial f/\partial x_2$ and $\partial f/\partial x_3$ on $\mathbb{R}^3$. This is a significant property which gives us a partial converse to Theorem 3.3.20(i).

3.3.29 Theorem.   Let $f : D \subseteq \mathbb{R}^m \to \mathbb{R}$ *be a function whose partial derivatives exist throughout a neighbourhood* $N(\mathbf{p}, \varepsilon)$ *of* $\mathbf{p} \in D$. *If* $\partial f/\partial x_j : N(\mathbf{p}, \varepsilon) \subseteq \mathbb{R}^m \to \mathbb{R}$ *is continuous at* $\mathbf{p}$ *for each* $j = 1, \ldots, m$, *then* f *is differentiable at* $\mathbf{p}$.

Proof.   Define a function $\eta : D_{\mathbf{p}} \subseteq \mathbb{R}^m \to \mathbb{R}$ to satisfy

3.3.30 $$f(\mathbf{p} + \mathbf{h}) - f(\mathbf{p}) = \frac{\partial f}{\partial x_1}(\mathbf{p})h_1 + \cdots + \frac{\partial f}{\partial x_m}(\mathbf{p})h_m + \|\mathbf{h}\|\eta(\mathbf{h}).$$

We prove the theorem by showing that under its hypothesis $\lim_{\mathbf{h} \to \mathbf{0}} \eta(\mathbf{h}) = 0$. It is clearly enough to confine ourselves to values of $\mathbf{h}$ such that $0 < \|\mathbf{h}\| < \varepsilon$. The left-hand side of 3.3.30 can be expressed as a 'telescopic sum' in which the inside terms cancel pairwise, leaving unpaired the first and last terms only, thus:

$$f(\mathbf{p} + \mathbf{h}) = -f(\mathbf{p}) =$$
$$f(p_1 + h_1, p_2 + h_2, \ldots, p_m + h_m) - f(p_1, p_2 + h_2, \ldots, p_m + h_m)$$
$$+ f(p_1, p_2 + h_2, p_3 + h_3, \ldots, p_m + h_m) - f(p_1, p_2, p_3 + h_3, + \ldots + p_m + h_m)$$
$$+ \ldots$$
$$+ f(p_1, p_2, \ldots, p_{m-1}, p_m + h_m) - f(p_1, p_2, \ldots, p_{m-1}, p_m).$$

In trying to find an alternative form for the jth line of this expression, there are two cases to consider. Remember that $\|\mathbf{h}\| < \varepsilon$.

[i] Suppose that $h_j \neq 0$. The two points of $\mathbb{R}^m$ involved in the jth

line lie in $N(\mathbf{p}, \varepsilon)$, as does the segment joining them. On that segment f is effectively a function of its jth coordinate alone. This function of x_j satisfies the conditions of the Mean-Value Theorem of elementary calculus on the closed interval with end points p_j and $p_j + h_j$. So we can replace the jth line by

$$\frac{\partial f}{\partial x_j}(\mathbf{q}_j)h_j$$

where for some $0 < \theta_j < 1$

3.3.31 $\quad \mathbf{q}_j = (p_1, \ldots, p_{j-1}, p_j + \theta_j h_j, p_{j+1} + h_{j+1}, \ldots, p_m + h_m).$

[ii] If $h_j = 0$, then the jth line is 0, and so is equal to the expression given in 3.3.31 for any choice of $0 < \theta_j < 1$.

In either case (with $\mathbf{q}_j$ appropriately chosen in the above manner for $j = 1, \ldots, m$) we have

3.3.32 $\qquad f(\mathbf{p} + \mathbf{h}) - f(\mathbf{p}) = \dfrac{\partial f}{\partial x_1}(\mathbf{q}_1)h_1 + \cdots + \dfrac{\partial f}{\partial x_m}(\mathbf{q}_m)h_m.$

From 3.3.30 and 3.3.32

$$\|\mathbf{h}\|\eta(\mathbf{h}) = \sum_{j=1}^{m} \left(\frac{\partial f}{\partial x_j}(\mathbf{q}_j) - \frac{\partial f}{\partial x_i}(\mathbf{p}) \right) h_j.$$

Now for each j, $|h_j| \leqslant \|\mathbf{h}\|$, so we can apply the triangle inequality to obtain

$$\|\mathbf{h}\|\,|\eta(\mathbf{h})| \leqslant \|\mathbf{h}\| \sum_{j=1}^{m} \left| \frac{\partial f}{\partial x_j}(\mathbf{q}_j) - \frac{\partial f}{\partial x_j}(\mathbf{p}) \right|.$$

Since $\|\mathbf{h}\| \neq 0$, we obtain

3.3.33 $\qquad |\eta(\mathbf{h})| \leqslant \displaystyle\sum_{j=1}^{m} \left| \frac{\partial f}{\partial x_j}(\mathbf{q}_j) - \frac{\partial f}{\partial x_j}(\mathbf{p}) \right|.$

For each j, however, $\lim_{h_j \to 0} \mathbf{q}_j = \mathbf{p}$ (by 3.3.31). Therefore, if $\partial f/\partial x_j$ is continuous at $\mathbf{p}$,

$$\lim_{h_j \to 0} \left| \frac{\partial f}{\partial x_j}(\mathbf{q}_j) - \frac{\partial f}{\partial x_j}(\mathbf{p}) \right| = 0.$$

Hence, from 3.3.33, $\lim_{\mathbf{h} \to 0} \eta(\mathbf{h}) = 0$ and the proof is complete.

3.3.34 Definition.   *A function* $f : D \subseteq \mathbb{R}^m \to \mathbb{R}$, *whose partial derivatives* (i) *exist throughout a neighbourhood of* $\mathbf{p} \in D$ *and* (ii) *are continuous at* $\mathbf{p}$, *is said to be* continuously differentiable *at* $\mathbf{p}$.

3.3.35 Definition.   *A function* $f : D \subseteq \mathbb{R}^m \to \mathbb{R}$ *is said to be* continuously differentiable, *or a* C^1 *function, if it is continuously differentiable at each point* $\mathbf{p} \in D$.

Theorem 3.3.29 tells us that if a function $f : D \subseteq \mathbb{R}^m \to \mathbb{R}$ is continuously differentiable at a point in D, then it is also differentiable there. The following example shows that there are functions which are differentiable at a point but which are not continuously differentiable there.

3.3.36 Example.   Consider the function $g : \mathbb{R} \to \mathbb{R}$ defined by

$$g(x) = \begin{cases} x^2 \sin(1/x), & \text{for } x \neq 0, \\ 0 & \text{for } x = 0. \end{cases}$$

We find (Exercise 3.3.9) that

$$g'(x) = \begin{cases} 2x \sin(1/x) - \cos(1/x), & \text{for } x \neq 0, \\ 0, & \text{for } x = 0. \end{cases}$$

It will be seen that g is continuously differentiable at all $x \neq 0$, and that g is differentiable at 0, but g' is not continuous there.

To fill out the picture further, Exercise 3.3.10 describes a function which is differentiable at a point but is not differentiable anywhere else, and Exercises 3.3.7, 8, 11 describe functions which are continuously differentiable everywhere except at a single point, where they are not differentiable.

Exercises 3.3

1.   Let $f : \mathbb{R}^2 \to \mathbb{R}$ be defind by $f(x_1, x_2) = x_1 + x_2$. Prove that, for any $\mathbf{p} \in \mathbb{R}^2$

$$\lim_{\mathbf{h} \to 0} \frac{f(\mathbf{p} + \mathbf{h}) - f(\mathbf{p})}{\|\mathbf{h}\|}$$

does not exist. This illustrates the difficulty of attempting to define the differentiability of functions $f : D \subseteq \mathbb{R}^m \to \mathbb{R}$, $m \geqslant 2$, by generalizing Definition 2.5.1.

2.   Prove that a linear function $L : \mathbb{R}^m \to \mathbb{R}$ is differentiable everywhere, and that it is equal to its own differential at all points in $\mathbb{R}^m$.

3. Prove from Definition 3.3.6 that the function $f : \mathbb{R}^2 \to \mathbb{R}$ defined by $f(x_1, x_2) = x_1^3 + x_2^3$, is differentiable everywhere. Find the linear function $L_{f,\mathbf{p}}$ that closely approximates $\delta_{f,\mathbf{p}}$ near $\mathbf{0}$.

Answer: $L_{f,\mathbf{p}}(\mathbf{h}) = 3p_1^2 h_1 + 3p_2^2 h_2$.

4. In Exercise 3 check your result against Theorem 3.3.22. Also write down the Jacobian matrix $J_{f,\mathbf{p}}$.

5. (a) Given that $f(v, s) = v^2/2s$, $s \neq 0$, calculate $(\partial f/\partial v)(v, s)$ and $(\partial f/\partial s)(v, s)$.
   (b) Find $\partial f/\partial x$ and $\partial f/\partial y$ where $f(x, y)$ is equal to (i) $\sqrt{(x^2 + y^2)}$ (ii) $(x - y)/(x + y)$, $x + y \neq 0$.
   (c) Given that $f(x, y, z) = x^2 y + y^2 z + z^2 x$, show that

$$\left(\frac{\partial f}{\partial x} + \frac{\partial f}{\partial y} + \frac{\partial f}{\partial z}\right)(x, y, z) = (x + y + z)^2$$

and that

$$x\frac{\partial f}{\partial x} + y\frac{\partial f}{\partial y} + z\frac{\partial f}{\partial z} = 3f.$$

6. (a) Given that $r(x, y) = \sqrt{(x^2 + y^2)}$, find $(\partial r/\partial x)(x, y)$.
   (b) Given that $x(r, \theta) = r\cos\theta$, find $(\partial x/\partial r)(r, \theta)$.
   Interpret these results geometrically with reference to Cartesian coordinates x, y and polar coordinates r, θ of points in $\mathbb{R}^2$.

7. Consider the function $f : \mathbb{R}^2 \to \mathbb{R}$ given by

$$f(x, y) = \begin{cases} \dfrac{2xy}{x^2 + y^2} & \text{when } (x, y) \neq (0, 0), \\ 0 & \text{when } (x, y) = (0, 0). \end{cases}$$

(a) Prove, using Definition 3.3.17, that $(\partial f/\partial x)(0, 0) = (\partial f/\partial y)(0, 0) = 0$. In Exercise 3.2.7 we saw that f is discontinuous at $(0, 0)$. Thus a function can have a discontinuity at a point where all its partial derivatives exist.
(b) Show that if $(x, y) \neq (0, 0)$ then

$$\frac{\partial f}{\partial x}(x, y) = \frac{2y(y^2 - x^2)}{(x^2 + y^2)^2},$$

and calculate $(\partial f/\partial y)(x, y)$, $(x, y) \neq (0, 0)$.
(c) Prove that the functions $\partial f/\partial x : \mathbb{R}^2 \to \mathbb{R}$ and $\partial f/\partial y : \mathbb{R}^2 \to \mathbb{R}$ are discontinuous at the origin.

Hint: consider the sequence $(x_k, y_k) = (1/k)(\cos\alpha, \sin\alpha)$, α fixed, as $k \to \infty$.

Observe that the discontinuity of at least one of $\partial f/\partial x$ and $\partial f/\partial y$ at the origin follows from the discontinuity of f. For if both were continuous, then, by Theorems 3.3.29 and 3.3.11, f would have to be continuous at the origin.

(d) Prove by the method of Example 3.3.27 that f is not differentiable at the origin.

8.   We have seen (Exercise 3.2.8) that the functions $f : \mathbb{R}^2 \to \mathbb{R}$ and $g : \mathbb{R}^2 \to \mathbb{R}$ given by

$$f(x, y) = \begin{cases} \dfrac{x^2 y}{x^2 + y^2} & \text{when } (x, y) \neq (0, 0) \\ 0 & \text{when } (x, y) = (0, 0) \end{cases}$$

and

$$g(x, y) = \begin{cases} \dfrac{2xy}{\sqrt{(x^2 + y^2)}} & \text{when } (x, y) \neq (0, 0) \\ 0 & \text{when } (x, y) = (0, 0) \end{cases}$$

are continuous on $\mathbb{R}^2$.

Prove for each of f and g that the partial derivative (a) exist on $\mathbb{R}^2$, (b) take the value 0 at $(0, 0)$, and (c) are discontinuous at the origin and continuous elsewhere. Show also that neither f nor g is differentiable at $(0, 0)$.

Hint: if f were differentiable at $(0, 0)$, formula 3.3.23 would give

$$f(\mathbf{h}) = \|\mathbf{h}\| \, \eta(\mathbf{h}), \qquad \text{where } \lim_{\mathbf{h} \to 0} \eta(\mathbf{h}) = 0.$$

Prove this false by considering the sequence $(\mathbf{h}_k)$, where $\mathbf{h}_k = (1/k, 1/k)$, $k \in \mathbb{N}$. How does the sequence $(f(\mathbf{h}_k)/\|\mathbf{h}_k\|)$ behave?

9.   Complete Example 3.3.36.

Hint: calculate $g'(x)$, $x \neq 0$, by standard techniques. Using the definition of the derivative, calculate

$$g'(0) = \lim_{h \to 0} (g(h) - g(0))/h.$$

Finally prove that g' is not continuous at 0.

10.   Consider the function $f : \mathbb{R} \to \mathbb{R}$ defined by

$$f(x) = \begin{cases} x^2 & \text{when } x \text{ is rational,} \\ 0 & \text{when } x \text{ is irrational.} \end{cases}$$

Prove that f is differentiable at 0, but not differentiable anywhere else.

Hint: for the last part show that f is discontinuous at $x \neq 0$ and apply Theorem 3.3.11.

11. Prove that the function $f : \mathbb{R} \to \mathbb{R}$ defined by

$$f(x) = \begin{cases} x \sin(1/x) & \text{when } x \neq 0, \\ 0 & \text{when } x = 0 \end{cases}$$

is continuously differentiable everywhere except at 0, where it is not differentiable. Is it continuous at 0?

12. A function $f : D \subseteq \mathbb{R}^m \to \mathbb{R}$ may or may not have the following properties at a point $\mathbf{p} \in D$: (a) continuity, (b) existence of partial derivatives, (c) continuity of partial derivatives (if they exist), (d) differentiability. List the combinations that can arise and try to find examples in the text or the exercises that illustrate them. Fill in the missing possibilities, if any.

13. Given that $f : D \subseteq \mathbb{R}^m \to \mathbb{R}$ and $g : D \subseteq \mathbb{R}^m \to \mathbb{R}$ are differentiable at $\mathbf{p} \in D$, prove that the functions $f + g$ and fg are differentiable at $\mathbf{p}$.

    Show also that the corresponding Jacobian matrices are

$$J_{f+g, \mathbf{p}} = J_{f, \mathbf{p}} + J_{g, \mathbf{p}}$$

and

$$J_{fg, \mathbf{p}} = f(\mathbf{p}) J_{g, \mathbf{p}} + J_{f, \mathbf{p}} g(\mathbf{p}).$$

Hint for the case fg: consider

$$\begin{aligned} (fg)(\mathbf{p} + \mathbf{h}) - (fg)(\mathbf{p}) &= f(\mathbf{p} + \mathbf{h}) g(\mathbf{p} + \mathbf{h}) - f(\mathbf{p}) g(\mathbf{p}) \\ &= (f(\mathbf{p} + \mathbf{h}) - f(\mathbf{p})) g(\mathbf{p} + \mathbf{h}) \\ &\quad + f(\mathbf{p})(g(\mathbf{p} + \mathbf{h}) - g(\mathbf{p})), \end{aligned}$$

and apply Definition 3.3.6 and Theorem 3.3.11.

14. Verify the Jacobian matrix formulae of Exercise 13 for the differentiable functions $f : \mathbb{R}^2 \to \mathbb{R}$ and $g : \mathbb{R}^2 \to \mathbb{R}$ given by $f(x_1, x_2) = x_1^2 + x_2^2$, $g(x_1, x_2) = \sin(x_1 x_2)$.

Hint: use Theorem 3.3.20(iii). Note that from elementary calculus

$$\frac{\partial(fg)}{\partial x_i} = f \frac{\partial g}{\partial x_i} + \frac{\partial f}{\partial x_i} g.$$

3.4 Differentiability and tangent planes

The differentiability of a function $\phi : \mathbb{R} \to \mathbb{R}$ is equivalent to the existence of a tangent line to the graph of ϕ at every point. In this section we consider the corresponding property for a function $f : D \subseteq \mathbb{R}^2 \to \mathbb{R}$ and then give a generalization to functions defined on higher-dimensional domains.

Suppose that $f : D \subseteq \mathbb{R}^2 \to \mathbb{R}$ is differentiable at $\mathbf{p} \in D$ with differential $L_{f,\mathbf{p}}$. Then there is a function $\eta : D_{\mathbf{p}} \subseteq \mathbb{R}^2 \to \mathbb{R}$ such that for all $\mathbf{x} \in D$,

3.4.1 $f(\mathbf{x}) = f(\mathbf{p}) + L_{f,\mathbf{p}}(\mathbf{x} - \mathbf{p}) + \|\mathbf{x} - \mathbf{p}\| \eta(\mathbf{x} - \mathbf{p}),$

$$\text{where } \lim_{\mathbf{x} \to \mathbf{p}} \eta(\mathbf{x} - \mathbf{p}) = 0.$$

See 3.3.7, replacing $\mathbf{p} + \mathbf{h}$ by $\mathbf{x}$.

The graph of f is the set G in $\mathbb{R}^3$ with equation $z = f(\mathbf{x})$. Consideration of 3.4.1 suggests that we compare G with the set T in $\mathbb{R}^3$ with equation

3.4.2 $$z = f(\mathbf{p}) + L_{f,\mathbf{p}}(\mathbf{x} - \mathbf{p}).$$

3.4.3 Lemma. *With the above notation, the set T defined by 3.4.2 is a plane in $\mathbb{R}^3$ through $(\mathbf{p}, f(\mathbf{p}))$ parallel to the graph S of $L_{f,\mathbf{p}}$.*

Proof. We know from Example 3.1.13 that S, the graph of $L_{f,\mathbf{p}}$, is a plane in $\mathbb{R}^3$. Now

$$T = \{(\mathbf{x}, f(\mathbf{p}) + L_{f,\mathbf{p}}(\mathbf{x} - \mathbf{p})) \in \mathbb{R}^3 \,|\, \mathbf{x} \in \mathbb{R}^2\}$$
$$= (\mathbf{p}, f(\mathbf{p})) + \{(\mathbf{x} - \mathbf{p}, L_{f,\mathbf{p}}(\mathbf{x} - \mathbf{p})) \in \mathbb{R}^3 \,|\, \mathbf{x} \in \mathbb{R}^2\}.$$

Hence $T = (\mathbf{p}, f(\mathbf{p})) + S$ as required.

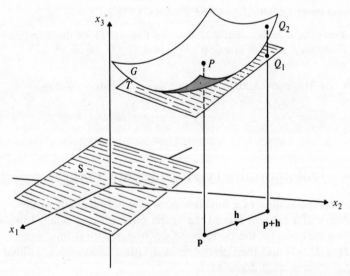

Fig. 3.13

The situation is illustrated in Fig. 3.13, where P is the point $(\mathbf{p}, f(\mathbf{p}))$.

If we move away from $\mathbf{p}$ to $\mathbf{p} + \mathbf{h}$ in $\mathbb{R}^2$, then the corresponding point Q_1 on the *plane* T has third coordinate

3.4.4
$$f(\mathbf{p}) + L_{f,\mathbf{p}}(\mathbf{h}).$$

On the other hand, the corresponding point Q_2 on the *graph* G has third coordinate

$$f(\mathbf{p} + \mathbf{h}) = f(\mathbf{p}) + L_{f,\mathbf{p}}(\mathbf{h}) + \|\mathbf{h}\|\eta(\mathbf{h}).$$

The vector $\overrightarrow{Q_1Q_2}$ indicates the error we make in assuming that the change in the value of f is linear as we move away from $\mathbf{p}$. The differentiability of f at $\mathbf{p}$ tells us that this error is 'small' in the sense that

$$\overrightarrow{Q_1Q_2} = (0, \|\mathbf{h}\|\eta(\mathbf{h}))$$

and so

3.4.5
$$\lim_{\mathbf{h}\to 0} \frac{\|\overrightarrow{Q_1Q_2}\|}{\|\mathbf{h}\|} = 0.$$

3.4.6 Definition. *Let $G \subseteq \mathbb{R}^3$ be the graph of a differentiable function $f : D \subseteq \mathbb{R}^2 \to \mathbb{R}$. For any point $\mathbf{p} \in D$, the plane in $\mathbb{R}^3$ with equation*

$$z = f(\mathbf{p}) + L_{f,\mathbf{p}}(\mathbf{x} - \mathbf{p}), \qquad \mathbf{x} = (x, y) \in \mathbb{R}^2,$$

is called the tangent plane *to G at $(\mathbf{p}, f(\mathbf{p}))$.*

The tangent plane to G at $(\mathbf{p}, f(\mathbf{p}))$ is the only plane which provides a close fit to G near $(\mathbf{p}, f(\mathbf{p}))$ in the sense that 3.4.5 is satisfied.

Conversely, for an arbitrary function f, if there is a plane such that the corresponding points Q_1 and Q_2 as in Fig. 3.13 satisfy condition 3.4.5, then f is differentiable at $\mathbf{p}$. The linear approximation $L_{f,\mathbf{p}}$ may be deduced from the equation of the plane by referring to 3.4.2.

By Theorem 3.3.20(ii) the equation of the tangent plane to the graph of f at $(a, b, f(a, b))$ is

3.4.7
$$z = f(a, b) + (x - a)\frac{\partial f}{\partial x}(a, b) + (y - b)\frac{\partial f}{\partial y}(a, b)$$

3.4.8 Example. The function $f(x, y) = x^2 + y^2$ has graph with equation

$z = x^2 + y^2$. There is a sketch of the graph in Fig. 3.4 (ii). We have

$$\frac{\partial f}{\partial x}(x, y) = 2x \quad \text{and} \quad \frac{\partial f}{\partial y}(x, y) = 2y.$$

The equation of the tangent plane to the graph at $(a, b, a^2 + b^2)$ is, by 3.4.7,

$$z = (a^2 + b^2) + (x - a)2a + (y - b)2b,$$

that is,

$$z = 2ax + 2by - (a^2 + b^2).$$

In particular the tangent plane at $(0, 0, 0)$ is $z = 0$, as we would expect on glancing at Fig. 3.14.

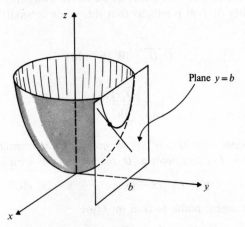

Plane $y = b$

Fig. 3.14 The graph $z = x^2 + y^2$

The partial derivatives have a geometrical interpretation. In the above example we calculate $(\partial f/\partial x)(a, b)$ by holding y constant at b. This means that we limit ourselves to the parabola $z = x^2 + b^2$ which is the cross section of the graph of f sliced by the plane $y = b$ (see Fig. 3.14). The equation $(\partial f/\partial x)(x, b) = 2x$ is a statement about the slope of this parabola at the point $(x, b, x^2 + b^2)$.

A sketch of the graph of a function can reveal points at which the partial derivatives do not exist. Consider for example the function f defined in Example 3.1.8. Its graph is sketched in Fig. 3.5. The fact that there are corners at the appropriate places tells us that $\partial f/\partial x$ does not exist at all points $(0, b)$, (b, b) and $(-b, b)$ in the domain of f, except at $(0, 0)$, where $(\partial f/\partial x)(0, 0) = 0$. A similar remark applies to $\partial f/\partial y$. (Note that $\partial f/\partial y$ exists at $(0, b)$ but not at $(a, 0)$, $a \neq 0$.)

According to Theorem 3.3.20, a function is not differentiable at points where a partial derivative does not exist. We have seen (Example 3.3.27) that the function f is not differentiable at $(0, 0)$, and this together with the above considerations shows that f is not differentiable anywhere along the lines $x = 0$, $y = 0$, $x = y$ and $x = -y$. Intuitively, the graph of f is too 'sharp' at such points for a tangent plane to fit closely to it.

The idea of the tangent plane to a graph in $\mathbb{R}^3$ is generalized as follows.

3.4.9 Definition. *Let $G \subseteq \mathbb{R}^m$ be the graph of a differentiable function $f : D \subseteq \mathbb{R}^{m-1} \to \mathbb{R}$. For any point $\mathbf{p} \in D$, the set $T \in \mathbb{R}^m$ with equation*

$$x_m = f(\mathbf{p}) + L_{f, \mathbf{p}}(\mathbf{x} - \mathbf{p}), \qquad \mathbf{x} = (x_1, \dots, x_{m-1}) \in \mathbb{R}^{m-1},$$

is called the tangent space *to G at $(\mathbf{p}, f(\mathbf{p}))$.*

The tangent space T is the translation through $(\mathbf{p}, f(\mathbf{p}))$ of the $(m-1)$-dimensional subspace of $\mathbb{R}^m$ which forms the graph of $L_{f, \mathbf{p}} : \mathbb{R}^{m-1} \to \mathbb{R}$. The tangent space has equation

3.4.10 $$x_m = f(\mathbf{p}) + (x_1 - p_1)\frac{\partial f}{\partial x_1}(\mathbf{p}) + \cdots + (x_{m-1} - p_{m-1})\frac{\partial f}{\partial x_{m-1}}(\mathbf{p}).$$

3.4.11 Example. The differentiable function $f : \mathbb{R}^3 \to \mathbb{R}$ defined by

$$f(x_1, x_2, x_3) = x_1^2 + x_2^2 + x_3^2$$

has graph $x_4 = x_1^2 + x_2^2 + x_3^2$ in $\mathbb{R}^4$. The tangent space to the graph at

$$(p_1, p_2, p_3, p_1^2 + p_2^2 + p_3^2)$$

is

$$x_4 = p_1^2 + p_2^2 + p_3^2 + 2p_1(x_1 - p_1) + 2p_2(x_2 - p_2) + 2p_3(x_3 - p_3)$$
$$= p_1 x_1 + p_2 x_2 + p_3 x_3 - (p_1^2 + p_2^2 + p_3^2).$$

Exercises 3.4

1. Define $f : \mathbb{R}^2 \to \mathbb{R}$ by $f(x, y) = x^2 - y^2$. Show that the equation of the tangent plane to the graph G of f at $(a, b, a^2 - b^2)$ is

   $$z = (a^2 - b^2) + 2a(x - a) - 2b(y - b).$$

   Sketch the graph G of f (Exercise 3.1.1(i)); its equation is $z = x^2 - y^2$. Fit the tangent planes for various choices of (a, b).

2. Sketch the graphs $z = f(x, y)$ and tangent planes at $(a, b, f(a, b))$ for

various choices of (a, b) when

(a) $f(x, y) = x^2 - y$,

(b) $f(x, y) = x + 3y$,

(c) $f(x, y) = xy$.

Consider in particular the cases $(a, b) = (0, 0)$ and $(a, b) = (1, 1)$.

3. In your sketches for Exercise 2 interpret geometrically the partial derivatives $(\partial f/\partial x)(a, b)$ as discussed in the text.

4. Given a function $f : D \subseteq \mathbb{R} \to \mathbb{R}$, the equation $z = f(x)$ can be interpreted as the equation of the graph G of f in the x, z plane. Show that the equation

$$z = f(a) + (x - a)\frac{\mathrm{d}f}{\mathrm{d}x}(a)$$

is the equation of the tangent line to G at $(a, f(a))$. Compare with Equation 3.4.7.

5. Consider the function $f : \mathbb{R}^2 \to \mathbb{R}$ of Exercise 3.3.8 given by

$$f(x, y) = \begin{cases} \dfrac{x^2 y}{x^2 + y^2} & \text{when } (x, y) \neq (0, 0) \\ 0 & \text{when } (x, y) = (0, 0). \end{cases}$$

Show that for any constant α the straight line through the origin parametrized by

$$(t\cos\alpha, t\sin\alpha, t\cos^2\alpha\sin\alpha), \qquad t \in \mathbb{R},$$

lies entirely in the graph G of f with equation $z = f(x, y)$. Hence a three-dimensional model of G can be constructed using thin straight rods (straws, for example). The 'wavy' nature of G near the origin suggests that no tangent plane can be fitted to G at the origin and hence that f is not differentiable at $(0, 0)$.

Does a similar analysis apply to the function g of Exercise 3.3.8?

3.5 Error estimation

In this section we discuss briefly a practical application of the linear approximation of differentiable functions to the estimation of how errors in measurements affect calculations based on those measurements.

Suppose that a physical quantity y is related to measurable variables $x_1, \ldots, x_m$ by the formula $y = f(x_1, \ldots, x_m)$. In an experiment to determine y, the recorded values of the variables form a vector $\mathbf{x} = (x_1, \ldots, x_m)$. These readings are however inaccurate, and the true values form the vector

$$\mathbf{x} + \Delta\mathbf{x} = (x_1 + \Delta x_1, \ldots, x_m + \Delta x_m).$$

The experimenter calculates the value of y as $f(\mathbf{x})$, whereas the true value is $f(\mathbf{x} + \Delta\mathbf{x})$. The resulting error Δy in the value of y is given by

$$\Delta y = f(\mathbf{x} + \Delta\mathbf{x}) - f(\mathbf{x}).$$

Suppose that f is differentiable at $\mathbf{x}$. Then, by 3.3.23, we obtain the approximation

3.5.1 $$\Delta y \approx \frac{\partial f}{\partial x_1}(\mathbf{x})\Delta x_1 + \cdots + \frac{\partial f}{\partial x_m}(\mathbf{x})\Delta x_m,$$

where the symbol $\approx$ indicates that the difference between the two sides is of the form $\|\Delta\mathbf{x}\|\eta(\Delta\mathbf{x})$, where $\eta(\Delta\mathbf{x}) \to 0$ as $\Delta\mathbf{x} \to \mathbf{0}$.

In a practical situation the values of $(\partial f/\partial x_1)(\mathbf{x}), \ldots, (\partial f/\partial x_m)(\mathbf{x})$ will be known, as will upper bounds for $|\Delta x_1|, \ldots, |\Delta x_m|$. We can therefore find an approximate upper bound for Δy by choosing $\Delta x_1, \ldots, \Delta x_m$ appropriately in 3.5.1.

Using classical (Leibniz) terminology, if $\Delta x_1, \ldots, \Delta x_m$ are the (infinitesimal) 'differentials' $dx_1, \ldots, dx_m$ respectively, then the approximation in 3.5.1 gives us an equation involving the (infinitesimal) 'differential' dy, where

3.5.2 $$dy = \frac{\partial f}{\partial x_1}dx_1 + \cdots + \frac{\partial f}{\partial x_m}dx_m.$$

This useful expression can be made respectable if $dy, dx_1, \ldots, dx_m$ are defined as differentials in our sense (as linear approximations), but for the purpose of this book it is best to regard 3.5.2 as a mnemonic.

3.5.3 *Example.* The (constant) acceleration a metres/(second)^2 of a vehicle is calculated from the formula

3.5.4 $$a = \frac{v^2}{2s}$$

where v metres/second is the speed of the vehicle when it has covered a distance s metres from the start of its journey. The speed is observed as $30.00 \, \mathrm{m\,s^{-1}}$ at a point $300.0 \, \mathrm{m}$ from the start. Given that the speed measurement is accurate to within $\pm 1.00 \, \mathrm{m\,s^{-1}}$ and the distance measurement is accurate to within $\pm 3.0 \, \mathrm{m}$, estimate the accuracy of the calculation of acceleration.

Solution.   Formula 3.5.4 defines a differentiable function $f : D \subseteq \mathbb{R}^2 \to \mathbb{R}$ given by

3.5.5 $$a = f(v, s) = \frac{v^2}{2s}$$

where $D = \{(v, s) \in \mathbb{R}^2 \mid s \neq 0\}$. By 3.5.1

3.5.6 $$\Delta a \approx \frac{v}{s}\Delta v - \frac{v^2}{2s^2}\Delta s.$$

Hence, when $v = 30$ and $s = 300$,

3.5.7 $$\Delta a \approx \frac{1}{10}\Delta v - \frac{1}{200}\Delta s.$$

Now the bounds of accuracy are $|\Delta v| \leqslant 1$ and $|\Delta s| \leqslant 3$. The right-hand side of 3.5.6 attains its maximum when $\Delta v = 1$ and $\Delta s = -3$ and its minimum when $\Delta v = -1$ and $\Delta s = 3$. Hence we have the approximation

3.5.8 $-0.115 \leqslant \Delta a \leqslant 0.115$.

A direct calculation from the formula

$$\Delta a = f(v + \Delta v, s + \Delta s) - f(v, s)$$

at the point $(v, s) = (30, 300)$ leads to the true bounds for the error in the acceleration

3.5.9 $-0.112 \leqslant \Delta a \leqslant 0.118$.

Exercises 3.5

1. A rectangular box has a square base. An edge of the base is measured to be 10 cm to an accuracy of 0.1 cm. The height is measured to be 20 cm to an accuracy of 0.1 cm. Using the formula volume = base area × height, the volume V of the box is calculated to be $100 \times 20 = 2000 \text{ cm}^3$. Estimate the accuracy of the calculation by using Formula 3.5.1.

Answer: $|\Delta V| \leqslant 50$.

Compare with the accurate bounds for the error.

Answer: $-49.601 \leqslant \Delta V \leqslant 50.401$.

2. If the error in a measurement $x \neq 0$ is Δx, the *relative error* is defined to be $\rho(x) = \Delta x / x$. For example, given a measurement 10 with error 0.2, the relative error is 0.02 or 2%. Prove that (a) $\rho(xy) \approx \rho(x) + \rho(y)$, (b) $\rho(x/y) \approx \rho(x) - \rho(y)$.

3. The radius r of a cylindrical tube is found from the formula $\pi r^2 l = V$. Given that the relative errors in the measurements of l and V are 0.2%

and 0.3% respectively, estimate the maximum relative error in the radius calculation.

Hint: prove that $2\rho(r) \approx \rho(V) - \rho(l)$ in the notation of Exercise 2.

Answer: $|\rho(r)| \leqslant 0.25\%$.

3.6 The Chain Rule. Rate of change along a path

The reader will be familiar with the rules for differentiating the product and quotient of two differentiable real-valued functions of $\mathbb{R}$. Namely

3.6.1   if $F(t) = x(t)y(t)$, then $F'(t) = x'(t)y(t) + x(t)y'(t)$, and

3.6.2   if $F(t) = x(t)/y(t)$, then $F'(t) = (x'(t)y(t) - x(t)y'(t))/y^2(t)$.

More generally, given m real-valued functions $x_1(t), \ldots, x_m(t)$ and given a function $f : \mathbb{R}^m \to \mathbb{R}$, one could ask about the differentiability of the function $F : \mathbb{R} \to \mathbb{R}$ defined by

3.6.3 $$F(t) = f(x_1(t), \ldots, x_m(t)).$$

If we define $g : \mathbb{R} \to \mathbb{R}^m$ by $g(t) = (x_1(t), \ldots, x_m(t))$, then we can interpret 3.6.3 as defining F as the composition $f \circ g$ of the two functions f and g.

In particular, if g is a path in $\mathbb{R}^m$, then $g(t)$ moves along the image of the path, and the derivative of $f \circ g$, if it exists, defines the rate of change of the scalar field f along the path g. For example, if the image of the path lies in a level set of f, then the rate of change along the path is 0.

The following theorem shows how the derivative of $f \circ g$ is related to those of f and g.

3.6.4 Theorem. *Chain Rule. Let $g : E \subseteq \mathbb{R} \to \mathbb{R}^m$ be defined on an open interval E and let $f : D \subseteq \mathbb{R}^m \to \mathbb{R}$ be defined on an open set D such that $g(E) \subseteq D$. Define $F : E \subseteq \mathbb{R} \to \mathbb{R}$ to be the composite function given by*

$$F(t) = (f \circ g)(t) = f(g(t)), \qquad t \in E.$$

Suppose that g is differentiable at $a \in E$ and that f is differentiable at $g(a) \in D$. Then F is differentiable at a and its differential is given by

3.6.5 $$L_{F,a} = L_{f,g(a)} \circ L_{g,a}.$$

The theorem will be proved in a more general situation in Section 4.4. Notice however that

$$\delta_{f \circ g, a}(h) = (f \circ g)(a + h) - (f \circ g)(a) = f(g(a + h)) - f(g(a))$$
$$= \delta_{f, g(a)}(g(a + h) - g(a)) = \delta_{f, g(a)}(\delta_{g, a}(h)).$$

Hence

3.6.6 $\delta_{f \circ g, a} = \delta_{f, g(a)} \circ \delta_{g, a}.$

The identity 3.6.5 will follow from the fact (Lemma 4.4.4) that the composition of the close linear approximations near 0 to $\delta_{f, g(a)}$ and $\delta_{g, a}$ is a close linear approximation near 0 to their composition.

3.6.7 Corollary.   *Let $g : E \subseteq \mathbb{R} \to \mathbb{R}^m$ be differentiable at $a \in E$, let $g(E) \subseteq D$ and let $f : D \subseteq \mathbb{R}^m \to \mathbb{R}$ be differentiable at $g(a)$. Then*

3.6.8 $J_{f \circ g, a} = J_{f, g(a)} J_{g, a}.$

Alternatively, putting $g(t) = (x_1(t), \ldots, x_m(t))$ and $F(t) = f(g(t)) = f(x_1(t), \ldots, x_m(t))$,

3.6.9 $$\frac{dF}{dt} = \frac{\partial f}{\partial x_1}\frac{dx_1}{dt} + \cdots + \frac{\partial f}{\partial x_m}\frac{dx_m}{dt},$$

where dF/dt, $dx_1/dt, \ldots, dx_m/dt$ are evaluated at a and $\partial f/\partial x_1, \ldots, \partial f/\partial x_m$ are evaluated at $g(a)$.

Proof.   The identity 3.6.5 between differentials leads to the identity 3.6.8 between representing matrices (Jacobians).
If we put $g(t) = (x_1(t), \ldots, x_m(t))$ and let $g(a) = \mathbf{p}$, then by Theorem 3.3.20 and 2.10.18,

$J_{F, a}$ is the 1×1 matrix $[F'(a)]$,

$J_{f, g(a)}$ is the $1 \times m$ matrix $\left[\dfrac{\partial f}{\partial x_1}(\mathbf{p}) \quad \cdots \quad \dfrac{\partial f}{\partial x_m}(\mathbf{p})\right]$

$J_{g, a}$ is the $m \times 1$ matrix $\begin{bmatrix} g'_1(a) \\ \vdots \\ g'_m(a) \end{bmatrix} = \begin{bmatrix} \dfrac{dx_1}{dt}(a) \\ \vdots \\ \dfrac{dx_m}{dt}(a) \end{bmatrix}$

Expression 3.6.9 now follows from 3.6.8.

The reader should notice the relationship between 3.6.9 and the formal expression 3.5.2 used in error estimation.

3.6.10 *Example*. Consider $f : D \subseteq \mathbb{R}^2 \to \mathbb{R}$ defined by $f(x, y) = x/y$, where $D = \{(x, y) \subseteq \mathbb{R}^2 | y \neq 0\}$. Then $(\partial f/\partial x)(x, y) = 1/y$ and $(\partial f/\partial y)(x, y) = -x/y^2$. Application of 3.6.9 now gives the rule for differentiating the quotient $x(t)/y(t)$ contained in 3.6.2. Similarly, consideration of $f(x, y) = xy$ leads to 3.6.1.

3.6.11 *Example*. If $F(t) = x(t)\sin(y(t)z(t))$ then, by 3.6.9,

$$F'(t) = x'(t)\sin(y(t)z(t)) + y'(t)x(t)z(t)\cos(y(t)z(t))$$
$$+ z'(t)x(t)y(t)\cos(y(t)z(t)).$$

3.6.12 *Example*. Consider the function $g :]-\pi/2, \pi/2[\to \mathbb{R}^2$ defined by

$$g(t) = (\tan t, \cos^2 t), \qquad t \in]-\pi/2, \pi/2[.$$

The image of g is known as the Witch of Agnesi (first studied by Fermat and later by Maria Agnesi). See Fig. 3.15.

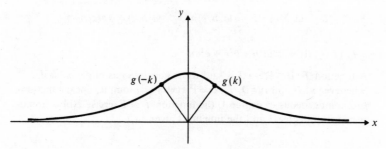

Fig. 3.15 $g(t) = (\tan t, \cos^2 t), -\pi/2 < t < \pi/2$

We can find the points at which the curve is closest to the origin as follows. Define a function $f : \mathbb{R}^2 \to \mathbb{R}$ by

$$f(x, y) = (x^2 + y^2)^{1/2} = \|(x, y)\|.$$

The composite function $F = f \circ g$ has derivative (by 3.6.9)

$$F'(t) = x(x^2 + y^2)^{-1/2}\sec^2 t - 2y(x^2 + y^2)^{-1/2}\sin t \cos t,$$

where $x = \tan t$ and $y = \cos^2 t$. It follows that

$$F'(t) = (x^2 + y^2)^{-1/2}\sin t(\sec^3 t - 2\cos^3 t).$$

In particular $F'(t) = 0$ when $t = 0$ and at the two values k and $-k$ in

$]-\pi/2, \pi/2[$ at which $\cos^2 k = 2^{-1/3}$. It will be found that $F(0) = 1$, and $F(\pm k) = 0.943$. Therefore $g(k)$ and $g(-k)$ are the required points on the curve.

Exercises 3.6

1. Given that $f(x, y) = \tan^{-1}(y/x)$, $x \neq 0$ and $g(t) = (x(t), y(t))$, where $x(t) = \cos t$, $y(t) = \sin t$, apply the Chain Rule in the form 3.6.9 to find $F'(a)$, where $F = f \circ g$. Interpret your result geometrically.

Answer: $F'(a) = 1$ for all a.

Obtain the Jacobian matrix expression 3.6.8.

2. (a) Using the Chain Rule in the form 3.6.9 in each of the following cases, calculate $(f \circ g)'(t)$:
    (i) $f(x_1, x_2) = x_1 x_2$, $g(t) = (\sin t, \cos t)$;
    (ii) $f(x, y) = x^2 y + y^3$, $g(t) = (t + 1, e^t)$.
    (b) If $f(x_1, x_2, x_3) = x_1^2 x_2 + x_2^2 x_3 + x_3^2 x_1$ and $g(t) = (ta, tb, tc)$, where a, b, c are constants, apply the Chain Rule 3.6.9 to calculate $(f \circ g)'(t)$. Show also that

$$a\frac{\partial f}{\partial x_1}(a, b, c) + b\frac{\partial f}{\partial x_2}(a, b, c) + c\frac{\partial f}{\partial x_3}(a, b, c) = 3f(a, b, c).$$

Answer: $(f \circ g)'(t) = 3t^3(a^2 b + b^2 c + c^2 a)$.

3. A function $f : D \subseteq \mathbb{R}^m \to \mathbb{R}$ is said to be *homogeneous* of degree k if, whenever $\mathbf{x} \in D$ and $t\mathbf{x} \in D$, $f(t\mathbf{x}) = t^k f(\mathbf{x})$. For example, linear functions are homogeneous of degree 1, the function f of Exercise 2(b) is homogeneous of degree 3 and the functions given by

$$f(x, y, z) = \frac{z}{\sqrt{(x^2 + y^2)}}, \qquad x^2 + y^2 \neq 0,$$

and

$$f(x, y, z) = \frac{1}{\sqrt{(x^2 + y^2 + z^2)}}, \qquad x^2 + y^2 + z^2 \neq 0,$$

are homogeneous of degrees 0 and -1 respectively.
    Prove *Euler's Theorem*, that a differentiable homogeneous function $f : D \subseteq \mathbb{R}^m \to \mathbb{R}$ of degree k satisfies the identity

$$p_1\frac{\partial f}{\partial x_1}(\mathbf{p}) + \cdots + p_m\frac{\partial f}{\partial x_m}(\mathbf{p}) = kf(\mathbf{p}), \qquad \mathbf{p} \in D.$$

Hint: use the method of Exercise 2(b).

4. Let $f : \mathbb{R}^2 \to \mathbb{R}$ be defined by

$$f(x, y) = \begin{cases} \dfrac{x^2 y}{x^2 + y^2} & \text{when } (x, y) \neq (0, 0) \\[2mm] 0 & \text{when } (x, y) = (0, 0). \end{cases}$$

In Exercise 3.3.8 we saw that f is not differentiable at $(0, 0)$ but that its partial derivatives exist there. Check that $(\partial f / \partial x)(0, 0) = (\partial f / \partial y)(0, 0) = 0$.
  Now define $g : \mathbb{R} \to \mathbb{R}^2$ by $g(t) = (x(t), y(t))$, where $x(t) = t$, $y(t) = t$, $t \in \mathbb{R}$. Given that $F = f \circ g$,
(a) prove that F is differentiable at $(0, 0)$ and show that $F'(0) = 1$.
(b) verify that

$$\frac{\partial f}{\partial x}(0, 0) \frac{\mathrm{d}x}{\mathrm{d}t}(0) + \frac{\partial f}{\partial y}(0, 0) \frac{\mathrm{d}y}{\mathrm{d}t}(0) = 0.$$

This example illustrates the breakdown of the Chain Rule 3.6.9 at a point where the function f is not differentiable.

5. The temperature in a region of space is given by the formula

$$f(x, y, z) = kx^2(y - z),$$

where k is a positive constant. An insect flies so that its position at time t is $g(t) = (t, t, 2t)$. Find the rate of change of temperature along its path.

Hint: Calculate $- T'(t)$, where $T = f \circ g$. This problem is solved most simply by determining $T(t)$ and then differentiating. Use it alternatively as an exercise on the Chain Rule.

3.7   Directional derivatives

We recall that the partial derivatives of $f : D \subseteq \mathbb{R}^m \to \mathbb{R}$ at $\mathbf{p} \in D$ are given by the formula 3.3.17

3.7.1 $\dfrac{\partial f}{\partial x_j}(\mathbf{p}) = \lim_{t \to 0} \dfrac{f(\mathbf{p} + t\mathbf{e}_j) - f(\mathbf{p})}{t}, \qquad j = 1, \dots, m.$

For each $t \in \mathbb{R}$ the vector $\mathbf{p} + t\mathbf{e}_j$ lies on the straight line through $\mathbf{p}$ in the direction $\mathbf{e}_j$. We may regard the partial derivative as the rate of change of $f(\mathbf{x})$ as $\mathbf{x}$ moves through $\mathbf{p}$ along this line (the case $m = 2$ is illustrated in Fig. 3.16(i)).
  The right-hand side of 3.7.1 is the derivative of $f(\mathbf{p} + t\mathbf{e}_j)$ with respect to t at $t = 0$. We have therefore an alternative expression for

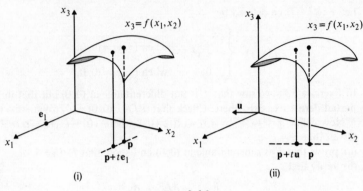

Fig. 3.16

the partial derivative

$$\frac{\partial f}{\partial x_j}(\mathbf{p}) = \frac{d}{dt} f(\mathbf{p} + t\mathbf{e}_j)\Big|_{t=0}$$

From this point of view there is no reason why we should restrict ourselves to lines in directions $\mathbf{e}_1, \ldots, \mathbf{e}_m$. For any unit vector $\mathbf{u} \in \mathbb{R}^m$, the straight line through $\mathbf{p}$ in direction $\mathbf{u}$ consists of the vectors $\mathbf{p} + t\mathbf{u}$, $t \in \mathbb{R}$. Accordingly we have the following generalization of 3.7.1 (see Fig. 3.16(ii)).

3.7.2 Definition.   *Given a function $f : D \subseteq \mathbb{R}^m \to \mathbb{R}$, a point $\mathbf{p} \in D$, and a unit vector $\mathbf{u} \in \mathbb{R}^m$, the* directional derivative *of f at $\mathbf{p}$ in direction $\mathbf{u}$ is defined by*

$$\frac{\partial f}{\partial \mathbf{u}}(\mathbf{p}) = \lim_{t \to 0} \frac{f(\mathbf{p} + t\mathbf{u}) - f(\mathbf{p})}{t} = \frac{d}{dt} f(\mathbf{p} + t\mathbf{u})\Big|_{t=0},$$

provided this limit exists.

Notice that the partial derivatives are directional derivatives and that

$$(\partial f/\partial x_j)(\mathbf{p}) = (\partial f/\partial \mathbf{e}_j)(\mathbf{p}), \qquad j = 1, \ldots, m.$$

The following example shows that the existence of all the partial derivatives is not enough to guarantee the existence of other directional derivatives.

3.7.3 Example.   Consider again (see Example 3.1.8) the function $f : \mathbb{R}^2 \to \mathbb{R}$

defined by

$$f(x, y) = \begin{cases} -|y| & \text{if } |y| \leqslant |x|, \\ -|x| & \text{if } |x| \leqslant |y|. \end{cases}$$

For any $t \in \mathbb{R}$ and any unit vector $\mathbf{u} \in \mathbb{R}^2$, $f(\mathbf{0} + t\mathbf{u}) = |t| f(\mathbf{u})$. Now $f(\mathbf{u})$ is constant and therefore $f(\mathbf{0} + t\mathbf{u})$ is differentiable as a function of t if and only if $f(\mathbf{u}) = 0$. This in turn is true if and only if $\mathbf{u}$ is $(\pm 1, 0)$ or $(0, \pm 1)$. The only directional derivatives at $\mathbf{0}$ which exist therefore are $(\partial f/\partial \mathbf{e}_1)(\mathbf{0})$, $(\partial f/\partial(-\mathbf{e}_1))(\mathbf{0})$, $(\partial f/\partial \mathbf{e}_2)(\mathbf{0})$, $(\partial f/\partial(-\mathbf{e}_2))(\mathbf{0})$. Each of these directional derivatives is 0. The sketch of the graph of f (Fig. 3.5) suggests the same result.

The following theorem shows however that if f is differentiable at $\mathbf{p} \in D$, then each directional derivative $(\partial f/\partial \mathbf{u})(\mathbf{p})$ exists and is a value of the differential. The corollary which follows it shows how the directional derivative is linearly related to the partial derivatives.

3.7.4 Theorem. Let $f : D \subseteq \mathbb{R}^m \to \mathbb{R}$ be differentiable at $\mathbf{p} \in D$. Then $(\partial f/\partial \mathbf{u})(\mathbf{p})$ exists for every unit vector $\mathbf{u} \in \mathbb{R}^m$.

Furthermore

[i] $\dfrac{\partial f}{\partial \mathbf{u}}(\mathbf{p}) = L_{f, \mathbf{p}}(\mathbf{u}),$

and, in the notation of Section 3.5,

[ii] $f(\mathbf{p} + t\mathbf{u}) \approx f(\mathbf{p}) + t\dfrac{\partial f}{\partial \mathbf{u}}(\mathbf{p}).$

Proof. Since f is differentiable at $\mathbf{p}$ and since $L_{f, \mathbf{p}}$ is linear, we have

3.7.5 $f(\mathbf{p} + t\mathbf{u}) - f(\mathbf{p}) = t L_{f, \mathbf{p}}(\mathbf{u}) + |t| \eta(t\mathbf{u}),$ $t\mathbf{u} \in D_{\mathbf{p}}$

where $\lim_{t \to 0} \eta(t\mathbf{u}) = 0$. Hence

$$\frac{f(\mathbf{p} + t\mathbf{u}) - f(\mathbf{p})}{t} = L_{f, \mathbf{p}}(\mathbf{u}) + \frac{|t|}{t}\eta(t\mathbf{u}) \qquad t \neq 0,\ t\mathbf{u} \in D_{\mathbf{p}}.$$

Taking the limit as t tends to 0 on both sides of this expression establishes (i). Replacing $L_{f, \mathbf{p}}(\mathbf{u})$ by $(\partial f/\partial \mathbf{u})(\mathbf{p})$ in 3.7.5 leads to (ii).

3.7.6 Corollary. Let $f : D \subseteq \mathbb{R}^m \to \mathbb{R}$ be differentiable at $\mathbf{p} \in D$. Then for every unit vector $\mathbf{u} = (u_1, \ldots, u_m) \in \mathbb{R}^m$,

$$\frac{\partial f}{\partial \mathbf{u}}(\mathbf{p}) = u_1 \frac{\partial f}{\partial x_1}(\mathbf{p}) + \cdots + u_m \frac{\partial f}{\partial x_m}(\mathbf{p}).$$

Proof.   The result follows from Theorem 3.7.4(i) by replacing **h** by **u** in Theorem 3.3.20(ii).

3.7.7 Example.   Let $f : D \subseteq \mathbb{R}^2 \to \mathbb{R}$ be defined by

$$f(x, y) = \sqrt{(9 - x^2 - y^2)}, \qquad D = \{(x, y) \in \mathbb{R}^2 \mid x^2 + y^2 < 9\},$$

and let $\mathbf{p} = (2, 1)$. The graph of f is an inverted hemi-spherical bowl. The partial derivatives of f are

$$\frac{\partial f}{\partial x}(x, y) = \frac{-x}{\sqrt{(9 - x^2 - y^2)}}, \qquad \frac{\partial f}{\partial y}(x, y) = \frac{-y}{\sqrt{(9 - x^2 - y^2)}}.$$

In particular, $(\partial f / \partial x)(\mathbf{p}) = -1$ and $(\partial f / \partial y)(\mathbf{p}) = -\frac{1}{2}$. The function is differentiable at **p** since (Theorem 3.3.29) the partial derivatives are continuous there. It follows from Corollary 3.7.6 that for any unit vector $\mathbf{u} \in \mathbb{R}^2$,

3.7.8 $$\frac{\partial f}{\partial \mathbf{u}}(\mathbf{p}) = -u_1 - \frac{1}{2}u_2.$$

When u_1 and u_2 are both positive $(\partial f / \partial \mathbf{u})(\mathbf{p})$ is negative and so $f(\mathbf{x})$ decreases as we move from **p** in the direction **u**.

The directional derivative in 3.7.8 is 0 when **u** is a unit vector such that $u_2 = -2u_1$. This is true if and only if $\mathbf{u} = \pm (1/\sqrt{5}, -2/\sqrt{5})$.

3.7.9 Example.   Let $f : \mathbb{R}^2 \to \mathbb{R}$ be defined by $f(x_1, x_2) = x_1^2 - x_2^2$, and let $\mathbf{p} = (-2, 1)$. By the above argument, for any unit vector $\mathbf{u} \in \mathbb{R}^2$, $(\partial f / \partial \mathbf{u})(\mathbf{p}) = -4u_1 - 2u_2$. Thus for example when $\mathbf{u} = (2/\sqrt{5}, 1/\sqrt{5})$ we have $(\partial f / \partial \mathbf{u})(\mathbf{p}) = -2/\sqrt{5}$. Hence the estimated value of $f(\mathbf{p} + t\mathbf{u})$ using Theorem 3.7.4(ii) is $3 - 2t\sqrt{5}$. The correct value is $3 - 2t\sqrt{5} + \frac{3}{5}t^2$.

Exercises 3.7

1.   Find the directional derivative $(\partial f / \partial \mathbf{u})(\mathbf{p})$ for $\mathbf{u} = (\frac{3}{5}, \frac{4}{5})$ and $\mathbf{p} = (0, -1)$, where

$$\text{(a) } f(x, y) = \sqrt{(x^2 + y^2)}, \qquad \text{(b) } f(x) = \frac{x - y}{x + y}, \qquad (x + y) \neq 0.$$

Hint: apply Corollary 3.7.6.

2.   The roof of an exhibition hall is constructed in the shape of a hemi-sphere rising from ground level. A workman is standing at a point on the roof at a height above ground level which is half the maximum height of the roof. When he faces due east the vertical axis through the centre of the building is directly behind him.

   Calculate the slope of his ascent or descent if he moves on the roof

(a) in an easterly direction; (b) in a westerly direction; (c) in a south-easterly direction.

In what direction must be set off in order to 'traverse' in a horizontal direction?

Hint: consider the surface of the roof as the graph of the function f, where $f(x, y) = \sqrt{(1 - x^2 - y^2)}$, $x^2 + y^2 \leqslant 1$, and choose x and y axes in directions south and east. The workman is then located at the point $(\mathbf{p}, f(\mathbf{p})) = (0, \frac{1}{2}\sqrt{3}, \frac{1}{2})$. To solve part (a) calculate $(\partial f/\partial \mathbf{u})(\mathbf{p})$ where $\mathbf{u} = (0, 1)$.

Answers: (a) descent at $60°$ to horizontal;   (b) ascent at $60°$;
   (c) descent at $\tan^{-1}\sqrt{\frac{3}{2}}$. Horizontal motion due north or south.

3.   Continuing Exercise 3.6.5, when the insect is at the point $(1, 1, 2)$ how should he change his course to proceed at constant temperature?

Hint: find unit vector $\mathbf{u} \in \mathbb{R}^3$ such that $(\partial f/\partial \mathbf{u})(1, 1, 2) = 0$.

Answer: any direction $\mathbf{u} = (u_1, u_2, u_3)$ such that $-u_1 + u_2 - u_3 = 0$ will do.

4.   Let $f : \mathbb{R}^2 \to \mathbb{R}$ be defined by

$$f(x, y) = \begin{cases} \dfrac{x^2 y}{x^2 + y^2} & \text{when } (x, y) \neq (0, 0) \\ 0 & \text{when } (x, y) = (0, 0). \end{cases}$$

Prove from Definition 3.7.2 that, given any unit vector $\mathbf{u} = (u_1, u_2) \in \mathbb{R}^2$, $(\partial f/\partial \mathbf{u})(\mathbf{0})$ exists, and

$$\frac{\partial f}{\partial \mathbf{u}}(\mathbf{0}) = \frac{u_1^2 u_2}{u_1^2 + u_2^2}.$$

In Exercise 3.6.4 we observed that $(\partial f/\partial x)(\mathbf{0}) = (\partial f/\partial y)(\mathbf{0}) = 0$. Hence the formula for $\partial f/\partial \mathbf{u}$ of Corollary 3.7.6 breaks down at $\mathbf{p} = \mathbf{0}$. Note that f is not differentiable at $\mathbf{0}$ (Exercise 3.3.8) although all its directional derivatives exist.

Are similar conclusions true for the function $g : \mathbb{R}^2 \to \mathbb{R}$ of Exercise 3.3.8?

3.8   The Gradient. Surfaces

We begin this section by solving the following problems concerning the directional derivative of a function $f : D \subseteq \mathbb{R}^m \to \mathbb{R}$ that is differentiable at $\mathbf{p} \in D$.

3.8.1   *Find all unit vectors $\mathbf{u} \in \mathbb{R}^m$ such that $(\partial f/\partial \mathbf{u})(\mathbf{p}) = 0$.*

3.8.2   *Find all unit vectors $\mathbf{u} \in \mathbb{R}^m$ such that $(\partial f/\partial \mathbf{u})(\mathbf{p})$ takes maximum value.*

The solutions of these two problems follow easily from Theorem 3.7.4 with the help of the following very important concept.

3.8.3 Definition.   *Let* $f : D \subseteq \mathbb{R}^m \to \mathbb{R}$ *be a function that is differentiable at* $\mathbf{p} \in D$. *The gradient of* f *at* $\mathbf{p}$ *is defined to be the vector*

$$(\operatorname{grad} f)(\mathbf{p}) = \left(\frac{\partial f}{\partial x_1}(\mathbf{p}), \dots, \frac{\partial f}{\partial x_m}(\mathbf{p}) \right) \in \mathbb{R}^m.$$

When f *is differentiable throughout* D, *then this expression defines a (vector-valued) function* $\operatorname{grad} f : D \subseteq \mathbb{R}^m \to \mathbb{R}^m$.

3.8.4 Example.   Define $f : \mathbb{R}^2 \to \mathbb{R}$ by $f(x, y) = x^2 - y^2$. Then
$$(\operatorname{grad} f)(x, y) = (2x, -2y).$$

3.8.5 Example.   Define $F : \mathbb{R}^3 \to \mathbb{R}$ by $F(x, y, z) = x^2 + y^2 + z^2$. Then
$$(\operatorname{grad} F)(x, y, z) = (2x, 2y, 2z).$$

We shall consider vector-valued functions in greater detail in later chapters. For the moment we continue our study of the function $\operatorname{grad} f$ by explaining its connection with differentials, directional derivatives and the Chain Rule.

3.8.6 Theorem.   *Let* $f : D \subseteq \mathbb{R}^m \to \mathbb{R}$ *be differentiable at* $\mathbf{p} \in D$. *Then*
   [i]   *the differential* $L_{f, \mathbf{p}}$ *is related to the gradient through the scalar product*

$$L_{f, \mathbf{p}}(\mathbf{h}) = (\operatorname{grad} f)(\mathbf{p}) \cdot \mathbf{h}, \qquad \mathbf{h} \in \mathbb{R}^m;$$

[ii] *for a given unit vector* $\mathbf{u} \in \mathbb{R}^m$, *the directional derivative* $(\partial f / \partial \mathbf{u})(\mathbf{p})$ *is expressible as the scalar product*

$$\frac{\partial f}{\partial \mathbf{u}}(\mathbf{p}) = (\operatorname{grad} f)(\mathbf{p}) \cdot \mathbf{u}.$$

Proof.   (i) Theorem 3.3.20(ii); (ii) Corollary 3.7.6.

3.8.7 Theorem   (*Chain Rule*).   *Let* $g : E \subseteq \mathbb{R} \to \mathbb{R}^m$ *be defined on an open interval* E, *let* $f : D \subseteq \mathbb{R}^m \to \mathbb{R}$ *be defined on an open set* D *such that* $g(E) \subseteq D$, *and let* $F = f \circ g$.
   Suppose that g *is differentiable at* $a \in E$ *and that* f *is differentiable at* $g(a) \in D$. *Then* F *is differentiable at* a *and*

$$F'(a) = (f \circ g)'(a) = (\operatorname{grad} f)(g(a)) \cdot g'(a).$$

Proof. Put $g(t) = (x_1(t), \ldots, x_m(t))$ and apply 3.6.9.

There is a striking similarity between this form of the Chain Rule and the Chain Rule of elementary calculus (see 1.6.11).

We can now solve the problems raised in 3.8.1 and 3.8.2. The solution is trivial when $(\text{grad } f)(\mathbf{p}) = \mathbf{0}$, for then $(\partial f/\partial \mathbf{u})(\mathbf{p}) = 0$ for all unit vectors $\mathbf{u} \in \mathbb{R}^m$. The non-trivial case is dealt with in the following theorem.

3.8.8 Theorem. *Let the function* $f : D \subseteq \mathbb{R}^m \to \mathbb{R}$ *be differentiable at* $\mathbf{p} \in D$ *and let* $(\text{grad } f)(\mathbf{p}) \neq \mathbf{0}$. *Then*

[i] *the directional derivative* $(\partial f/\partial \mathbf{u})(\mathbf{p})$ *takes maximum value if and only if* $\mathbf{u}$ *is the unit vector in the direction* $(\text{grad } f)(\mathbf{p})$. *The maximum value is* $\|(\text{grad } f)(\mathbf{p})\|$;

[ii] $(\partial f/\partial \mathbf{u})(\mathbf{p}) = 0$ *if and only if* $\mathbf{u}$ *is a unit vector orthogonal to* $(\text{grad } f)(\mathbf{p})$.

Proof. Immediate from Theorem 3.8.6(ii).

Notice that Theorem 3.8.8 tells us that the direction of maximum rate of change is orthogonal to the directions of zero rate of change. The gradient takes on even more significance if we consider 3.8.1 and 3.8.2 from a geometrical point of view and in particular examine how $(\text{grad } f)(\mathbf{p})$ is related to the level set of f which contains $\mathbf{p}$. Let the level set be $S = \{\mathbf{x} \in \mathbb{R}^m \,|\, f(\mathbf{x}) = f(\mathbf{p})\}$. Since f is constant in S, it is reasonable to expect that $(\partial f/\partial \mathbf{u})(\mathbf{p})$ will be zero when $\mathbf{u}$ is 'tangential' to S at $\mathbf{p}$. It would follow that $(\partial f/\partial \mathbf{u})(\mathbf{p})$ takes maximum value when $\mathbf{u}$ is a unit vector 'normal' to the level set S through $\mathbf{p}$. This in turn suggests that $(\text{grad } f)(\mathbf{p})$ is 'normal' to the level set S.

In attempting to apply these ideas to general functions $f : D \subseteq \mathbb{R}^m \to \mathbb{R}$ we meet the difficulty that we do not have a definition of tangent lines and normals to arbitrary sets. We avoid this problem by using $(\text{grad } f)(\mathbf{p})$ to *define* the concepts (Definition 3.8.16). But first we consider some illustrative examples and introduce the important notion of a surface in $\mathbb{R}^m$.

3.8.9 Example. Consider again the function $f : \mathbb{R}^2 \to \mathbb{R}$ given by $f(x, y) = x^2 - y^2$. The level set S through $\mathbf{p} = (-2, 1)$ is the hyperbola

$$x^2 - y^2 = f(-2, 1) = 3.$$

We know from elementary analytic geometry that the tangent to the hyperbola at $(-2, 1)$ has slope -2. The unit vector $\mathbf{u} = (-1/\sqrt{5}, 2/\sqrt{5})$ is in this direction. It is straightforward to check that

$$\frac{\partial f}{\partial \mathbf{u}}(-2, 1) = -\frac{1}{\sqrt{5}}\frac{\partial f}{\partial x}(-2, 1) + \frac{2}{\sqrt{5}}\frac{\partial f}{\partial y}(-2, 1) = 0.$$

Similarly we know that the normal to S through $(-2, 1)$ has slope $\frac{1}{2}$. The vector $(\mathrm{grad}\, f)(-2, 1) = (-4, -2)$ is in the direction of the normal (see Fig. 3.17(i)).

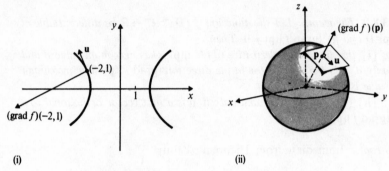

(i)   (ii)

Fig. 3.17 (i) Hyperbola $f(x, y) = x^2 - y^2 = 3$
            (ii) Sphere $f(x, y, z) = x^2 + y^2 + z^2 = 9$

3.8.10 Example.   The level sets of the function $f : \mathbb{R}^3 \to \mathbb{R}$ given by $f(x, y, z) = x^2 + y^2 + z^2$ are concentric spheres centre $\mathbf{0}$. In particular the level set S through $\mathbf{p} = (1, 2, 2)$ is the sphere with equation

$$x^2 + y^2 + z^2 = f(1, 2, 2) = 9.$$

The unit vector $\mathbf{u} = (0, 1/\sqrt{2}, -1/\sqrt{2})$ is orthogonal to the radius vector through $\mathbf{p}$ (see Fig. 3.17(ii)). Hence $\mathbf{u}$ is the direction of a tangent line to the sphere at $\mathbf{p}$. It is straightforward to check that

$$\frac{\partial f}{\partial \mathbf{u}}(1, 2, 2) = 0\frac{\partial f}{\partial x}(1, 2, 2) + \frac{1}{\sqrt{2}}\frac{\partial f}{\partial y}(1, 2, 2) - \frac{1}{\sqrt{2}}\frac{\partial f}{\partial z}(1, 2, 2) = 0.$$

Finally, $(\mathrm{grad}\, f)(1, 2, 2) = (2, 4, 4)$, a vector which is a scalar multiple of the radius vector through $\mathbf{p}$. It is therefore in the direction of the normal to the sphere at $\mathbf{p}$.

3.8.11 Definition.   *A set $S \subseteq \mathbb{R}^m$ is called a* surface *if S is a level set of a C^1 function $f : D \subseteq \mathbb{R}^m \to \mathbb{R}$ such that $(\mathrm{grad}\, f)(\mathbf{x}) \neq \mathbf{0}$ for all $\mathbf{x} \in S$.*

3.8.12 Example.   The sphere $x^2 + y^2 + z^2 = 9$ is a surface in $\mathbb{R}^3$. It is the level set corresponding to the value 9 of the C^1 function $f : \mathbb{R}^3 \to \mathbb{R}$ given by $f(x, y, z) = x^2 + y^2 + z^2$, and $(\text{grad } f)(x, y, z) \neq (0, 0, 0)$ at points on the sphere.

Similarly, the hyperbola $x^2 - y^2 = 3$ is a surface in $\mathbb{R}^2$. It is a level set of the C^1 function $f : \mathbb{R}^2 \to \mathbb{R}$ given by $f(x, y) = x^2 - y^2$. We observe that $(\text{grad } f)(x, y) \neq (0, 0)$ at points on the hyperbola.

Notice that the branch of the hyperbola containing the point $(-2, 1)$ is also defined as the level set corresponding to 0 of the differentiable function $g(x, y) = x + \sqrt{(y^2 + 3)}$, and that $(\text{grad } g)(x, y) \neq (0, 0)$ everywhere. At a point (x, y) on the hyperbola the vectors $(\text{grad } f)(x, y)$ and $(\text{grad } g)(x, y)$ must both be in the direction of the normal to the hyperbola (Example 3.8.9) and so $(\text{grad } g)(x, y)$ is a scalar multiple of $(\text{grad } f)(x, y)$. For example, $(\text{grad } g)(-2, 1) = (1, 1/2)$, and $(\text{grad } f)(-2, 1) = (-4, -2)$.

The condition in Definition 3.8.11 that f should be continuously differentiable is there to ensure that the normal lines to S (which we shall define) change direction continuously over S. The requirement that the gradient shall be non-zero is there to exclude awkward points as the following example illustrates.

3.8.13 *Example.* The function $f : \mathbb{R}^3 \to \mathbb{R}$ defined by $f(x, y, z) = x^2 + y^2 - z^2$ has as level set corresponding to 0 the right circular cone $z = \pm\sqrt{(x^2 + y^2)}$. See Fig. 3.18(i). At the apex, $(\text{grad } f)(0) = 0$. Such points must be avoided to allow sensible definitions of normal and tangent plane to a surface at a point on it.

Note that the level sets $x^2 + y^2 - z^2 = c \neq 0$ are surfaces. If $c = a^2 > 0$ the level set is a hyperboloid of one sheet (Fig. 3.18(ii)), and if $c = -a^2 < 0$ it is a hyperboloid of two sheets (Fig. 3.18(iii)).

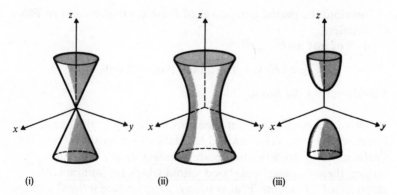

(i)   (ii)   (iii)

Fig. 3.18 (i) Cone $x^2 + y^2 - z^2 = 0$; (ii) Hyperboloid $x^2 + y^2 - z^2 = a^2$; (iii) Hyperboloid $x^2 + y^2 - z^2 = -a^2$

In view of the above comments we have the following definition.

3.8.14 Definition. *A function* $f : D \subseteq \mathbb{R}^m \to \mathbb{R}$ *is said to be* smooth *if it is continuously differentiable and if* $(\operatorname{grad} f)(\mathbf{x}) \neq \mathbf{0}$ *for all* $\mathbf{x} \in D$.

We can now say that a surface is a level set of a smooth function (Exercise 3.8.10). An important class of surfaces is considered in the following theorem.

3.8.15 Theorem. *The graph of a* C^1 *function* $f : D \subseteq \mathbb{R}^{m-1} \to \mathbb{R}$ *is a surface in* $\mathbb{R}^m$.

Proof. Consider the function $F : D \times \mathbb{R} \subseteq \mathbb{R}^m \to \mathbb{R}$ defined by the rule

3.8.16 $F(\mathbf{x}, x_m) = f(\mathbf{x}) - x_m, \qquad \mathbf{x} \in D, \, x_m \in \mathbb{R}.$

The graph G of f is the level set of F corresponding to the value 0, that is

$$G = \{(\mathbf{x}, x_m) \in \mathbb{R}^m \mid f(\mathbf{x}) - x_m = 0, \, \mathbf{x} \in D\}.$$

To prove that G is a surface in $\mathbb{R}^m$ we show that (i) F is a C^1 function and (ii) $(\operatorname{grad} F)(\mathbf{x}, x_m) \neq (\mathbf{0}, 0)$ for all $\mathbf{x} \in D, \, x_m \in \mathbb{R}$.

[i] It follows from 3.8.16 that for each $i = 1, \ldots, m-1$ and each $\mathbf{x} \in D, \, x_m \in \mathbb{R}$

$$\frac{\partial F}{\partial x_i}(\mathbf{x}, x_m) = \frac{\partial f}{\partial x_i}(\mathbf{x}) \quad \text{and} \quad \frac{\partial F}{\partial x_m}(\mathbf{x}, x_m) = -1.$$

Therefore the partial derivatives of F are continuous and so F is a C^1 function.

[ii] For any $\mathbf{x} \in D, \, x_m \in \mathbb{R}$

$$(\operatorname{grad} F)(\mathbf{x}, x_m) = ((\operatorname{grad} f)(\mathbf{x}), -1) \neq (\mathbf{0}, 0).$$

This completes the proof.

One of the most important theorems in this book, the Implicit Function Theorem (Theorem 4.8.1), establishes a local converse to Theorem 3.8.15. It shows that corresponding to any point in a surface, there is a neighbourhood within which the surface is the graph of a C^1 function. That is to say, every surface is 'locally graph-like'.

We are now in a position to define the normal and the tangent space to a surface at a point on it. Before we do that, however, we prove the following theorem by way of justification.

3.8.17 Theorem. *Let S be a surface which is a level set of a smooth function $f : D \subseteq \mathbb{R}^m \to \mathbb{R}$ and let $\mathbf{q}$ be a point in S. Then for any differentiable path $\alpha : E \subseteq \mathbb{R} \to \mathbb{R}^m$ such that $\alpha(E) \subseteq S$ and any $a \in E$ such that $\alpha(a) = \mathbf{q}$, the tangent vector $\alpha'(a)$ is orthogonal to the vector $(\operatorname{grad} f)(\mathbf{q})$.*

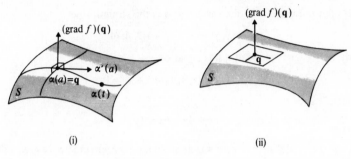

Fig. 3.19

Proof.   The theorem is illustrated in Fig. 3.19(i). Since $\alpha(E) \subseteq S$ we have

$$f(\alpha(t)) = f(\mathbf{q}) \qquad \text{for all } t \in E.$$

We obtain the derivative at a by using the Chain Rule in the form 3.8.7:

$$(\operatorname{grad} f)(\alpha(a)) \cdot \alpha'(a) = 0.$$

This is the required result.

Theorem 3.8.17 tells us that $(\operatorname{grad} f)(\mathbf{q})$ is orthogonal to every curve in S through $\mathbf{q}$. We are led to the following definitions.

3.8.18 Definition. *Let the surface S in $\mathbb{R}^m$ be a level set of a smooth function $f : D \subseteq \mathbb{R}^m \to \mathbb{R}$. Then, for any $\mathbf{q} \in S$,*
   [i] *the straight line through $\mathbf{q}$ in direction $(\operatorname{grad} f)(\mathbf{q})$ is called the* normal line *to the surface S at $\mathbf{q}$,*
   [ii] *the set of all vectors $\mathbf{x}$ such that $(\mathbf{x} - \mathbf{q}) \cdot (\operatorname{grad} f)(\mathbf{q}) = 0$ is called the* tangent space *to S at $\mathbf{q}$ (tangent line when $m = 2$, tangent plane when $m = 3$).*

The tangent space to S at $\mathbf{q}$ is the translation of an $(m-1)$-dimensional subspace of $\mathbb{R}^m$ through $\mathbf{q}$. The situation is illustrated in Fig. 3.19(ii).

3.8.19 Example.   The ellipsoid $x^2 + 2y^2 + 3z^2 = 6$ is a surface since it is a level set of the smooth function $f : \mathbb{R}^3 \setminus \{\mathbf{0}\} \to \mathbb{R}$ defined by

$$f(x, y, z) = x^2 + 2y^2 + 3z^2.$$

Consider the point $\mathbf{q} = (1, 1, 1)$ on the ellipsoid. Since $(\text{grad } f)(1, 1, 1) = (2, 4, 6)$,

[i]   the normal line to the surface at $\mathbf{q}$ is the straight line

$$(x, y, z) = (1, 1, 1) + t(2, 4, 6);$$

[ii]   the tangent plane at $\mathbf{q}$ has equation

$$((x, y, z) - (1, 1, 1)) \cdot (2, 4, 6) = 0,$$

namely,

$$2x + 4y + 6z = 12.$$

The above definition of a tangent space to a surface S is given in terms of a smooth function which has the surface as a level set. In general there are many different smooth functions with this property. We shall show in Exercise 4.8.9 (once we have proved the Implicit Function Theorem) that they all determine the same tangent space to S. We can however prove this result now in the particular case when S is a graph of a C^1 function. (We know from Theorem 3.8.15 that such a graph is a surface.) The following theorem shows that if G is the graph of a C^1 function $f : D \subseteq \mathbb{R}^{m-1} \to \mathbb{R}$ and if $F : D \times \mathbb{R} \subseteq \mathbb{R}^m \to \mathbb{R}$ is any smooth function having G as a level set, then the equation of the tangent space to G at $(\mathbf{p}, f(\mathbf{p}))$, as calculated by applying the above definition to F, is

$$x_m = f(\mathbf{p}) + L_{f, \mathbf{p}}(\mathbf{x} - \mathbf{p}), \qquad \mathbf{x} \in \mathbb{R}^{m-1}, \ \mathbf{p} \in D.$$

Since this equation depends on f and $\mathbf{p}$ alone, it follows that all appropriate smooth functions F determine the same tangent space. We also observe that this equation is the equation of the tangent space to the graph G of f as given in Section 3.4. The two definitions of tangent spaces to G (Definitions 3.4.9 and 3.8.18(ii)) are therefore consistent.

3.8.20 Theorem.   *Let the surface* $G \subseteq \mathbb{R}^m$ *be a level set of a smooth function* $F : D \times \mathbb{R} \subseteq \mathbb{R}^m \to \mathbb{R}$ *and also the graph of a* C^1 *function*

$f : D \subseteq \mathbb{R}^{m-1} \to \mathbb{R}$. *Then in the sense of Definition 3.8.18(ii), the equation of the tangent space to G at $(\mathbf{p}, f(\mathbf{p})) \in G$ is*

$$x_m = f(\mathbf{p}) + (x_1 - p_1)\frac{\partial f}{\partial x_1}(\mathbf{p}) + \cdots + (x_{m-1} - p_{m-1})\frac{\partial f}{\partial x_{m-1}}(\mathbf{p}).$$

Proof. Since G is both a level set of F and the graph of f, there exists $k \in \mathbb{R}$ such that

$$F(\mathbf{x}, f(\mathbf{x})) = k \qquad \text{for all } \mathbf{x} \in D.$$

For each $j = 1, \ldots, m-1$, taking partial derivatives of this expression with respect to x_j, we obtain (by the Chain Rule)

$$\frac{\partial F}{\partial x_j}(\mathbf{p}, f(\mathbf{p})) + \frac{\partial F}{\partial x_m}(\mathbf{p}, f(\mathbf{p}))\frac{\partial f}{\partial x_j}(\mathbf{p}) = 0.$$

Hence

$$(\text{grad } F)(\mathbf{p}, f(\mathbf{p})) = -\frac{\partial F}{\partial x_m}(\mathbf{p}, f(\mathbf{p}))\left(\frac{\partial f}{\partial x_1}(\mathbf{p}), \ldots, \frac{\partial f}{\partial x_{m-1}}(\mathbf{p}), -1\right).$$

Therefore, since F is smooth, $(\partial F/\partial x_m)(\mathbf{p}, f(\mathbf{p})) \neq 0$ and from 3.8.18(ii) the equation of the tangent space to G at $(\mathbf{p}, f(\mathbf{p}))$ is

$$((\mathbf{x}, x_m) - (\mathbf{p}, f(\mathbf{p})) \cdot \left(\frac{\partial f}{\partial x_1}(\mathbf{p}), \ldots, \frac{\partial f}{\partial x_{m-1}}(\mathbf{p}), -1\right) = 0.$$

The result follows.

We close this section by proving a theorem which generalizes the fundamental result that if the derivative of a real-valued function $f : E \subseteq \mathbb{R} \to \mathbb{R}$ is zero on the interval E, then f is a constant function. We need a preparatory definition.

3.8.21 Definition. *An open subset D of $\mathbb{R}^m$ is path connected if, given any two vectors $\mathbf{a}$ and $\mathbf{b}$ in D, there is a path $\alpha : [0, 1] \subseteq \mathbb{R} \to \mathbb{R}^m$ in D such that $\alpha(0) = \mathbf{a}$ and $\alpha(1) = \mathbf{b}$.*

We state without proof that if such a path α exists then there is a differentiable path with the same property.

3.8.22 Theorem. *Let D be an open path connected subset of $\mathbb{R}^m$ and let $f : D \subseteq \mathbb{R}^m \to \mathbb{R}$ be a differentiable function such that $(\text{grad } f)(\mathbf{x}) = \mathbf{0}$ for all $\mathbf{x} \in D$. Then f is a constant function.*

Proof.   It is enough to prove that, for any two vectors **a** and **b** in D, $f(\mathbf{a}) = f(\mathbf{b})$. Let $\alpha : [0, 1] \subseteq \mathbb{R} \to \mathbb{R}^m$ be a differentiable path in D such that $\alpha(0) = \mathbf{a}$ and $\alpha(1) = \mathbf{b}$. Then $f \circ \alpha : [0, 1] \subseteq \mathbb{R} \to \mathbb{R}^m$ has derivative given by

$$(f \circ \alpha)'(t) = (\text{grad } f)(\alpha(t)) \cdot \alpha'(t) = 0.$$

Hence $f \circ \alpha$ is a constant function (Exercise 1.6.3) and therefore $(f \circ \alpha)(0) = (f \circ \alpha)(1)$. It follows that $f(\mathbf{a}) = f(\mathbf{b})$.

Exercises 3.8

1. Find $(\text{grad } f)(x, y)$ when

    (a) $f(x, y) = \sqrt{(x^2 + y^2)}$,   (b) $f(x) = \dfrac{x - y}{x + y}$, $x + y \neq 0$.

    Hence find $(\partial f / \partial \mathbf{u})(\mathbf{p})$ when $\mathbf{u} = (\frac{3}{5}, \frac{4}{5})$, $\mathbf{p} = (0, -1)$. Compare with Exercise 3.7.1.

2. For the following functions $f : \mathbb{R}^2 \to \mathbb{R}$ and $g : \mathbb{R} \to \mathbb{R}^2$ calulate $(f \circ g)'(t)$ from the formula $(f \circ g)'(t) = (\text{grad } f)(g(t)) \cdot g'(t)$.
    (a) $f(x_1, x_2) = x_1 x_2$, $g(t) = (\sin t, \cos t)$;
    (b) $f(x, y) = x^2 y + y^3$, $g(t) = (t + 1, e^t)$.
    Compare with Exercise 3.6.2.

3. Continuing Exercise 3.6.5, when the insect is at the point $(1, 1, 2)$ and the temperature in space is given by $f(x, y, z) = kx^2(y - z)$, what course should he take to warm up as quickly as possible?

Hint: find **u** such that $(\partial f / \partial \mathbf{u})(1, 1, 2)$ is a maximum from Theorem 3.8.8(i).

Check: by Theorem 3.8.8(ii) the direction of maximum rate of increase of temperature at $(1, 1, 2)$ must be orthogonal to any direction of constant temperature at $(1, 1, 2)$ as calculated in Exercise 3.7.3.

4. Let $f : \mathbb{R}^2 \to \mathbb{R}$ be the function defined by $f(x, y) = x^2 - y^2$. Sketch the level set

    $$S = \{(x, y) \in \mathbb{R}^2 \,|\, f(x, y) = -1\}.$$

    On your sketch draw at points **p** in S the vector $(\text{grad } f)(\mathbf{p})$, where (a) $\mathbf{p} = (0, 1)$, (b) $\mathbf{p} = (1, \sqrt{2})$, (c) $p = (1, -\sqrt{2})$. Observe that in each case $(\text{grad } f)(\mathbf{p})$ is normal to the level set.

5. Repeat Exercise 4 for various level sets of the functions of Exercise 3.1.1.

6. Sketch the hyperboloid of two sheets $x^2 - y^2 - z^2 = 1$. Show that it is a surface according to Definition 3.8.11. Find (i) the normal at **q**, (ii) the tangent plane at **q** to the hyperboloid when (a) $\mathbf{q} = (1, 0, 0)$;

(b) $\mathbf{q} = (-1, 0, 0)$; (c) $\mathbf{q} = (2, 0, \sqrt{3})$; (d) $\mathbf{q} = (\sqrt{3}, 1, -1)$. Sketch the normals and tangent planes.

Answer to part (c): the normal to the hyperboloid at $(2, 0, \sqrt{3})$ is the line $(x, y, z) = (2, 0, \sqrt{3}) + t(4, 0, -2\sqrt{3})$; the tangent plane at $(2, 0, \sqrt{3})$ has equation $2x - \sqrt{3}z = 1$.

7. Prove that a plane in $\mathbb{R}^3$ is a surface.

8. Let $F : \mathbb{R}^3 \setminus \{\mathbf{0}\} \to \mathbb{R}$ be defined by

$$F(\mathbf{r}) = \frac{1}{r}, \qquad \mathbf{r} \neq \mathbf{0}$$

where $\mathbf{r} = (x, y, z)$ and $r = \|\mathbf{r}\| = \sqrt{(x^2 + y^2 + z^2)}$. Prove that

$$(\operatorname{grad} F)(\mathbf{r}) = -\frac{1}{r^3}\mathbf{r}.$$

Show that $(\operatorname{grad} F)(a, b, c)$ is normal to the sphere $r^2 = a^2 + b^2 + c^2$ at the point (a, b, c). Find the equation of the tangent plane to this sphere at (a, b, c).

Answer: $ax + by + cz = a^2 + b^2 + c^2$.

9. Let $F : \mathbb{R}^3 \to \mathbb{R}$ be defined by $F(x, y, z) = y^3 - z^3$. Prove that

$$(\operatorname{grad} F)(x, 0, 0) = (0, 0, 0), \qquad x \in \mathbb{R}.$$

Is the level set

$$S = \{(x, y, z) \in \mathbb{R}^3 \mid F(x, y, z) = 0\}$$

a surface in $\mathbb{R}^3$?

Hint: note that Definition 3.8.11 does not apply to the function F. This does *not* imply that S is not a surface in $\mathbb{R}^3$. Prove that $y^3 - z^3 = 0$ if and only if $y - z = 0$. Hence show that S is a surface in $\mathbb{R}^3$.

10. Let $S \subseteq \mathbb{R}^m$ be a surface. Prove that S is a level set of a *smooth* function $f : E \subseteq \mathbb{R}^m \to \mathbb{R}$.

Hint: starting from Definition 3.8.11, prove that the set $K = \{\mathbf{x} \in D \mid (\operatorname{grad} f)(\mathbf{x}) = \mathbf{0}\}$ is closed. (Compare Exercise 3.2.9.) Then f is smooth on the open domain $E = D \setminus K$, and $S \subseteq E$.

11. Prove that the cone $S = \{(x, y, z) \in x^2 + y^2 - z^2 = 0\}$ (see Example 3.8.13) is not a surface.

Hint: Suppose to the contrary that there exists a smooth function $f : E \subseteq \mathbb{R}^3 \to \mathbb{R}$ such that

$$S = \{(x, y, z) \in E \mid f(x, y, z) = 0\}.$$

Consider the three differentiable paths α, β, γ in S given by

$$\alpha(t) = (t, 0, t), \qquad \beta(t) = (0, t, t), \qquad \gamma(t) = (t, t, \sqrt{2}t),$$
$$t \in [-1, 1].$$

Then $\alpha(0) = \beta(0) = \gamma(0) = \mathbf{0}$, the apex of the cone. Prove that the tangent vectors $\alpha'(0)$, $\beta'(0)$, $\gamma'(0)$ are linearly independent. Argue by contradiction from Exercise 10.

12. Let $f : \mathbb{R}^3 \to \mathbb{R}$ be defined by $f(x, y, z) = x^2 - y^2$, $(x, y, z) \in \mathbb{R}^3$. Show that f is not a smooth function on the level set $S = \{(x, y, z) \in \mathbb{R}^3 \,|\, f(x, y, z) = 0\}$. Sketch S.

3.9   The Mean-Value Theorem

The Mean-Value Theorem of elementary calculus can be extended as follows.

3.9.1 Theorem.   *Let the function* $f : D \subseteq \mathbb{R}^m \to \mathbb{R}$ *be differentiable and let* $\mathbf{p}$ *lie in* D. *Suppose that for some non-zero vector* $\mathbf{h} \in \mathbb{R}^m$ *the line segment joining* $\mathbf{p}$ *and* $\mathbf{p} + \mathbf{h}$ *is a subset of* D. *Then there exists a point* $\mathbf{c} = \mathbf{p} + \theta\mathbf{h}, 0 < \theta < 1$, *in that line segment such that*

$$f(\mathbf{p} + \mathbf{h}) - f(\mathbf{p}) = h_1 \frac{\partial f}{\partial x_1}(\mathbf{c}) + \cdots + h_m \frac{\partial f}{\partial x_m}(\mathbf{c}).$$

3.9.2 Corollary.   *With the notation and hypothesis of Theorem* 3.9.1

$$f(\mathbf{p} + \mathbf{h}) - f(\mathbf{p}) = \|\mathbf{h}\| \frac{\partial f}{\partial \mathbf{u}}(\mathbf{c})$$

where $\mathbf{u} = \|\mathbf{h}\|^{-1}\mathbf{h}$ *is the unit vector in the direction of* $\mathbf{h}$.

Proof of Theorem 3.9.1.   Since we are working on the line segment joining $\mathbf{p}$ and $\mathbf{p} + \mathbf{h}$ we can reduce our problem to one concerning a function $F : [0, 1] \subseteq \mathbb{R} \to \mathbb{R}$ by defining

3.9.3 $$F(t) = f(\mathbf{p} + t\mathbf{h}), \qquad t \in [0, 1].$$

Notice that F is the composition of f with the differentiable function $g : [0, 1] \subseteq \mathbb{R} \to \mathbb{R}^m$ defined by $g(t) = \mathbf{p} + t\mathbf{h}, t \in [0, 1]$.

The Mean-Value Theorem applies to $F = f \circ g$ since F is continuous on $[0, 1]$ and differentiable on $]0, 1[$. Therefore there exists $0 < \theta < 1$ such that

3.9.4 $f(\mathbf{p} + \mathbf{h}) - f(\mathbf{p}) = F(1) - F(0) = F'(\theta).$

By the Chain Rule 3.6.9

3.9.5 $F'(\theta) = h_1 \dfrac{\partial f}{\partial x_1}(\mathbf{p} + \theta\mathbf{h}) + \cdots + h_m \dfrac{\partial f}{\partial x_m}(\mathbf{p} + \theta\mathbf{h}).$

The result follows from 3.9.4 and 3.9.5 by taking $\mathbf{c} = \mathbf{p} + \theta\mathbf{h}$.

Proof of Corollary 3.9.2.   By Corollary 3.7.6

3.9.6 $\dfrac{\partial f}{\partial \mathbf{u}}(\mathbf{c}) = u_1 \dfrac{\partial f}{\partial x_1}(\mathbf{c}) + \cdots + u_m \dfrac{\partial f}{\partial x_m}(\mathbf{c})$

and therefore, multiplying 3.9.6 by $\|\mathbf{h}\|$

3.9.7 $\|\mathbf{h}\| \dfrac{\delta f}{\delta \mathbf{u}}(\mathbf{c}) = h_1 \dfrac{\partial f}{\partial x_1}(\mathbf{c}) + \cdots + h_m \dfrac{\partial f}{\partial x_m}(\mathbf{c}).$

Combining 3.9.7 and Theorem 3.9.1 gives the required result.

3.9.8 *Example.* We now take a second look at our estimation of the acceleration in Example 3.5.3. The relationship is $a = f(v, s) = v^2/2s$ and the observed values are $(v, s) = (30, 300)$ with possible errors given by $|\Delta v| \leq 1$ and $|\Delta s| \leq 3$. We know from the direct solution 3.5.9 that if the true acceleration is $a_t \, m s^{-2}$, then $-0.112 \leq a_t - a \leq 0.118$. We cannot hope to improve on that inequality since all values in that range could occur, given the error bounds on v and s.

The Mean-Value Theorem tells us that

3.9.9 $a_t - a = \Delta v \dfrac{\partial f}{\partial v}(v + \theta\Delta v, s + \theta\Delta s) + \Delta s \dfrac{\partial f}{\partial s}(v + \theta\Delta v, s + \theta\Delta s)$

for some $0 < \theta < 1$.
Hence

$$a_t - a = \Delta v \frac{v + \theta \Delta v}{s + \theta \Delta s} - \Delta s \frac{1}{2}\left(\frac{v + \theta \Delta v}{s + \theta \Delta s}\right)^2.$$

We can now find an upper bound for $|a_t - a|$ by taking $\Delta v = 1$, $\Delta s = -3$ and $\theta = 1$, giving

$$|a_t - a| \leq \frac{31}{297} + \frac{3}{2}\left(\frac{31}{297}\right)^2 = 0.121.$$

We therefore have $-0.121 \leq a_t - a \leq 0.121$. As expected this range contains the achievable range given above.

It is interesting to note that the approximation 3.5.8 which was obtained by neglecting a term $\|\Delta\mathbf{x}\|\eta(\Delta\mathbf{x})$ can also be obtained from 3.9.9 by taking $\theta = 0$. We saw in Example 3.5.3 that this leads to $-0.115 \leqslant a_t - a \leqslant 0.115$, which does not contain the achievable range as a subset.

Of course in this simple example a direct calculation is most appropriate. But the example illustrates how the Mean-Value Theorem provides a correct upper bound for the error, which a crude application of differentiability at (30, 300) did not do.

Exercises 3.9

1. Let $f : \mathbb{R}^2 \to \mathbb{R}$ be defined by $f(x_1, x_2) = x_1^2 x_2$. Obtain the expression for $f(\mathbf{p} + \mathbf{h}) - f(\mathbf{p})$ of Theorem 3.9.1 for the case $\mathbf{p} = (10, 20)$, $\mathbf{h} = (0.1, 0.1)$.

2. Prove that, if $f(x, y) = e^x \cos y$, then there exists $0 < \theta < 1$ such that

$$f(x, y) = 1 + xe^{\theta x}\cos\theta y - ye^{\theta x}\sin\theta y.$$

    Deduce that provided $|x|$ and $|y|$ are 'small', the polynomial $1 + x$ is a reasonable approximation to $f(x, y)$.

    Hint: In Theorem 3.9.1 take $\mathbf{p} = \mathbf{0}$ and $\mathbf{h} = (x, y)$.

3. By the method of Exercise 2 obtain a polynomial of degree 1 in $h_1 = (x + 1)$ and $h_2 = (y - 1)$ which is a reasonable approximation to $\sqrt{(1 + x + 4y)}$ when x is close to -1 and y is close to 1.

    Hint: In Theorem 3.9.1 take $\mathbf{p} = (-1, 1)$ and $\mathbf{p} + \mathbf{h} = (x, y)$ and consider small values of $h_1 = x + 1$ and $h_2 = y - 1$.

    Answer: $2 + \frac{1}{4}h_1 + h_2$.

4. Consider again the rectangular box of Exercise 3.5.1. Estimate the accuracy of the calculation for the volume V by applying the Mean-Value Theorem in the manner of Example 3.9.8. (Use the calculations of Exercise 1.)

3.10   Higher-order derivatives

In the next section we propose to prove Taylor's Theorem which generalizes the Mean-Value Theorem 3.9.1 and Corollary 3.9.2. The theorem is conveniently stated in terms of higher-order directional derivatives. However, for the purpose of calculation there is a useful alternative version that involves higher-order partial derivatives. As a preliminary to Taylor's Theorem we will consider higher-order derivatives in this section.

3.10.1 Definition. *The nth-order directional derivative of the function* $f : D \subseteq \mathbb{R}^m \to \mathbb{R}$ *in the direction of a unit vector* $\mathbf{u} \in \mathbb{R}^m$ *is the function* $\partial^n f / \partial \mathbf{u}^n : D \subseteq \mathbb{R}^m \to \mathbb{R}$ *defined inductively by the rule*

$$\frac{\partial^{r+1} f}{\partial \mathbf{u}^{r+1}} = \frac{\partial}{\partial \mathbf{u}} \left(\frac{\partial^r f}{\partial \mathbf{u}^r} \right), \qquad r = 1, \ldots, n-1,$$

whenever these derivatives exist.

For the case $m = 1$, with $\mathbf{u}$ the unit vector in the positive direction in $\mathbb{R}$, the directional derivatives are simply the ordinary derivatives $f', f'', \ldots$.

Recall from Section 3.7 that for arbitrary m the directional derivative $\delta f / \delta \mathbf{e}_j$ in the direction $\mathbf{e}_j$ in $\mathbb{R}^m$ is by definition equal to the partial derivative $\partial f / \partial x_j$. Similarly the higher-order derivative $\partial^n f / \partial \mathbf{e}_j^n$ is denoted by $\partial^n f / \partial x_j^n$. This is in agreement with the following general definition of higher-order partial derivatives.

3.10.2 Definition. *The partial derivatives of the partial derivatives of a function* $f : D \subseteq \mathbb{R}^m \to \mathbb{R}$, *provided they exist, are called* second-order *partial derivatives. The second-order partial derivative*

$$\frac{\partial}{\partial x_j} \left(\frac{\partial f}{\partial x_i} \right)$$

is denoted by

$$\frac{\partial^2 f}{\partial x_j \partial x_i}$$

if $i \neq j$ *and by*

$$\frac{\partial^2 f}{\partial x_i^2}$$

if $i = j$. *The notation for third-order partial derivatives is*

$$\frac{\partial^3 f}{\partial x_k \partial x_j \partial x_i} = \frac{\partial}{\partial x_k} \left(\frac{\partial^2 f}{\partial x_j \partial x_i} \right).$$

Similar notation applies to fourth and higher orders.

3.10.3 Example. Define $f : \mathbb{R}^3 \to \mathbb{R}$ by

$$f(x_1, x_2, x_3) = x_1^3 x_2 - x_1 x_3^2, \qquad \mathbf{x} \in \mathbb{R}^3.$$

Then $\partial f/\partial x_1(\mathbf{x}) = 3x_1^2 x_2 - x_3^2$ and $\partial f/\partial x_2(\mathbf{x}) = x_1^3$. Hence

$$\frac{\partial^2 f}{\partial x_1^2}(\mathbf{x}) = 6x_1 x_2, \qquad \frac{\partial^2 f}{\partial x_2 \partial x_1}(\mathbf{x}) = 3x_1^2 \quad \text{and} \quad \frac{\partial^2 f}{\partial x_1 \partial x_2}(\mathbf{x}) = 3x_1^2.$$

Finally,

$$\frac{\partial^3 f}{\partial x_2 \partial x_1^2}(\mathbf{x}) = 6x_1, \; \frac{\partial^3 f}{\partial x_1 \partial x_2 \partial x_1}(\mathbf{x}) = 6x_1 \quad \text{and} \quad \frac{\partial^3 f}{\partial x_1^2 \partial x_2}(\mathbf{x}) = 6x_1.$$

It is no coincidence that the two mixed second-order partial derivatives and the three third-order partial derivatives are equal, as the following theorem shows.

3.10.4 Theorem. *Let $f : D \subseteq \mathbb{R}^2 \to \mathbb{R}$ be a function such that*
[i] *$\partial f/\partial x_1$, $\partial f/\partial x_2$ and $\partial^2 f/\partial x_2 \partial x_1$ exist throughout D, and*
[ii] *$\partial^2 f/\partial x_2 \partial x_1$ is continuous at $\mathbf{p} \in D$.*
Then $\partial^2 f/\partial x_1 \partial x_2$ exists at $\mathbf{p}$ and

$$\frac{\partial^2 f}{\partial x_1 \partial x_2}(\mathbf{p}) = \frac{\partial^2 f}{\partial x_2 \partial x_1}(\mathbf{p}).$$

Proof. We need to express the relevant partial derivatives in terms of limits.

$$\frac{\partial f}{\partial x_1}(\mathbf{x}) = \lim_{h_1 \to 0} \frac{f(x_1 + h_1, x_2) - f(x_1, x_2)}{h_1},$$

$$\frac{\partial^2 f}{\partial x_2 \partial x_1}(\mathbf{p}) = \lim_{h_2 \to 0} \frac{1}{h_2} \left(\lim_{h_1 \to 0} \frac{f(p_1 + h_1, p_2 + h_2) - f(p_1, p_2 + h_2)}{h_1} \right.$$

$$\left. - \lim_{h_1 \to 0} \frac{f(p_1 + h_1, p_2) - f(p_1, p_2)}{h_1} \right).$$

Therefore

$$\frac{\partial^2 f}{\partial x_2 \partial x_1}(\mathbf{p}) = \lim_{h_2 \to 0} \lim_{h_1 \to 0} \frac{F(h_1, h_2)}{h_1 h_2},$$

where

3.10.5
$$F(h_1, h_2) = f(p_1 + h_1, p_2 + h_2) - f(p_1, p_2 + h_2)$$
$$- f(p_1 + h_1, p_2) + f(p_1, p_2).$$

Similarly, we find that

$$\frac{\partial^2 f}{\partial x_1 \partial x_2}(\mathbf{p}) = \lim_{h_1 \to 0} \lim_{h_2 \to 0} \frac{F(h_1, h_2)}{h_1 h_2},$$

provided that this limit exists.

We intend to show that under the hypothesis of the theorem

3.10.6 $$\lim_{h_1 \to 0} \lim_{h_2 \to 0} \frac{F(h_1, h_2)}{h_1 h_2} = \frac{\partial^2 f}{\partial x_2 \partial x_1}(\mathbf{p}).$$

The result will follow.

For fixed h_2, let $g(x_1) = f(x_1, p_2 + h_2) - f(x_1, p_2)$. The domain of g is an open subset of $\mathbb{R}$ and, since $\partial f / \partial x_1$ exists, g is differentiable. The Mean-Value Theorem implies then that

$$\begin{aligned}
F(h_1, h_2) &= g(p_1 + h_1) - g(p_1) \qquad \text{(by 3.10.5)} \\
&= h_1 g'(p_1 + \phi h_1) \qquad \text{for some } 0 < \phi < 1 \\
&= h_1 \left(\frac{\partial f}{\partial x_1}(p_1 + \phi h_1, p_2 + h_2) - \frac{\partial f}{\partial x_1}(p_1 + \phi h_1, p_2) \right).
\end{aligned}$$

A second application of the Mean-Value Theorem is possible since $(\partial/\partial x_2)(\partial f/\partial x_1)$ exists. Therefore

$$F(h_1, h_2) = h_1 h_2 \frac{\partial^2 f}{\partial x_2 \partial x_1}(p_1 + \phi h_1, p_2 + \theta h_2), \qquad \text{for some } 0 < \theta < 1.$$

By the continuity of $\partial^2 f / \partial x_2 \partial x_1$ at $\mathbf{p}$,

$$F(h_1, h_2) = h_1 h_2 \left(\frac{\partial^2 f}{\partial x_2 \partial x_1}(\mathbf{p}) + \eta(\mathbf{h}) \right), \qquad \text{where } \lim_{\mathbf{h} \to 0} \eta(\mathbf{h}) = 0.$$

Expression 3.10.6 follows.

3.10.7 Corollary. *Let $f : D \subseteq \mathbb{R}^m \to \mathbb{R}$ be a function such that for particular i and j,*

[i] $\dfrac{\partial f}{\partial x_i}, \dfrac{\partial f}{\partial x_j}, \dfrac{\partial^2 f}{\partial x_j \partial x_i}$ *exist throughout D, and*

[ii] $\dfrac{\partial^2 f}{\partial x_j \partial x_i}$ *is continuous at $\mathbf{p} \in D$.*

Then $\partial^2 f / \partial x_i \partial x_j$ exists at $\mathbf{p}$ and

$$\frac{\partial^2 f}{\partial x_i \partial x_j}(\mathbf{p}) = \frac{\partial^2 f}{\partial x_j \partial x_i}(\mathbf{p}).$$

Proof.   Fix x_r at p_r except when $r = i$ or j. Then f can be regarded as acting on $\mathbb{R}^2$ and Theorem 3.10.4 applies.

3.10.8 *Example*.   Consider again the function $f(x_1, x_2, x_3) = x_1^3 x_2 - x_1 x_3^2$ of Example 3.10.3. Clearly all partial derivatives are continuous. It is no surprise, in view of Theorem 3.10.4, that

$$\frac{\partial^2 f}{\partial x_2 \partial x_1}(\mathbf{x}) = \frac{\partial^2 f}{\partial x_1 \partial x_2}(\mathbf{x}) \quad \text{and} \quad \frac{\partial^3 f}{\partial x_2 \partial x_1^2}(\mathbf{x}) = \frac{\partial^3 f}{\partial x_1 \partial x_2 \partial x_1}(\mathbf{x}) = \frac{\partial^3 f}{\partial x_1^2 \partial x_2}(\mathbf{x}).$$

We now consider how directional derivatives can be expressed in terms of partial derivatives. For first-order derivatives the relation is given by Corollary 3.7.6, which states that if $f : D \subseteq \mathbb{R}^m \to \mathbb{R}$ is differentiable, then the derivative in the direction of the unit vector $\mathbf{u} = (u_1, \ldots, u_m)$ is given by

3.10.9 $$\frac{\partial f}{\partial \mathbf{u}} = u_1 \frac{\partial f}{\partial x_1} + \cdots + u_m \frac{\partial f}{\partial x_m} = \sum_i u_i \frac{\partial f}{\partial x_i}$$

We can think of the process of forming the function $\partial f / \partial \mathbf{u} : D \subseteq \mathbb{R}^m \to \mathbb{R}$ from the differentiable function $f : D \subseteq \mathbb{R}^m \to \mathbb{R}$ as a transformation of f by the operator $\partial / \partial \mathbf{u}$. In these terms 3.10.9 gives an identity between operators

3.10.10 $$\frac{\partial}{\partial \mathbf{u}} = u_1 \frac{\partial}{\partial x_1} + \cdots + u_m \frac{\partial}{\partial x_m},$$

provided we restrict the action of the operators to differentiable functions.

Suppose now that the function f has continuous first-order partial derivatives throughout D. By Theorem 3.3.29, f is differentiable, and so we have the expression 3.10.9 for $\partial f / \partial \mathbf{u}$. Moreover, by 3.10.9, $\partial f / \partial \mathbf{u}$ is continuous since the partial derivatives are continuous.

Suppose in addition that the second-order partial derivatives of f are all continuous throughout D. By Theorem 3.3.29 the first-order partial derivatives are differentiable and hence, by 3.10.9, so is $\partial f / \partial \mathbf{u}$. Therefore, applying the operator 3.10.10,

3.10.11 $$\frac{\partial^2 f}{\partial \mathbf{u}^2} = \left(u_1 \frac{\partial}{\partial x_1} + \cdots + u_m \frac{\partial}{\partial x_m} \right) \frac{\partial f}{\partial \mathbf{u}}$$

$$= \left(u_1 \frac{\partial}{\partial x_1} + \cdots + u_m \frac{\partial}{\partial x_m} \right) \left(u_1 \frac{\partial f}{\partial x_1} + \cdots + u_m \frac{\partial f}{\partial x_m} \right)$$

$$= \sum_{j, i} u_j u_i \frac{\partial^2 f}{\partial x_j \partial x_i}.$$

It follows that $\partial^2 f/\partial^2 \mathbf{u}^2$ is continuous since the second-order derivatives are.

Similarly, if in addition the third-order partial derivatives are all continuous throughout D then, by Theorem 3.3.29, the second-order partial derivatives are differentiable and hence, by 3.10.11, so is $\partial^2 f/\partial \mathbf{u}^2$. Therefore by 3.10.10,

$$
\begin{aligned}
\frac{\partial^3 f}{\partial \mathbf{u}^3} &= \left(u_1 \frac{\partial}{\partial x_1} + \cdots + u_m \frac{\partial}{\partial x_m} \right) \frac{\partial^2 f}{\partial \mathbf{u}^2} \\
&= \left(u_1 \frac{\partial}{\partial x_1} + \cdots + u_m \frac{\partial}{\partial x_m} \right) \sum_{j,i} u_j u_i \frac{\partial^2 f}{\partial x_j \partial x_i} \\
&= \sum_{k,j,i} u_k u_j u_i \frac{\partial^3 f}{x_k x_j x_i}.
\end{aligned}
$$

It follows that $\partial^3 f/\partial \mathbf{u}^3$ is continuous since the third-order derivatives are.

The above process leads to the general result stated in the following theorem.

3.10.12 Definition. *A function $f : D \subseteq \mathbb{R}^m \to \mathbb{R}$ all of whose partial derivatives up to order n are continuous throughout D is said to be n* times continuously differentiable *or a C^n function.*

3.10.13 Theorem. *Let $f : D \subseteq \mathbb{R}^m \to \mathbb{R}$ be a C^n function, and let $\mathbf{u}$ be a unit vector in $\mathbb{R}^m$. Then the functions $f, \partial f/\partial \mathbf{u}, \ldots, \partial^{n-1} f/\partial \mathbf{u}^{n-1}$ are differentiable, $\partial^n f/\partial \mathbf{u}^n$ is continuous and, for $r = 1, \ldots, n$,*

3.10.14
$$
\begin{aligned}
\frac{\partial^r f}{\partial \mathbf{u}^r} &= \left(u_1 \frac{\partial}{\partial x_1} + \cdots + u_m \frac{\partial}{\partial x_m} \right)^r f \\
&= \sum_{i_r, \ldots, i_1} u_{i_r} \cdots u_{i_1} \frac{\partial^r f}{\partial x_{i_r} \cdots \partial x_{i_1}}.
\end{aligned}
$$

Proof. Continue the above process.

3.10.15 Remark. The notation

$$
\left(u_1 \frac{\partial}{\partial x_1} + \cdots + u_m \frac{\partial}{\partial x_m} \right)^r
$$

in 3.10.14 indicates an r-fold application of the operator 3.10.10. In view of the conditions on f, this is meaningful.

3.10.16 *Example.* In the case of a C^2 function $f : D \subseteq \mathbb{R}^2 \to \mathbb{R}$,

$$\frac{\partial^2 f}{\partial \mathbf{u}^2} = \left(u_1 \frac{\partial}{\partial x_1} + u_2 \frac{\partial}{\partial x_2} \right)^2 f$$

$$= u_1^2 \frac{\partial^2 f}{\partial x_1^2} + u_1 u_2 \frac{\partial^2 f}{\partial x_1 \partial x_2} + u_2 u_1 \frac{\partial^2 f}{\partial x_2 \partial x_1} + u_2^2 \frac{\partial^2 f}{\partial x_2^2}$$

$$= u_1^2 \frac{\partial^2 f}{\partial x_1^2} + 2 u_1 u_2 \frac{\partial^2 f}{\partial x_1 \partial x_2} + u_2^2 \frac{\partial^2 f}{\partial x_2^2}.$$

The last step is obtained by an application of Theorem 3.10.4 to the C^2 function f.

Similarly, if f is a C^3 function, then, by Theorem 3.10.4,

$$\frac{\partial^3 f}{\partial \mathbf{u}^3} = \left(u_1 \frac{\partial}{\partial x_1} + u_2 \frac{\partial}{\partial x_2} \right)^3 f$$

$$= u_1^3 \frac{\partial^3 f}{\partial x_1^3} + 3 u_1^2 u_2 \frac{\partial^3 f}{\partial x_1^2 \partial x_2} + 3 u_1 u_2^2 \frac{\partial^3 f}{\partial x_1 \partial x_2^2} + u_2^3 \frac{\partial^3 f}{\partial x_2^3}.$$

The similarity between these expressions and the expansions of $(a + b)^2$ and $(a + b)^3$ continues through higher orders and makes the expression for $\partial^n f / \partial \mathbf{u}^n$ easy to remember.

Exercises 3.10

1. Compute the value at (x, y) taken by the second-order partial derivatives $\partial^2 f / \partial x^2$, $\partial^2 f / \partial x \partial y$, $\partial^2 f / \partial y \partial x$ and $\partial^2 f / \partial y^2$ for each of the following C^2 functions $f : \mathbb{R}^2 \to \mathbb{R}$. Check in each case that the mixed second-order partial derivatives are equal.

$$\text{(a) } f(x, y) = x^3 y; \qquad \text{(b) } f(x, y) = \sin(x^3 y).$$

Show also in each case that $\partial^3 f / \partial x \partial y \partial x = \partial^3 f / \partial x^2 \partial y$.

2. For the functions f of Exercise 1 compute, using 3.10.11, $(\partial^2 f / \partial \mathbf{u}^2)(x, y)$, where $\mathbf{u}$ is a unit vector (u_1, u_2). Verify your earlier calculations of $\partial^2 f / \partial x^2$ and $\partial^2 f / \partial y^2$ by choosing $\mathbf{u} = (1, 0)$ and $\mathbf{u} = (0, 1)$.

3. The following partial differential equations are of some importance in classical physics.

(a) *Laplace's Equation:* $\dfrac{\partial^2 f}{\partial x^2} + \dfrac{\partial^2 f}{\partial y^2} + \dfrac{\partial^2 f}{\partial z^2} = 0$;

(b) *One-dimensional Wave Equation:* $\dfrac{\partial^2 f}{\partial t^2} - c^2 \dfrac{\partial^2 f}{\partial x^2} = 0$, c constant;

(c) *One-dimensional Heat Equation:* $\dfrac{\partial f}{\partial t} - k \dfrac{\partial^2 f}{\partial x^2} = 0$, k constant.

Verify the following respective solutions of equations (a), (b) and (c):

(a) $f(x, y, z) = 1/r$, where $r = \sqrt{(x^2 + y^2 + z^2)} \neq 0$;

(b) $f(x, t) = \sin(x - ct)$, or more generally,

$f(x, t) = \phi(x - ct)$, where $\phi : \mathbb{R} \to \mathbb{R}$ is any real-valued twice-differentiable function on $\mathbb{R}$;

(c) $f(x, t) = e^{-kt}\sin x$.

4. Consider the function $f : \mathbb{R}^2 \to \mathbb{R}$ defined by

$$f(x, y) = xy\frac{x^2 - y^2}{x^2 + y^2}, \qquad (x, y) \neq (0, 0), \qquad f(0, 0) = 0.$$

Prove that

$$\frac{\partial^2 f}{\partial x \partial y}(x, y) = \frac{\partial^2 f}{\partial y \partial x}(x, y) \qquad \text{when } (x, y) \neq (0, 0).$$

Show also that

$$\frac{\partial^2 f}{\partial x \partial y}(0, 0) = 1 \qquad \text{and} \qquad \frac{\partial^2 f}{\partial y \partial x}(0, 0) = -1.$$

Deduce by Theorem 3.10.4 that neither of the mixed second-order partial derivatives is continuous at $(0, 0)$, and prove this by direct calculation.

Hint: the first part is a routine calculation. For the second part show that

$$\frac{\partial f}{\partial y}(x, 0) = \lim_{k \to 0} (f(x, k) - f(x, 0))/k = x$$

and hence that $(\partial^2 f/\partial x \partial y)(0, 0) = 1$.

3.11   Taylor's Theorem

The method of Section 3.9 can be used to extend Taylor's Theorem of elementary calculus (the General Mean-Value Theorem) to any suitable function $f : D \subseteq \mathbb{R}^m \to \mathbb{R}$ near a point $\mathbf{p} \in D$. We again consider the composition of f with a function g whose image contains the straight line segment in D joining two distinct points $\mathbf{p}$ and $\mathbf{p} + \mathbf{h}$.

Let E be an open interval in $\mathbb{R}$ containing $[0, 1]$ such that $\mathbf{p} + t\mathbf{h} \in D$ for all $t \in E$. Let $g : E \subseteq \mathbb{R} \to \mathbb{R}^m$ be given by $g(t) = \mathbf{p} + t\mathbf{h}$, $t \in E$. Define a function $F : E \subseteq \mathbb{R} \to \mathbb{R}$ by

3.11.1 $F(t) = (f \circ g)(t) = f(\mathbf{p} + t\mathbf{h}), \qquad t \in E.$

We know from Taylor's theorem that provided F is n times differentiable on E there exists $0 < \theta < 1$ such that

3.11.2 $\quad f(\mathbf{p} + \mathbf{h}) - f(\mathbf{p}) = F(1) - F(0)$
$$= F'(0) + \frac{F''(0)}{2!} + \cdots + \frac{F^{(n-1)}(0)}{(n-1)!} + \frac{F^{(n)}(\theta)}{n!}.$$

Our problem is to interpret these higher derivatives of F in terms of the given function f.

Suppose that f is differentiable on D. Then Theorem 3.8.7 (the Chain Rule) implies that F is differentiable and

3.11.3 $\qquad F'(t) = (\text{grad } f)(\mathbf{p} + t\mathbf{h}) \cdot \mathbf{h}, \qquad t \in E.$

Hence by Theorem 3.8.6(ii)

3.11.4 $\qquad\qquad F'(t) = \|\mathbf{h}\| \frac{\partial f}{\partial \mathbf{u}}(\mathbf{p} + t\mathbf{h})$

where $\mathbf{u} = \|\mathbf{h}\|^{-1}\mathbf{h}$ is the unit vector in the direction of $\mathbf{h}$.

Suppose now in addition that the function $\partial f / \partial \mathbf{u} : D \subseteq \mathbb{R}^m \to \mathbb{R}$ is itself differentiable in D. The same argument can be used to deduce from 3.11.4 that F' is differentiable and that

3.11.5 $\qquad F''(t) = \|\mathbf{h}\|^2 \frac{\partial^2 f}{\partial \mathbf{u}^2}(\mathbf{p} + t\mathbf{h}), \qquad t \in E.$

The process begun in 3.11.4 and 3.11.5 can now be continued. A simple inductive argument shows that if $f, \partial f / \partial \mathbf{u}, \ldots, \partial^{n-1} f / \partial \mathbf{u}^{n-1}$ are differentiable, then F is n times differentiable and

3.11.6 $\qquad F^{(r)}(t) = \|\mathbf{h}\|^r \frac{\partial^r f}{\partial \mathbf{u}^r}(\mathbf{p} + t\mathbf{h}), \qquad t \in E, r = 1, \ldots, n.$

We can now state and prove the following extension of Taylor's Theorem.

3.11.7 *Theorem* (Taylor). *Let* $\mathbf{p}$ *and* $\mathbf{p} + \mathbf{h}$ *be two distinct points in an open subset D of $\mathbb{R}^m$ such that the straight line segment joining* $\mathbf{p}$ *and* $\mathbf{p} + \mathbf{h}$ *lies in D. Let* $\mathbf{u}$ *be the unit vector in direction* $\mathbf{h}$. *Consider a function* $f : D \subseteq \mathbb{R}^m \to \mathbb{R}$ *such that, for some $n \in \mathbb{N}$, the functions*

$$f, \frac{\partial f}{\partial \mathbf{u}}, \ldots, \frac{\partial^{n-1} f}{\partial \mathbf{u}^{n-1}}$$

are all differentiable in D.

Then there exists $0 < \theta < 1$ such that

3.11.8
$$f(\mathbf{p} + \mathbf{h}) = f(\mathbf{p}) + \|\mathbf{h}\| \frac{\partial f}{\partial \mathbf{u}}(\mathbf{p}) + \frac{\|\mathbf{h}\|^2}{2!} \frac{\partial^2 f}{\partial \mathbf{u}^2}(\mathbf{p}) + \cdots$$
$$+ \frac{\|\mathbf{h}\|^{n-1}}{(n-1)!} \frac{\partial^{n-1} f}{\partial \mathbf{u}^{n-1}}(\mathbf{p}) + \frac{\|\mathbf{h}\|^n}{n!} \frac{\partial^n f}{\partial \mathbf{u}^n}(\mathbf{p} + \theta\mathbf{h}).$$

Proof. Since D is open in $\mathbb{R}^m$ we can choose E, an open interval in $\mathbb{R}$, such that $[0, 1] \subseteq E$ and $\mathbf{p} + t\mathbf{h} \in D$ for all $t \in E$. Define $F : E \subseteq \mathbb{R} \to \mathbb{R}$ by the rule $F(t) = f(\mathbf{p} + t\mathbf{h})$, $t \in E$. Then by the above inductive argument and by 3.11.6 the function F is n times differentiable in E. That is, F satisfies the hypothesis of Taylor's theorem of elementary calculus. Substituting for $F^{(r)}$ from 3.11.6 in 3.11.2, we obtain the required result.

We note in passing that the hypothesis in Theorem 3.11.7 could be weakened. By just considering f on the segment joining $\mathbf{p}$ and $\mathbf{p} + \mathbf{h}$ and by considering $\partial f / \partial \mathbf{u}$ and higher-order directional derivatives from first principles we could prove 3.11.8 by just assuming that f is well behaved on the segment. We have chosen the above approach since it is simpler, fits in with the more applicable form of the theorem (Theorem 3.11.10) and relies on the link between differentiability and linear approximations.

For a fixed vector $\mathbf{p} \in D$, 3.11.8 expresses $f(\mathbf{p} + \mathbf{h})$ as a polynomial in $\|\mathbf{h}\|$ plus a remainder term

3.11.9
$$R_n = \frac{\|\mathbf{h}\|^n}{n!} \frac{\partial^n f}{\partial \mathbf{u}^n}(\mathbf{p} + \theta\mathbf{h}).$$

In many important examples the remainder term can be made as small as we like by taking large enough values of n. To evaluate the polynomial and the remainder we need to be able to calculate the higher-order directional derivatives. Theorem 3.10.13 gives an expression for directional derivatives in terms of partial derivatives. In order to use that expression we strengthen the hypothesis of Taylor's Theorem and assume n times continuous differentiability of f. It is this version of Taylor's Theorem which is useful for applications.

3.11.10 Theorem. *Let $\mathbf{p}$ and $\mathbf{p} + \mathbf{h}$ be two distinct points in an open subset D of $\mathbb{R}^m$ such that the straight line segment joining $\mathbf{p}$ and $\mathbf{p} + \mathbf{h}$ lies in D. Let $f : D \subseteq \mathbb{R}^m \to \mathbb{R}$ be a function which, for some $n \in \mathbb{N}$, is n*

times continuously differentiable on D. Then there exists $0 < \theta < 1$ *such that*

3.11.11 $\quad f(\mathbf{p} + \mathbf{h}) = f(\mathbf{p}) + \sum_{r=1}^{n-1} \frac{1}{r!} \left[\left(h_1 \frac{\partial}{\partial x_1} + \cdots + h_m \frac{\partial}{\partial x_m} \right)^r f \right](\mathbf{p}) + R_n$

where

3.11.12 $\quad R_n = \frac{1}{n!} \left[\left(h_1 \frac{\partial}{\partial x_1} + \cdots + h_m \frac{\partial}{\partial x_m} \right)^n f \right](\mathbf{p} + \theta \mathbf{h}).$

Proof.   Let **u** be the unit vector in direction **h**. By Theorem 3.10.13 the hypothesis of this theorem implies the hypothesis of Theorem 3.11.7. The conclusion of the theorem follows from the conclusion of Theorem 3.11.7 by a second reference to Theorem 3.10.13, bearing in mind that $\|\mathbf{h}\|^r u_i^r = h_i^r$, for $i = 1, \ldots, m$.

We call 3.11.11 the *n*th *order Taylor expansion of* f *at* **p**. The first-order expansion is that obtained from the Mean-Value Theorem (Theorem 3.9.1): $f(\mathbf{p} + \mathbf{h}) = f(\mathbf{p}) + R_1$.

3.11.13 *Example.*   Consider the function $f : \mathbb{R}^2 \to \mathbb{R}$ defined by $f(x_1, x_2) = x_1^2 x_2$ near $\mathbf{p} = (10, 20)$. The partial derivatives are as follows.

$$(\partial f / \partial x_1)(\mathbf{p}) = 2p_1 p_2 = 400; \qquad (\partial f / \partial x_2)(\mathbf{p}) = p_1^2 = 100;$$
$$(\partial^2 f / \partial x_1^2)(\mathbf{p}) = 40; \qquad (\partial^2 f / \partial x_2^2)(\mathbf{p}) = 0$$

and $\qquad (\partial^2 f / \partial x_1 \partial x_2)(\mathbf{p}) = (\partial^2 f / \partial x_2 \partial x_1)(\mathbf{p}) = 2p_1 = 20.$

Taking $h = (0.1, 0.2)$ we obtain
$f(10.1, 20.2) = f(10, 20) + R_1 = 2000 + R_1,$
$f(10.1, 20.2) = 2000 + 400h_1 + 100h_2 + R_2 = 2060 + R_2,$
$f(10.1, 20.2) = 2000 + 400h_1 + 100h_2 + \frac{1}{2}(40h_1^2 + 2 \times 20 \times h_1 h_2 + 0h_2^2) + R_3$
$\qquad\qquad = 2060.6 + R_3.$
In fact, $f(10.1, 20.2) = 2060.602$, so that $R_1 = 60.602$, $R_2 = 0.602$ and $R_3 = 0.002$.

This example shows how the Taylor expansion can be used to estimate the value of a function in the vicinity of a point **p**. The importance of Theorem 3.11.10 lies in the expression for the remainder 3.11.12.

We now consider the remainder term R_n in more detail. Remember that the function $f : D \subseteq \mathbb{R}^m \to \mathbb{R}$ is *n* times continuously differentiable.

From 3.11.12, using the fact that $\|\mathbf{h}\|^n u_i^n = h_i^n$ for $i = 1, \ldots, m$, where $\mathbf{u}$ is the unit vector in the direction of $\mathbf{h}$,

$$R_n = \frac{\|\mathbf{h}\|^n}{n!}\left[\left(u_1\frac{\partial}{\partial x_1} + \cdots + u_m\frac{\partial}{\partial x_m}\right)^n f\right](\mathbf{p} + \theta\mathbf{h}).$$

In particular the nth-order partial derivatives of f are continuous and so we can express the remainder in the form

3.11.14 $R_n = \dfrac{\|\mathbf{h}\|^n}{n!}\left[\left(u_1\dfrac{\partial}{\partial x_1} + \cdots + u_m\dfrac{\partial}{\partial x_m}\right)^n f\right](\mathbf{p}) + \|\mathbf{h}\|^n\eta(\mathbf{h})$

where $\lim_{\mathbf{h} \to 0} \eta(\mathbf{h}) = 0$. The function η depends of course on our choice of n.

From 3.11.11 we obtain

3.11.15

$$f(\mathbf{p} + \mathbf{h}) = f(\mathbf{p}) + \sum_{r=1}^{n}\frac{1}{r!}\left[\left(h_1\frac{\partial}{\partial x_1} + \cdots + h_m\frac{\partial}{\partial x_m}\right)^r f\right](\mathbf{p}) + \|\mathbf{h}\|^n\eta(\mathbf{h})$$

where $\lim_{\mathbf{h} \to 0} \eta(\mathbf{h}) = 0$.

3.11.16 Definition.   *Let* $f : D \subseteq \mathbb{R}^m \to \mathbb{R}$ *be a* C^n *function and let* $\mathbf{p} \in D$. *Define a function* $T_n : \mathbb{R}^m \to \mathbb{R}$ *by*

$$T_n(\mathbf{h}) = \sum_{r=1}^{n}\frac{1}{r!}\left[\left(h_1\frac{\partial}{\partial x_1} + \cdots + h_m\frac{\partial}{\partial x_m}\right)^r f\right](\mathbf{p}), \qquad \mathbf{h} \in \mathbb{R}^m.$$

Then $f(\mathbf{p}) + T_n(\mathbf{h})$ *is called the* **Taylor polynomial** *of degree n of f at* $\mathbf{p}$. *It is a polynomial in* $h_1, \ldots, h_m$.

Referring to Example 3.11.13 the first two Taylor polynomials of the function $f : \mathbb{R}^2 \to \mathbb{R}$ defined by $f(x_1, x_2) = x_1^2 x_2$ are

$$T_1(\mathbf{h}) = 2000 + 400h_1 + 100h_2,$$
$$T_2(\mathbf{h}) = 2000 + 400h_1 + 100h_2 + 20h_1^2 + 20h_1 h_2.$$

We can now express 3.11.15 in terms of the difference function and the polynomial T_n as follows:

3.11.17 $\delta_{f,\,\mathbf{p}}(\mathbf{h}) = f(\mathbf{p} + \mathbf{h}) - f(\mathbf{p}) = T_n(\mathbf{h}) + \|\mathbf{h}\|^n\eta(\mathbf{h})$

where $\lim_{\mathbf{h} \to 0} \eta(\mathbf{h}) = 0$.

When $n = 1$, 3.11.17 simply becomes 3.3.7. The polynomial function T_1 is the unique linear function (the differential) $L_{f,\,\mathbf{p}}$ that closely approximates $\delta_{f,\,\mathbf{p}}$ near the origin. In this sense T_n is a generalization of the differential. To explore this further we use the following extension of 'close approximation' (compare Definition 3.3.5).

3.11.18 Definition.   Let $g : N \subseteq \mathbb{R}^m \to \mathbb{R}$ and $g^* : M \subseteq \mathbb{R}^m \to \mathbb{R}$ be two functions, both of whose open domains contain $\mathbf{0}$. We say that g and g^* closely approximate each other to the nth degree near $\mathbf{0}$ if there is a function $\eta : N \cap M \subseteq \mathbb{R}^m \to \mathbb{R}$ such that

$$g^*(\mathbf{h}) - g(\mathbf{h}) = \|\mathbf{h}\|^n \eta(\mathbf{h}), \qquad\qquad \mathbf{h} \in N \cap M$$

and $\lim_{\mathbf{h} \to \mathbf{0}} \eta(\mathbf{h}) = 0$.

The above condition can be written

3.11.19 $g(\mathbf{0}) = g^*(\mathbf{0})$ and $\displaystyle\lim_{\mathbf{h} \to \mathbf{0}} \frac{|g^*(\mathbf{h}) - g(\mathbf{h})|}{\|\mathbf{h}\|^n} = 0.$

Notice that if g^* closely approximates g to the nth degree near $\mathbf{0}$, then it also closely approximates g to the rth degree for all $r < n$. So a higher-degree approximation is 'better' than a lower-degree approximation.

We now have the following generalization of Theorem 3.3.13.

3.11.20 Theorem.   Let $f : D \subseteq \mathbb{R}^m \to \mathbb{R}$ be n times continuously differentiable and let $\mathbf{p} \in D$. Then the polynomial T_n of Definition 3.11.16 is the only nth degree polynomial that closely approximates $\delta_{f,\mathbf{p}}$ to the nth degree near $\mathbf{0}$.

Proof.   The relation 3.11.15 establishes that T_n is a sufficiently close approximation. The fact that it is the only one follows from the fact that if two nth-degree polynomials are close approximates to the nth-degree near $\mathbf{0}$ then they are equal. See Exercise 3.11.4.

3.11.21 Example.   Find the best approximation to the function $f(x, y) = e^x \cos y$ by a second degree polynomial near $\mathbf{0}$.

The best second-degree approximation is the Taylor polynomial $f(\mathbf{0}) + T_2(\mathbf{x})$. We could calculate the partial derivatives of f up to second order and solve our problem by substituting in the expression

$$f(\mathbf{0}) + x\frac{\partial f}{\partial x}(\mathbf{0}) + y\frac{\partial f}{\partial y}(\mathbf{0}) + \frac{1}{2!}\left(x^2\frac{\partial^2 f}{\partial x^2}(\mathbf{0}) + 2xy\frac{\partial^2 f}{\partial x \partial y}(\mathbf{0}) + y^2\frac{\partial^2 f}{\partial y^2}(\mathbf{0}) \right).$$

Alternatively we could use the known series for e^x and $\cos y$ as follows.

$$e^x = 1 + x + \tfrac{1}{2}x^2 + x^2\alpha(x), \qquad \text{where } \lim_{x \to 0} \alpha(x) = 0,$$

$$\cos y = 1 - \tfrac{1}{2}y^2 + y^2\beta(y), \qquad \text{where } \lim_{y \to 0} \beta(y) = 0.$$

Multiplying these two series together, we have

3.11.22 $$e^x \cos y = 1 + x + \tfrac{1}{2}x^2 - \tfrac{1}{2}y^2 + R$$

where R involves terms of the form $y^2\beta(y)$ and $x^2\alpha(x)$ and others of higher than second order. Hence

$$\lim_{(x, y) \to (0, 0)} R/\|(x, y)\|^2 = 0$$

and, from 3.11.22, $1 + x + \tfrac{1}{2}x^2 - \tfrac{1}{2}y^2$ closely approximates $e^x \cos y$ to the second degree. By Theorem 3.11.20, $1 + x + \tfrac{1}{2}x^2 - \tfrac{1}{2}y^2$ is the required approximation.

3.11.23 Example. Obtain a second-degree polynomial suitable for estimating the values of $f(x, y) = \sqrt{(1 + x + 4y)}$ near $(-1, 1)$.

We require the Taylor polynomial of degree 2 of f at $\mathbf{p} = (-1, 1)$. Define (h, k) by the rule $(x, y) = (-1, 1) + (h, k)$.
Method 1. Calculate all partial derivatives of f up to the second order at $(-1, 1)$. Then from 3.11.15

$$f(x, y) = f((-1, 1) + (h, k))$$
$$= f(-1, 1) + T_2(h, k) + \|(h, k)\|^2 \eta(h, k).$$

The required polynomial is $f(-1, 1) + T_2(h, k)$.
Method 2. As in the previous example we may reduce the problem to an application of Taylor's theorem for functions defined on $\mathbb{R}$. We have

$$f(x, y) = f(-1 + h, 1 + k) = \sqrt{[1 + (-1 + h) + 4(1 + k)]} = \sqrt{(4 + t)}$$

where $t = h + 4k$. Now by the Binomial Theorem (Taylor's Theorem!)

$$\sqrt{(4 + t)} = 2\left(1 + \frac{t}{4}\right)^{1/2} = 2\left(1 + \frac{t}{8} - \frac{t^2}{128} + t^2\eta(t)\right)$$

where $\lim_{t \to 0} \eta(t) = 0$. Hence

$$f(-1 + h, 1 + k) = 2\left(1 + \tfrac{1}{8}(h + 4k) - \tfrac{1}{128}(h + 4k)^2\right) + R$$

where $\lim_{(h, k) \to (0, 0)} R/(h^2 + k^2) = 0$.
The required Taylor polynomial at $(-1, 1)$ is therefore

3.11.24 $$2 + \tfrac{1}{4}h + k - \tfrac{1}{64}h^2 - \tfrac{1}{8}hk - \tfrac{1}{4}k^2.$$

By taking $h = -0.1$ and $k = -0.1$ we obtain an estimate of 1.8711 for $f(-1.1, 0.9)$ from this polynomial. The actual value of $f(-1.1, 0.9)$ (correct to four decimal places) is 1.8708.

Warning.   The student may be tempted in this example to expand $\sqrt{(1 + x + 4y)}$ by the Binomial Theorem in the form $\sqrt{(1 + u)}$, where $u = x + 4y$. This is inappropriate for this problem because we are interested in values of (x, y) near $(-1, 1)$ which correspond to values of u near 3. The Taylor polynomial of $\sqrt{(1 + u)}$ of degree 2 is uninformative near $u = 3$, for here the remainder term is large.

3.11.25 Example.   We now take a further look at our estimation of the acceleration in Example 3.5.3. The relationship is $a = f(v, s) = v^2/2s$ and the observed values are $(v, s) = (30, 300)$ with possible errors given by $|\Delta v| \leqslant 1$ and $|\Delta s| \leqslant 3$. Letting the true acceleration be $a_t \, \mathrm{m\,s^{-2}}$ we have

[i] the possible range is $1.388 \leqslant a_t \leqslant 1.618$ (see 3.5.9);

[ii] the approximate range given by 3.5.7 (effectively the Taylor polynomial of degree 1 at (30, 300)) is $1.385 \leqslant a_t \leqslant 1.615$,

[iii] the approximate range given by the Mean-value Theorem (3.9.9) is $-1.379 \leqslant a_t \leqslant 1.621$.

We now look at the estimate provided by the Taylor polynomial of degree 2 at (30, 300). Using the indirect technique developed in the previous examples,

$$a_t = \tfrac{1}{2}(v + \Delta v)^2 (s + \Delta s)^{-1} = \frac{1}{2s}(v + \Delta v)^2 \left(1 + \frac{\Delta s}{s}\right)^{-1}$$

$$= \frac{1}{2s}(v^2 + 2v\Delta v + \Delta v^2)\left(1 - \frac{\Delta s}{s} + \left(\frac{\Delta s}{s}\right)^2 + \cdots\right)$$

$$= \frac{v^2}{2s} + \frac{v}{s}\Delta v - \frac{v^2}{2s^2}\Delta s + \frac{\Delta v^2}{2s} - \frac{v}{s^2}\Delta v\,\Delta s + \frac{v^2}{2s^3}\Delta s^2 + R.$$

where R involves terms of higher than second order in Δv and Δs.

The Taylor polynomial of degree 2 near $(v, s) = (30, 300)$ is therefore

$$\frac{v^2}{2s} + \frac{v}{s}\Delta v - \frac{v^2}{2s^2}\Delta s + \frac{1}{2s}\Delta v^2 - \frac{v}{s^2}\Delta v\,\Delta s + \frac{v^2}{2s^3}\Delta s^2.$$

This clearly takes its maximum value when $\Delta v = 1$ and $\Delta s = -3$ and its minimum value when $\Delta v = -1$ and $\Delta s = 3$. To three places of decimals the resulting approximation is $1.388 \leqslant a_t \leqslant 1.618$. We have therefore come very close to the achievable range.

It must be stressed that before applying Taylor's Theorem to a function f one should check that the continuity conditions on the partial derivatives of f are satisfied. We took this for granted in the above examples, since well-known functions were involved. Failure of the conditions often manifests itself in the breakdown of calculations. For example, suppose that we are looking for a Taylor polynomial approximating $f(x, y) = \sqrt{(1 + x + 4y)}$ near $(x, y) = (3, -1)$. We begin with the substitution $x = 3 + h$, $y = -1 + k$ and obtain $f(3 + h, 1 + k) = \sqrt{(h + 4k)}$. What next? Putting $t = h + 4k$ fails, for there is no polynomial in t that closely approximates $\sqrt{t}$ near the origin. The trouble can be diagnosed by calculating $(\partial f/\partial x)(x, y)$. It does not exist at $(3, -1)$.

Exercises 3.11

1. For each of the following functions f, obtain the second degree Taylor polynomial $f(2, 1) + T_2(h, k)$ suitable for estimating the values of $f(2 + h, 1 + k)$ for numerically small values of h, k. For the case $h = 0.2$, $k = -0.1$ compare your estimate with the accurate value.

    (a) $f(x, y) = x^2y^2$;   (b) $f(x, y) = \ln(1 + x + 2y)$
    (c) $f(x, y) = e^x \sin y$.

Answers: (a) $4 + 4h + 8k + h^2 + 8hk + 4k^2$;
  (b) $\ln 5 + \frac{1}{50}(10h + 20k - h^2 - 4hk - 4k^2)$.

    Compare your estimates with those obtained from the Taylor polynomial of degree 3 of f at $(2, 1)$.

2. Find the best approximation to the functions of Exercise 1 by a second degree polynomial near $(0, 0)$.

Answers: (a) 0;   (b) $x + 2y - \frac{1}{2}(x^2 + 4xy + 4y^2)$;   (c) $y + xy$.

3. Do the following limits exist?

    (a) $\displaystyle\lim_{(x, y) \to (0, 0)} \frac{\sin(xy)}{x}$ (b) $\displaystyle\lim_{(x, y) \to (0, 0)} \frac{\cos(xy) - 1}{x^2y}$

Hint: consider Taylor expansions with remainder near $(0, 0)$.

Answer: Both limits exist and are 0.

4. Let $f(x_1, \ldots, x_m)$ and $f^*(x_1, \ldots, x_m)$ be two polynomials of degree n. Prove that if f^* closely approximates f to the nth degree near 0 (Definition 3.11.18), then $f = f^*$.

Hint: in the expression $f^*(\mathbf{h}) - f(\mathbf{h}) = \|\mathbf{h}\|^n \eta(\mathbf{h})$, prove that $\eta(\mathbf{h}) = 0$, $\mathbf{h} \in \mathbb{R}^m$.)

5. Prove that close approximation to the nth degree near $\mathbf{0}$ (Definition 3.11.18) defines an equivalence relation on the set of functions $f : N \subseteq \mathbb{R}^m \to \mathbb{R}$ whose domains are open sets containing $\mathbf{0}$.

3.12   Extreme points

Remember that we are considering functions $f : D \subseteq \mathbb{R}^m \to \mathbb{R}$ whose domain D is an open subset of $\mathbb{R}^m$.

3.12.1 Definition.   [i] *The function f is said to have a* local maximum *at $\mathbf{p} \in D$ if there is a neighbourhood N of $\mathbf{p}$ such that*

$$f(\mathbf{x}) \leqslant f(\mathbf{p}) \quad \text{for all } \mathbf{x} \in N.$$

[ii] *The function f is said to have a* local minimum *at $\mathbf{p}$ if there is a neighbourhood N of $\mathbf{p}$ such that*

$$f(\mathbf{x}) \geqslant f(\mathbf{p}) \quad \text{for all } \mathbf{x} \in N.$$

3.12.2 Definition.   *We say that $\mathbf{p} \in D$ is an* extreme point *of the function f if f has either a local maximum or a local minimum at $\mathbf{p}$. If $\mathbf{p}$ is an extreme point of f, then $f(\mathbf{p})$ is called an* extreme value *of f.*

In the case $m = 2$, provided f is continuous, the graph of f will look like a landscape. If $(\mathbf{p}, f(\mathbf{p}))$ is a mountain peak, then f has a local maximum at $\mathbf{p}$. If $(\mathbf{p}, f(\mathbf{p}))$ is at the bottom of a valley, then f has a local minimum at $\mathbf{p}$. Notice however that if $(\mathbf{p}, f(\mathbf{p}))$ is in the middle of a plain, then f has both a local maximum and a local minimum at the point $\mathbf{p}$.

3.12.3 Theorem.   *Let $f : D \subseteq \mathbb{R}^m \to \mathbb{R}$ have an extreme point at $\mathbf{p} \in D$ and let $\mathbf{u}$ be a unit vector in $\mathbb{R}^m$ such that $(\partial f / \partial \mathbf{u})(\mathbf{p})$ exists. Then $(\partial f / \partial \mathbf{u})(\mathbf{p}) = 0$.*

Proof.   If f has a local maximum at $\mathbf{p}$, then $f(\mathbf{p} + t\mathbf{u}) - f(\mathbf{p}) \leqslant 0$ for all numerically small t. Hence

$$\lim_{t \to 0+} \frac{f(\mathbf{p} + t\mathbf{u}) - f(\mathbf{p})}{t} \leqslant 0 \quad \text{and} \quad \lim_{t \to 0-} \frac{f(\mathbf{p} + t\mathbf{u}) - f(\mathbf{p})}{t} \geqslant 0.$$

It follows that $(\partial f / \partial \mathbf{u})(\mathbf{p}) \leqslant 0$ and $(\partial f / \partial \mathbf{u})(\mathbf{p}) \geqslant 0$. Hence $(\partial f / \partial \mathbf{u})(\mathbf{p}) = 0$. A similar argument applies if f has a local minimum at $\mathbf{p}$.

3.12.4 Corollary.   *Let $\mathbf{p} \in D$ be an extreme point of a differentiable function $f : D \subseteq \mathbb{R}^m \to \mathbb{R}$. Then*

[i] $\dfrac{\partial f}{\partial x_j}(\mathbf{p}) = 0$ *for $j = 1, \ldots, m$;*

[ii] $L_{f, \mathbf{p}} : \mathbb{R}^m \to \mathbb{R}$ *is the zero transformation.*

Proof. (i) $\dfrac{\partial f}{\partial x_j}(\mathbf{p}) = \dfrac{\partial f}{\partial \mathbf{e}_j}(\mathbf{p}) = 0$ for $i = 1, \ldots, m$, by Theorem 3.12.3.

(ii) Immediate from (i) and Theorem 3.3.20.

For the case $m = 2$ this Corollary tells us that if $\mathbf{p}$ is an extreme point, then the tangent plane to the graph of f at $(\mathbf{p}, f(\mathbf{p}))$ is horizontal. Our experience of landscapes, however, suggests that there may be points on the graph which do not correspond to extreme points but where nevertheless the tangent planes are horizontal. (See Fig. 3.20). We are led to the following definition.

3.12.5 Definition. *Let* $f : D \subseteq \mathbb{R}^m \to \mathbb{R}$ *be a differentiable function. Any point* $\mathbf{p} \in D$ *for which* $L_{f,\mathbf{p}}$ *is the zero transformation is called a* critical point *of* f. *Equivalently* (*see* 3.3.20(*ii*)) *the critical points are those points* $\mathbf{p} \in D$ *for which* $(\partial f / \partial x_j)(\mathbf{p}) = 0$ *for all* $j = 1, \ldots, m$.

In the case $m = 2$, $\mathbf{p}$ is a critical point if and only if the graph of f has a horizontal tangent plane at $(\mathbf{p}, f(\mathbf{p}))$. Corollary 3.12.4 tells us that extreme points of differentiable functions are also critical points.

The following examples explore this relationship further.

3.12.6 Example. Define $f : \mathbb{R} \to \mathbb{R}$ by the rule $f(x) = |x|$. Then f has a local minimum at 0. But 0 is not a critical point of f since f is not differentiable at 0.

3.12.7 Example. Define $f : \mathbb{R} \to \mathbb{R}$ by the rule $f(x) = x^3$. The function is strictly increasing and so has no extreme points. But $f'(0) = 0$, and so 0 is a critical point of f.

3.12.8 Example. Define $f : \mathbb{R}^2 \to \mathbb{R}$ by the rule $f(x, y) = x^2 - y^2$. The graph of f is sketched in Fig. 3.20. Now f is differentiable and $(\partial f / \partial x)(x, y) = 2x$ and $(\partial f / \partial y)(x, y) = -2y$. It follows that f has only one critical point, the origin $(0, 0)$ where it takes the value 0. The tangent plane at $(0, 0)$ is the plane $z = 0$ in $\mathbb{R}^3$. Now $f(h, 0) = h^2 > 0$ for $h \neq 0$ and $f(0, k) = -k^2 < 0$ for $k \neq 0$. Hence in any neighbourhood of $(0, 0)$ the function takes values greater than $f(0, 0)$ and values less than $f(0, 0)$. So $(0, 0)$ is not an extreme point of f.

The graph of f is the surface $z = x^2 - y^2$ in $\mathbb{R}^3$. The horizontal sections (the intersection of the graph with the planes $z = c$) are hyperbolas. The vertical sections (the intersection of the graph with the planes $y = c$ and $x = c$) are parabolas. For this reason the surface is called a hyperbolic paraboloid. The saddle-like shape of this surface gives us the following definition.

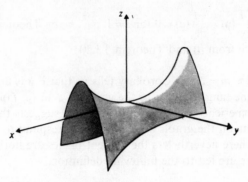

Fig. 3.20 Graph $z = x^2 - y^2$

3.12.9 Definition.   *A point* $\mathbf{p} \in D$ *is called a* saddle point *of a diffe-rentiable function* $f : D \subseteq \mathbb{R}^m \to \mathbb{R}$ *if* $\mathbf{p}$ *is a critical point but not an extreme point of* f.

Do not be misled by the name—some very peculiar saddles turn up as the graphs of functions near a saddle point.

3.12.10 Example.   An amusing example is that of a 'monkey saddle' which allows for the monkey's anatomy (Fig. 3.21(i)). This is illustrated by the graph of the function $f : \mathbb{R}^2 \to \mathbb{R}$ defined by

$$f(x, y) = x^3 - 3xy^2 = x(x - \sqrt{3}y)(x + \sqrt{3}y).$$

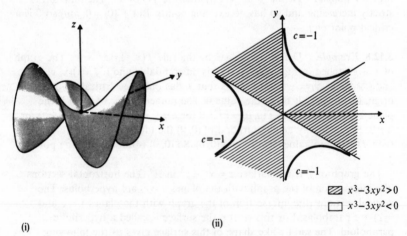

(i)   (ii)

Fig. 3.21 (i) Graph $z = x^3 - 3xy^2$ (ii) $x^3 - 3xy^2 = c$

The function is differentiable. The partial derivatives are $(\partial f/\partial x)(x, y) = 3x^2 - 3y^2$ and $(\partial f/\partial y)(x, y) = -6xy$. The only critical point of the function therefore is the origin $(0, 0)$. This point can be identified as a 'monkey', saddle point by marking the regions of $\mathbb{R}^2$ in the neighbourhood of $(0, 0)$ in which f takes positive and negative values. See Fig. 3.21(ii). For example, f takes positive values when $x > 0$ and $x > \sqrt{3}y$ and $x > -\sqrt{3}y$. More detailed information is obtainable by drawing the level sets of f in $\mathbb{R}^2$.

Experience of elementary calculus suggests that it is important to develop a technique for finding and identifying extreme points of differentiable functions. Corollary 3.12.4 tells us that we can narrow the search by first picking out the critical points—those points where the partial derivatives all vanish. We shall use our work on Taylor expansions to establish conditions which will, in many cases, enable us to pick out extreme points from among the critical points and to identify which ones correspond to local maxima and which to local minima.

Let $\mathbf{p}$ be a critical point of a twice continuously differentiable function $f : D \subseteq \mathbb{R}^m \to \mathbb{R}$. Since D is an open set in $\mathbb{R}^m$, there exists $\varepsilon > 0$ such that $N(\mathbf{p}, \varepsilon) \subseteq D$. The straight line segment joining $\mathbf{p}$ and $\mathbf{p} + \mathbf{h}$ lies in D for any vector $\mathbf{h} \in \mathbb{R}^m$ such that $\|\mathbf{h}\| < \varepsilon$. By 3.11.15, for such a vector $\mathbf{h}$, since the first order partial derivatives of f all vanish at $\mathbf{p}$,

3.12.11

$$f(\mathbf{p} + \mathbf{h}) - f(\mathbf{p}) = \frac{1}{2}\left[\left(h_1\frac{\partial}{\partial x_1} + \cdots + h_m\frac{\partial}{\partial x_m}\right)^2 f\right](\mathbf{p}) + \|\mathbf{h}\|^2\eta(\mathbf{h}),$$

where $\lim_{\mathbf{h} \to \mathbf{0}}\eta(\mathbf{h}) = 0$. The second-order partial derivatives are continuous and therefore, by the symmetry established in Corollary 3.10.7,

3.12.12 $\quad\left[\left(h_1\dfrac{\partial}{\partial x_1} + \cdots + h_m\dfrac{\partial}{\partial x_m}\right)^2 f\right](\mathbf{p})$

$$= \left(h_1^2\frac{\partial^2 f}{\partial x_1^2}(\mathbf{p}) + \cdots + 2h_1 h_2\frac{\partial^2 f}{\partial x_1 \partial x_2}(\mathbf{p}) + \cdots\right).$$

The right-hand side of 3.12.12 is a quadratic polynomial $q(\mathbf{h})$ where q is a quadratic form on $\mathbb{R}^m$ (Section 1.4). In this case $q(\mathbf{h}) = [\mathbf{h}]^t A [\mathbf{h}]$, where A is the symmetric $m \times m$ matrix $[a_{ij}]$ with

3.12.13 $\qquad a_{ij} = \dfrac{\partial^2 f}{\partial x_i \partial x_j}(\mathbf{p}), \qquad i, j = 1, \ldots, m,$

and [**h**] is the column whose entries are the coordinates $h_1, \ldots, h_m$ of **h**. With this notation 3.12.11 becomes

3.12.14 $f(\mathbf{p} + \mathbf{h}) - f(\mathbf{p}) = \frac{1}{2}[\mathbf{h}]^t A[\mathbf{h}] + \|\mathbf{h}\|^2 \eta(\mathbf{h}),$ $\|\mathbf{h}\| < \varepsilon.$

We also know from Theorem 1.4.6 that all eigenvalues of A are real and that if $\lambda_{\min}$ is the minimum eigenvalue and $\lambda_{\max}$ is the maximum eigenvalue, then

3.12.15 $\|\mathbf{h}\|^2 \lambda_{\min} \leqslant [\mathbf{h}]^t A[\mathbf{h}] \leqslant \|\mathbf{h}\|^2 \lambda_{\max},$ $\mathbf{h} \in \mathbb{R}^m.$

It follows from 3.12.14 that

3.12.16 $\|\mathbf{h}\|^2 (\frac{1}{2} \lambda_{\min} + \eta(\mathbf{h})) \leqslant f(\mathbf{p} + \mathbf{h}) - f(\mathbf{p})$
$\leqslant \|\mathbf{h}\|^2 (\frac{1}{2} \lambda_{\max} + \eta(\mathbf{h})),$ $\|\mathbf{h}\| < \varepsilon.$

We can now state and prove our main result. Recall that the symmetric matrix A is said to be positive definite if $[\mathbf{h}]^t A[\mathbf{h}] > 0$ for all $\mathbf{h} \neq \mathbf{0}$, it is said to be negative definite if $[\mathbf{h}]^t A[\mathbf{h}] < 0$ for all $\mathbf{h} \neq \mathbf{0}$ and it is indefinite if $[\mathbf{h}]^t A[\mathbf{h}]$ takes both positive and negative values. Moreover, the matrix A is positive definite (negative definite) if and only if all the eigenvalues of A are positive (negative), and it is indefinite if and only if there are both positive and negative eigenvalues (see Theorem 1.4.12). We can therefore decide the nature of A if we have an estimation of the largest and smallest eigenvalues of A.

3.12.17 Theorem.   *Suppose that the C^2 function $f : D \subseteq \mathbb{R}^m \to \mathbb{R}$ has a critical point at $\mathbf{p} \in D$. Define a (symmetric) $m \times m$ matrix $A = [a_{ij}]$ by the rule given in 3.12.13.*
  [i]   *If A is positive definite, then f has a local minimum at $\mathbf{p}$.*
  [ii]   *If A is negative definitive, then f has a local maximum at $\mathbf{p}$.*
  [iii]   *If A is indefinite, then $\mathbf{p}$ is a saddle point of f.*

Proof.   Choose $\varepsilon > 0$ such that for $\|\mathbf{h}\| < \varepsilon$ the straight line segment joining $\mathbf{p}$ and $\mathbf{p} + \mathbf{h}$ is contained in D. We therefore have identity 3.12.11 and its consequences. The results will follow from 3.12.16 where $\lambda_{\min}$ and $\lambda_{\max}$ are respectively the minimum and maximum eigenvalues of A.

  [i] If A is positive definite then, by Theorem 1.4.12, $\lambda_{\min} > 0$. Now since $\lim_{\mathbf{h} \to \mathbf{0}} \eta(\mathbf{h}) = 0$ we can find $\delta > 0$ such that

3.12.18 $|\eta(\mathbf{h})| < \frac{1}{2} \lambda_{\min}$ whenever $\|\mathbf{h}\| < \delta.$

Therefore if $\|\mathbf{h}\| < \min\{\varepsilon, \delta\}$, then from 3.12.16 and 3.12.18

$$0 < \|\mathbf{h}\|^2 (\tfrac{1}{2}\lambda_{\min} + \eta(\mathbf{h})) \leqslant f(\mathbf{p} + \mathbf{h}) - f(\mathbf{p}).$$

It follows that f has a local minimum at $\mathbf{p}$.

[ii] If A is negative definite then again by Theorem 1.4.12, $\lambda_{\max} < 0$. We can find $\delta > 0$ such that

$$|\eta(\mathbf{h})| < -\tfrac{1}{2}\lambda_{\max} \qquad \text{whenever } \|\mathbf{h}\| < \delta.$$

Therefore if $\|\mathbf{h}\| < \min\{\varepsilon, \delta\}$, then from 3.12.16 and 3.12.18

$$0 > \|\mathbf{h}\|^2 (\tfrac{1}{2}\lambda_{\max} + \eta(\mathbf{h})) \geqslant f(\mathbf{p} + \mathbf{h}) - f(\mathbf{p}).$$

It follows that f has a local maximum at $\mathbf{p}$.

[iii] If A is indefinite, then (Theorem 1.4.12) it has both positive and negative eigenvalues. In particular $\lambda_{\max} > 0$ and $\lambda_{\min} < 0$. Let $[\mathbf{v}_{\max}]$ and $[\mathbf{v}_{\min}]$ be any unit eigenvectors of A corresponding to $\lambda_{\max}$ and $\lambda_{\min}$ respectively. Then $A[\mathbf{v}_{\max}] = \lambda_{\max}[\mathbf{v}_{\max}]$, and from 3.12.14

$$f(\mathbf{p} + s\mathbf{v}_{\max}) - f(\mathbf{p}) = s^2(\tfrac{1}{2}\lambda_{\max} + \eta(s\mathbf{v}_{\max})).$$

Similarly,

$$f(\mathbf{p} + s\mathbf{v}_{\min}) - f(\mathbf{p}) = s^2(\tfrac{1}{2}\lambda_{\min} + \eta(s\mathbf{v}_{\min})).$$

Therefore, by the argument used in [i] and [ii], for all small enough s

$$f(\mathbf{p} + s\mathbf{v}_{\max}) - f(\mathbf{p}) > 0 \quad \text{and} \quad f(\mathbf{p} + s\mathbf{v}_{\min}) - f(\mathbf{p}) < 0.$$

Hence $\mathbf{p}$ is a saddle point of f.

Remark. Theorem 3.12.17 generalizes the familiar test for local maxima and local minima of functions $f : \mathbb{R} \to \mathbb{R}$ in terms of the sign of $f''(x)$ (Exercise 3.12.5).

3.12.19 Example. The origin $(0, 0)$ is a critical point of the function $f : \mathbb{R}^2 \to \mathbb{R}$ defined by $f(x, y) = x^2 + y^2$. The associated matrix of second-order partial derivatives at $(0, 0)$ is

$$\begin{bmatrix} 2 & 0 \\ 0 & 2 \end{bmatrix}.$$

As expected, this is positive definite, indicating a minimum.

3.12.20 Example. The origin $(0, 0)$ is a critical point of the function $f(x, y) = x^2 - y^2$ considered in Example 3.12.8. The associated matrix of second-order partial derivatives at (0, 0) is

$$\begin{bmatrix} 2 & 0 \\ 0 & -2 \end{bmatrix}$$

This is an indefinite matrix, indicating that (0, 0) is a saddle point (see Fig. 3.20).

Theorem 3.12.17 does not give a complete answer to our problem. The theorem tells us nothing if the matrix of second derivatives at the critical point is either positive semi-definite or negative semi-definite. In such cases a direct approach from first principles is usually appropriate.

3.12.21 *Example.*   The origin is a critical point of all three functions on $\mathbb{R}^2$,

$$f(x, y) = x^4 + y^4, \qquad g(x, y) = x^4 - y^4 \quad \text{and} \quad k(x, y) = -x^4 - y^4.$$

The matrix of second derivatives at (0, 0) is the zero matrix in all three cases and yet f, g and k have respectively a maximum, a saddle and a minimum at (0, 0).

In order to apply Theorem 3.12.17 we need to be able to recognize the nature of the symmetric matrix A. The most direct method is to take the polynomial $[\mathbf{x}]^t A[\mathbf{x}]$ and by completing squares express it as the sum and difference of squares. Alternatively one can examine the eigenvalues of A.

A useful test for positive definiteness is given by the following set of determinant conditions.

3.12.22 *Theorem.*   *Let A be an $m \times m$ symmetric matrix and let A_r be the $r \times r$ submatrix which is obtained by taking just the first r rows and the first r columns of A. The matrix A is positive definite if and only if the determinants $\det A_r$ are positive for $r = 1, \ldots, m$.*

Proof.   A proof can be found G. Hadley, *Linear Algebra.* The case $m = 2$ is covered in Exercise 3.12.6.

3.12.23 *Example.*   The 3×3 symmetric matrix A is positive definite if and only if

$$a_{11} > 0, \qquad \begin{vmatrix} a_{11} & a_{12} \\ a_{21} & a_{22} \end{vmatrix} > 0 \quad \text{and} \quad \begin{vmatrix} a_{11} & a_{12} & a_{13} \\ a_{21} & a_{22} & a_{23} \\ a_{31} & a_{32} & a_{33} \end{vmatrix} > 0.$$

3.12.24 Definition. *Let* $f : D \subseteq \mathbb{R}^m \to \mathbb{R}$ *be a* C^2 *function with a critical point at* $\mathbf{p} \in D$. *Let* $A = (a_{ij})$ *be the* $m \times m$ *symmetric matrix defined by* 3.12.13. *The determinant of* A *is called the* discriminant *of* f *at* $\mathbf{p}$ *and is denoted by* $\Delta_f(\mathbf{p})$.

In these terms Theorem 3.12.17 gives us information about the nature of a critical point $\mathbf{p}$ of f when $\Delta_f(\mathbf{p}) \neq 0$.

3.12.25 Example. In the case $m = 2$,

$$\Delta_f(\mathbf{p}) = \frac{\partial^2 f}{\partial x_1^2}(\mathbf{p}) \frac{\partial^2 f}{\partial x_2^2}(\mathbf{p}) - \left(\frac{\partial^2 f}{\partial x_1 \partial x_2}(\mathbf{p}) \right)^2.$$

For $m = 2$ we can state Theorem 3.12.17 in the following form.

3.12.26 Theorem. *Let* $\mathbf{p}$ *be a critical point of a* C^2 *function* $f : D \subseteq \mathbb{R}^2 \to \mathbb{R}$. *Then*

[i] *f has a local minimum at* $\mathbf{p}$ *if* $\dfrac{\partial^2 f}{\partial x_1^2}(\mathbf{p}) > 0$ *and* $\Delta_f(\mathbf{p}) > 0$,

[ii] *f has a local maximum at* $\mathbf{p}$ *if* $\dfrac{\partial f}{\partial x_1^2}(\mathbf{p}) < 0$ *and* $\Delta_f(\mathbf{p}) > 0$,

[iii] *$\mathbf{p}$ is a saddle point of* f *if* $\Delta_f(\mathbf{p}) < 0$.

Proof. Let A be the 2×2 matrix defined in relation to f at $\mathbf{p}$ by 3.12.13.

[*i*] By Theorem 3.12.22, if $(\partial^2 f / \partial x_1^2)(\mathbf{p}) > 0$ and $\Delta_f(\mathbf{p}) > 0$ then A is positive definite. It follows from Theorem 3.12.17(i) that f has a local minimum at $\mathbf{p}$.

[*ii*] Define a function $g : D \subseteq \mathbb{R}^2 \to \mathbb{R}$ by $g(\mathbf{x}) = -f(\mathbf{x})$. Then $\mathbf{p}$ is also a critical point of g. If f satisfies the hypothesis of [ii], then g satisfies the hypothesis of [i]. Hence g has a local minimum at $\mathbf{p}$ and therefore f has a local maximum at $\mathbf{p}$.

[*iii*] The product of the eigenvalues of A (with multiplicity allowed for) is $\det A = \Delta_f(\mathbf{p})$. Hence if $\Delta_f(\mathbf{p}) < 0$, then A has a positive and a negative eigenvalue. Therefore A is indefinite and Theorem 3.12.17(iii) implies that $\mathbf{p}$ is a saddle point of f.

3.12.27 Example. Consider the function $f : \mathbb{R}^2 \to \mathbb{R}$ defined by

$$f(x_1, x_2) = x_1^3 + x_2^3 - 6x_1 x_2.$$

The first-order partial derivatives are

$$\frac{\partial f}{\partial x_1}(\mathbf{x}) = 3x_1^2 - 6x_2 \qquad \text{and} \qquad \frac{\partial f}{\partial x_2}(\mathbf{x}) = 3x_2^2 - 6x_1.$$

The critical points are located at (x_1, x_2) where $3x_1^2 = 6x_2$ and $3x_2^2 = 6x_1$, giving $(0, 0)$ and $(2, 2)$ as the only solutions. The second-order partial derivatives are

$$\frac{\partial^2 f}{\partial x_1^2}(\mathbf{x}) = 6x_1, \qquad \frac{\partial^2 f}{\partial x_2^2}\lambda(\mathbf{x}) = 6x_2, \qquad \frac{\partial^2 f}{\partial x_1 \partial x_2}(\mathbf{x}) = -6.$$

Hence $\Delta_f(\mathbf{x}) = 36x_1 x_2 - 36$. By Theorem 3.12.26, $(0, 0)$ is a saddle point since $\Delta_f(0, 0) = -36 < 0$. Similarly f has a local minimum at $(2, 2)$ since $\Delta_f(2, 2) = 108 > 0$ and $(\partial^2 f/\partial x_1^2)(2, 2) = 12 > 0$. Since f is differentiable, all its extreme points are critical points and so there are no other local maxima or minima.

Notice that although the value at the local minimum $(2, 2)$ is -8 the function takes values less than -8 since $f(x_1, 0) = x_1^3$.

3.12.28 *Example*.   Consider again the function $f(x, y) = x^3 - 3xy^2$ of Example 3.12.10. We found then that the only critical point is $(0, 0)$. However $\Delta_f(x, y) = -36x^2 - 36y^2$ and in particular $\Delta_f(0, 0) = 0$. In this case Theorem 3.12.26 is uninformative and the direct approach taken earlier is appropriate.

3.12.29 *Example*.   Consider the function $f : \mathbb{R}^3 \to \mathbb{R}$ defined by $f(x, y, z) = xy + 2xz + 2yz$. We find that

$$\frac{\partial f}{\partial x}(x, y, z) = y + 2z, \qquad \frac{\partial f}{\partial y}(x, y, z) = x + 2z, \qquad \frac{\partial f}{\partial z}(x, y, z) = 2x + 2y$$

and deduce that $(0, 0, 0)$ is the only critical point. Calculation of the 3×3 matrix A of second-order partial derivatives at $(0, 0, 0)$ (see 3.12.13) gives

$$A = \begin{bmatrix} 0 & 1 & 2 \\ 1 & 0 & 2 \\ 2 & 2 & 0 \end{bmatrix}.$$

It will be found that A has two negative and one positive eigenvalues. Hence A is indefinite and by Theorem 3.12.17(iii) $(0, 0, 0)$ is a saddle point of f.

Our example 3.12.29 illustrates a general method. Sometimes one can find a shorter route towards the solution. Here, for example, we need only note that $f(h, k, 0) = hk$ and $f(-h, k, 0) = -hk$ to conclude that f takes both positive and negative values in every neighbourhood of the origin.

Exercises 3.12

1.   Determine the nature of the critical points of the following functions $f : \mathbb{R}^3 \to \mathbb{R}$ by the method of Theorem 3.12.17.

(a) $f(x, y, z) = x^2 + y^2 + z^2 + xy$;

(b) $f(x, y, z) = xy + xz$.

Find an alternative short method, if possible.

Answers: (a) local minimum at $(0, 0, 0)$. Complete the square.

(b) saddle points at $(0, k, -k)$, any $k \in \mathbb{R}$.

2. Determine the nature of the critical points of the following functions
   $f : \mathbb{R}^2 \to \mathbb{R}$ by the method of Theorem 3.12.26.
   (a) $f(x, y) = x^5 y + xy^5 + xy$;
   (b) $f(x, y) = x^3 + y^2 - 3x$;
   (c) $f(x, y) = \sin x + \sin y + \cos(x + y)$;
   (d) $f(x, y) = x^2 + y^2 + (1/x^2 y^2)$, $xy \neq 0$.

Answers: (a) saddle point at $(0, 0)$;   (b) local minimum -2 at $(1, 0)$,
   saddle point at $(-1, 0)$;   (c) local minimum -3 at $(3\pi/2, 3\pi/2)$, local
   maximum $\frac{3}{2}$ at $(\pi/6, \pi/6)$ and $(5\pi/6, 5\pi/6)$, saddle points at $(\frac{1}{2}\pi, \frac{1}{2}\pi)$,
   $(\frac{1}{2}\pi, -\frac{1}{2}\pi)$, $(3\pi/2, -3\pi/2)$, further critical points by periodicity;
   (d) local minimum 3 at $(\pm 1, \pm 1)$.

3. Determine the nature of the critical points of the following functions
   $f : \mathbb{R}^2 \to \mathbb{R}$. Where the method of Theorem 3.12.26 fails, proceed either
   by inspection or by developing the Taylor expansion of f at the critical
   point to at least third order.
   (a) $f(x, y) = (x + y)^2 + x^4$;
   (b) $f(x, y) = (x + y)e^{-xy}$;
   (c) $f(x, y) = (y - x^2)(y - 2x^2)$.

Answers: (a) local minimum at $(0, 0)$ by inspection;
   (b) $(\pm 1/\sqrt{2}, \pm 1/\sqrt{2})$;   (c) saddle point at $(0, 0)$. Sketch a sign table
   for f near $(0, 0)$ in $\mathbb{R}^2$, indicating that $f(x, y) < 0$ when $x^2 < y < 2x^2$ and
   $f(x, y) > 0$ when $y < x^2$ or $y > 2x^2$.

4. Find the shortest distance from the origin of $\mathbb{R}^3$ to the surface $xyz = 1$.

Hint: find the minimum of $x^2 + y^2 + z^2$, where $z = 1/xy$. Use the calculations
of Exercise 2 (d).

5. Apply Theorem 3.12.17 to a C^2 function $f : D \subseteq \mathbb{R} \to \mathbb{R}$ and prove in
   particular that if $p \in D$ is a critical point of f (so $f'(p) = 0$) and if $f''(p)$ is
   positive, then f has a local minimum at p.

Note: part (iii) of Theorem 3.12.17 does not apply since a 1×1 matrix has
   only one eigenvalue.

6. Prove that a 2×2 real symmetric matrix $A = [a_{ij}]$ is positive definite if
   and only if

$$a_{11} > 0 \quad \text{and} \quad \begin{vmatrix} a_{11} & a_{12} \\ a_{21} & a_{22} \end{vmatrix} > 0.$$

Hint: let λ_1, λ_2 be the eigenvalues of A. By Exercise 1.4.2, $\lambda_1\lambda_2 = \det A$. Now the condition $a_{11} > 0$ means that if $\mathbf{h} = (1, 0)$, then $[\mathbf{h}]^t A[\mathbf{h}] = a_{11} > 0$, and hence that A is not negative definite. Deduce that the two conditions $a_{11} > 0$ and $\det A > 0$ hold if and only if $\lambda_1 > 0$ and $\lambda_2 > 0$.

7.   Decide which of the local minima and local maxima of f calculated in Exercises 1, 2, and 3 are absolute minima or maxima of f. (For example, the local minimum of f at $(1, 0)$ in Exercise 2(b) is not the absolute minimum of f.)

Vector-valued functions of $\mathbb{R}^m$

4.1 Introduction

The vector-valued functions which we consider in this chapter are those of the form $f : D \subseteq \mathbb{R}^m \to \mathbb{R}^n$, $m \in \mathbb{N}$, $n \in \mathbb{N}$, where D is an open subset of $\mathbb{R}^m$. We have considered the particular cases $m = 1$ and $n = 1$ in Chapters 2 and 3 respectively. Many of the new ideas in this chapter are simply generalizations of those in the earlier ones. We rely heavily upon the results of Chapter 3 by relating properties of vector-valued functions to properties of their real-valued coordinate functions which we now define.

4.1.1 Definition. The coordinate functions *of* $f : D \subseteq \mathbb{R}^m \to \mathbb{R}^n$ *are functions* $f_i : D \subseteq \mathbb{R}^m \to \mathbb{R}$, $i = 1, \ldots, n$ *defined by the rule*

$$f(\mathbf{x}) = (f_1(\mathbf{x}), \ldots, f_n(\mathbf{x})), \qquad \mathbf{x} \in D.$$

The function f *is then conveniently expressed as* $f = (f_1, \ldots, f_n)$.

As in the case of real-valued functions we are sometimes helped in picturing a function by considering its level sets. The *level set corresponding to* $\mathbf{c} \in \mathbb{R}^n$ of the function $f : D \subseteq \mathbb{R}^m \to \mathbb{R}^n$ is (compare 3.1.3)

4.1.2 $$\{\mathbf{x} \in D \,|\, f(\mathbf{x}) = \mathbf{c}\}.$$

Although we can only sketch the graph of f if $m + n \leq 3$ (and all possible such cases have already been considered) we can draw level sets of f for arbitrary n provided $m \leq 3$.

4.1.3 Example. Define $f : \mathbb{R}^3 \to \mathbb{R}^2$ by $f(\mathbf{x}) = (x_1^2 + x_2^2 + x_3^2, x_1 + x_2 + x_3)$. The coordinate functions of f are f_i, $i = 1, 2$, defined by $f_1(\mathbf{x}) = x_1^2 + x_2^2 + x_3^2$ and $f_2(\mathbf{x}) = x_1 + x_2 + x_3$. The level set corresponding to $(-1, 1)$ is empty. The level set corresponding to $(1, 1)$ is

$$\{(x_1, x_2, x_3) \in \mathbb{R}^3 \,|\, x_1^2 + x_2^2 + x_3^2 = 1 \quad \text{and} \quad x_1 + x_2 + x_3 = 1\}.$$

This set is a circle – the intersection of a sphere and a plane in $\mathbb{R}^3$.

4.1.4 *Example.* We have seen how to associate a vector-valued function grad $f : D \subseteq \mathbb{R}^m \to \mathbb{R}^m$ with a differentiable real-valued function f on D. The coordinate functions of grad f are the partial derivative functions $\partial f / \partial x_i : D \subseteq \mathbb{R}^m \to \mathbb{R}$, $i = 1, \ldots, m$.

The level set of grad f corresponding to $\mathbf{0}$ is the set of critical points of f (see Definition 3.12.5).

Vector-valued functions $F : D \subseteq \mathbb{R}^m \to \mathbb{R}^m$ whose domain and image are subsets of the same Euclidean space, as in the case of grad f considered in the above example, are particularly significant from a physical point of view. They are called *vector fields*. When m is 2 or 3 we can picture $F(\mathbf{p})$ (provided that it is not $\mathbf{0}$) as an arrow emanating from $\mathbf{p}$.

A curve in D whose tangent at each of its points $\mathbf{p}$ is in the direction of the field vector $F(\mathbf{p})$ at that point is called a *field line of F*. In the case of fluid motion, field lines are also called *stream lines* (see the following examples).

4.1.5 *Example.* Figure 4.1 illustrates three examples of vector fields and field lines arising in physical situations.

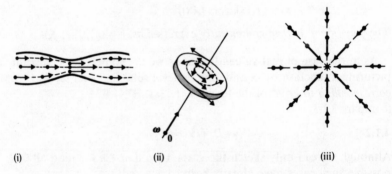

(i)   (ii)   (iii)

Fig. 4.1 (i) Fluid flow; (ii) rotating body; (iii) gravitational field

(a) *A velocity field describing the steady flow of a fluid in a pipe.* At each point in the fluid an arrow indicates the magnitude and direction of the velocity at that point. The illustration indicates that the fluid flows fastest at the narrowest part of the pipe. The study of hydrodynamics concerns the search for vector functions (fields) $F : D \subseteq \mathbb{R}^3 \to \mathbb{R}^3$ which most accurately describe fluid flow subject to given physical conditions, in the sense that $\mathbf{v} = F(\mathbf{p})$ corresponds to the velocity at the point with position vector $\mathbf{p}$. A speck of dust in the fluid will be carried along a field line.

(b) *The velocity field of a rigid body rotating about a fixed axis with angular speed* ω *radians/sec.* This field $F : D \subseteq \mathbb{R}^3 \to \mathbb{R}^3$ is given by

$$\mathbf{v} = F(\mathbf{r}) = \omega \wedge \mathbf{r}$$

where ω represents the angular velocity vector and $\mathbf{v}$ corresponds to the velocity of the point on the body with position vector $\mathbf{r}$ relative to a right-handed Cartesian coordinate system with origin on the axis of rotation. The field lines are circles in planes orthogonal to the axis with centres on it.

(c) *The gravitational field due to a particle of mass M.* This is described by the function $F : \mathbb{R}^3 \setminus \{\mathbf{0}\} \to \mathbb{R}^3$, where

4.1.6 $$F(\mathbf{r}) = -\frac{GM}{r^3}\mathbf{r}, \qquad \mathbf{r} \neq \mathbf{0}.$$

Here $\mathbf{r} = (x, y, z)$ is measured relative to axes with origin at the particle and $r = \|\mathbf{r}\|$. The vector $F(\mathbf{r})$ indicates the magnitude and direction of the force of attraction exerted by the mass M on a particle of unit mass with position vector $\mathbf{r}$. The constant G is called the gravitational constant. Expression 4.1.6 is Newton's celebrated inverse square law. It is so called because the magnitude of the attractive force at $\mathbf{r}$ is proportional to the inverse of the square of r:

$$\|F(\mathbf{r})\| = \frac{GM}{r^3}\|\mathbf{r}\| = \frac{GM}{r^2}.$$

The field lines, or lines of force, are straight lines through the origin.

Finally we note that we can combine vector-valued functions as in Definition 1.5.4.

4.1.7 Example. Let $\mathbf{u}$ be a unit vector in $\mathbb{R}^m$ and let $g : \mathbb{R}^m \to \mathbb{R}$ be the constant function defined by $g(\mathbf{x}) = \mathbf{u}$ for all $\mathbf{x} \in \mathbb{R}^m$. For any differentiable function $f : D \subseteq \mathbb{R}^m \to \mathbb{R}$ the function $(\operatorname{grad} f) \cdot g : D \subseteq \mathbb{R}^m \to \mathbb{R}$ is defined by

$$((\operatorname{grad} f) \cdot g)(\mathbf{x}) = (\operatorname{grad} f)(\mathbf{x}) \cdot g(\mathbf{x}) = (\operatorname{grad} f)(\mathbf{x}) \cdot \mathbf{u}, \qquad \mathbf{x} \in D.$$

By Theorem 3.8.6 however, $(\operatorname{grad} f)(\mathbf{x}) \cdot \mathbf{u} = (\partial f / \partial \mathbf{u})(\mathbf{x})$. We therefore have that $(\operatorname{grad} f) \cdot g = \partial f / \partial \mathbf{u}$. This relationship is often written $\mathbf{u} \cdot \operatorname{grad} f = \partial f / \partial \mathbf{u}$ or alternatively, in operator form, $\mathbf{u} \cdot \operatorname{grad} = \partial / \partial \mathbf{u}$ (see 3.10.10).

Exercises 4.1

1. Define $f : \mathbb{R}^3 \to \mathbb{R}^2$ by $f(x, y, z) = (x^2 + y^2 - z^2, y)$. Prove that the level set of f corresponding to $(0, c)$ is a hyperbola. Interpret the result geometrically with a sketch.

2. Define $f : \mathbb{R}^2 \to \mathbb{R}$ by $f(x, y) = x^2 + y^2$. Prove that the gradient function $\operatorname{grad} f : \mathbb{R}^2 \to \mathbb{R}^2$ satisfied $(\operatorname{grad} f)(x, y) = (2x, 2y)$. Sketch the gradient (vector) field in $\mathbb{R}^2$ and show that the field lines of $\operatorname{grad} f$ are lines

through the origin. In the same sketch draw a selection of level sets of f. Relate your sketch to Theorem 3.8.17 and Definition 3.8.18(i).

3. Repeat Exercise 2 with $f : \mathbb{R}^2 \to \mathbb{R}$ defined by $f(x, y) = x^2 - y^2$. (Consider level sets of f corresponding to $c > 0$, $c = 0$ and $c < 0$.)

4. Sketch the following vector fields $F : \mathbb{R}^2 \to \mathbb{R}^2$. In each case draw some field lines.

    (a) $F(x, y) = (1, \frac{1}{2}x^2)$ (b) $F(x, y) = (-y, x)$
    (c) $F(x, y) = (\frac{1}{4}x, \frac{1}{4})$.

Answers: Field lines given by (a) $\alpha(t) = (t, \frac{1}{6}t^3 + k)$, k constant;   (b) circles centred at origin;   (c) $\alpha(t) = (t, k + \ln|t|)$, k constant, $t \neq 0$.

5. Sketch the three-dimensional vector field $F : \mathbb{R}^3 \to \mathbb{R}^3$ given by $F(\mathbf{r}) = (1/r)\mathbf{r}$, $\mathbf{r} \neq \mathbf{0}$, where $\mathbf{r} = (x, y, z)$ and $r = \|\mathbf{r}\|$.

Note: $F(\mathbf{r}) = \hat{\mathbf{r}}$ in the notation 2.9.13.

4.2 Continuity and limits

The definition and properties of continuous vector-valued functions on $\mathbb{R}^m$ follow naturally from the work done in Sections 2.3, 2.4 and 3.2. Accordingly we shall merely state a theorem when the proof is a simple extension of one given earlier. The reader is recommended to supply a proof in each case. Remember that we are considering functions whose domains are open subsets of $\mathbb{R}^m$. In particular every point of the domain D is a cluster point of D. There may of course be other cluster points of D that do not belong to D.

4.2.1 Definition.   *The function* $f : D \subseteq \mathbb{R}^m \to \mathbb{R}^n$ *is said to be continuous at* $\mathbf{p} \in D$ *if* $f(\mathbf{a}_k) \to f(\mathbf{p})$ *whenever* $\mathbf{a}_k \to \mathbf{p}$. *The function is continuous if it is continuous at every point of* D.

4.2.2 Theorem.   *The function* $f : D \subseteq \mathbb{R}^m \to \mathbb{R}^n$ *is continuous at* $\mathbf{p} \in D$ *if and only if for each* $i = 1, \ldots, n$ *the coordinate function* $f_i : D \subseteq \mathbb{R}^m \to \mathbb{R}$ *is continuous at* $\mathbf{p}$. (Compare Theorem 2.3.2).

4.2.3 Example.   The function $f : \mathbb{R}^2 \to \mathbb{R}^3$ defined by

$$f(x, y) = \begin{cases} (x + y, x + 1, y^2 + 2) & \text{when } (x, y) \neq (0, 0), \\ (1, 1, 2) & \text{when } (x, y) = (0, 0) \end{cases}$$

is discontinuous at $(0, 0)$ and continuous elsewhere. The coordinate functions f_2 and f_3 are continuous everywhere, but f_1 is not continuous at $(0, 0)$.

4.2.4 *Corollary.* *A function* $f : D \subseteq \mathbb{R}^m \to \mathbb{R}$ *is continuously differentiable if and only if* grad $f : D \subseteq \mathbb{R}^m \to \mathbb{R}^m$ *is continuous.* (See Theorem 3.3.29).

4.2.5 *Corollary.* *Any linear function* $f : \mathbb{R}^m \to \mathbb{R}^n$ *is continuous.*

Proof. The coordinate functions of a linear function are themselves linear, and, by Theorem 3.2.2, they are therefore continuous. The result follows from Theorem 4.2.2.

4.2.6 *Definition.* *Given a cluster point* $\mathbf{p}$ *of* $D \subseteq \mathbb{R}^m$, *a point* $\mathbf{q}$ *of* $\mathbb{R}^n$, *and a function* $f : D \subseteq \mathbb{R}^m \to \mathbb{R}^n$, *we write* $\lim_{\mathbf{x} \to \mathbf{p}} f(\mathbf{x}) = \mathbf{q}$ *if* $f(\mathbf{a}_k) \to \mathbf{q}$ *whenever* $\mathbf{a}_k \to \mathbf{p}$, *where the sequence* $(\mathbf{a}_k)$ *lies in* D *and* $\mathbf{a}_k \neq \mathbf{p}$ *for all* $k \in \mathbb{N}$. (Compare Definitions 2.4.5 and 3.2.18).

4.2.7 *Theorem.* *Given a function* $f : D \subseteq \mathbb{R}^m \to \mathbb{R}^n$ *and* $\mathbf{p}$ *a cluster point of* D, *then* $\lim_{\mathbf{x} \to \mathbf{p}} f(\mathbf{x}) = \mathbf{q}$ *if and only if to each* $\varepsilon > 0$ *there corresponds* $\delta > 0$ *such that* $\| f(\mathbf{x}) - \mathbf{q} \| < \varepsilon$ *whenever* $\mathbf{x} \in D$ *and* $0 < \| \mathbf{x} - \mathbf{p} \| < \delta$.

4.2.8 *Theorem.* *The function* $f : D \subseteq \mathbb{R}^m \to \mathbb{R}^n$ *is continuous at* $\mathbf{p} \in D$ *if and only if* $\lim_{\mathbf{x} \to \mathbf{p}} f(\mathbf{x}) = f(\mathbf{p})$.

4.2.9 *Theorem.* *The function* $f : D \subseteq \mathbb{R}^m \to \mathbb{R}^n$ *is continuous at* $\mathbf{p} \in D$ *if and only if to each* $\varepsilon > 0$ *there corresponds* $\delta > 0$ *such that* $f(\mathbf{x}) \in N(f(\mathbf{p}), \varepsilon)$ *whenever* $\mathbf{x} \in N(p, \delta)$.

We can use Theorem 4.2.9 to relate the above definition of continuity with a special case of that given in accounts of General Topology.

4.2.10 *Theorem.* *A function* $f : D \subseteq \mathbb{R}^m \to \mathbb{R}^n$, *where* D *is an open subset of* $\mathbb{R}^m$, *is continuous if and only if for each open subset* V *of* $\mathbb{R}^n$ *the set*

$$f^{-1}(V) = \{ \mathbf{x} \in \mathbb{R}^m | \mathbf{x} \in D, f(\mathbf{x}) \in V \}$$

is open in $\mathbb{R}^m$.

Proof. [i] Let f be continuous and let V be an open subset of $\mathbb{R}^n$. We must show that every point $\mathbf{p} \in f^{-1}(V)$ is an interior point of $f^{-1}(V)$. If $f(\mathbf{p}) \in V$ then there exists $\varepsilon > 0$ such that $N(f(\mathbf{p}), \varepsilon) \subseteq V$. By

Theorem 4.2.9 there exists $\delta > 0$ such that $f(\mathbf{x}) \in N(f(\mathbf{p}), \varepsilon)$ whenever $\mathbf{x} \in N(\mathbf{p}, \delta)$. Therefore $f(\mathbf{x}) \in V$ whenever $\mathbf{x} \in N(\mathbf{p}, \delta)$ and so $N(\mathbf{p}, \delta) \subseteq f^{-1}(V)$. It follows that $\mathbf{p}$ is an interior point of $f^{-1}(V)$ and, since this is true of every point of $f^{-1}(V)$, that $f^{-1}(V)$ is open in $\mathbb{R}^m$.

[*ii*] Assume that $f^{-1}(V)$ is open in $\mathbb{R}^m$ for each open subset V of $\mathbb{R}^n$. We must show that f is continuous at every point $\mathbf{p} \in D$. Given any $\varepsilon > 0$, $N(f(\mathbf{p}), \varepsilon)$ is open in $\mathbb{R}^n$. Hence $f^{-1}(N(f(\mathbf{p}), \varepsilon))$ is open in $\mathbb{R}^m$. But $\mathbf{p} \in f^{-1}(N(f(p), \varepsilon))$ and so there exists $\delta > 0$ such that $N(\mathbf{p}, \delta) \subseteq f^{-1}(N(f(p), \varepsilon)) \subseteq D$. Therefore $f(\mathbf{x}) \in N(f(\mathbf{p}), \varepsilon))$ whenever $\mathbf{x} \in N(\mathbf{p}, \delta)$. It follows from Theorem 4.2.9 that f is continuous at $\mathbf{p}$ and hence that f is continuous.

Exercises 4.2

1. Given that the functions $f : D \subseteq \mathbb{R}^m \to \mathbb{R}^n$, $g : D \subseteq \mathbb{R}^m \to \mathbb{R}^n$ and $\phi : D \subseteq \mathbb{R}^m \to \mathbb{R}$ are continuous at $\mathbf{p} \in D$, prove that the functions $f + g$, ϕf, $f \cdot g$ and (for the case $n = 3$) $f \wedge g$ are continuous at $\mathbf{p}$. (Consider the coordinate functions.)

2. Given $g : E \subseteq \mathbb{R}^l \to \mathbb{R}^m$ and $f : D \subseteq \mathbb{R}^m \to \mathbb{R}^n$ such that $g(E) \subseteq D$, prove that if g is continuous at $\mathbf{p} \in E$ and f is continuous at $g(\mathbf{p}) \in D$, then the composite function $f \circ g$ is continuous at $\mathbf{p}$.

4.3   Differentiability

The differentiability of a function $f : D \subseteq \mathbb{R}^m \to \mathbb{R}^n$ at $\mathbf{p} \in D$ has already been defined for the case $m = 1$ in Section 2.10 and the case $n = 1$ in Section 3.3. The definitions were concerned with the possibility of finding a close linear approximation (the differential) to the difference, $f(\mathbf{p} + \mathbf{h}) - f(\mathbf{p})$, near $\mathbf{h} = \mathbf{0}$. There is no difficulty in extending the earlier work to the general situation.

4.3.1 Definition.   *Given a function* $f : D \subseteq \mathbb{R}^m \to \mathbb{R}^n$ *and a point* $\mathbf{p} \in D$, *the* difference function $\delta_{f, \mathbf{p}} : D_{\mathbf{p}} \subseteq \mathbb{R}^m \to \mathbb{R}^n$ *is defined by*

$$\delta_{f, \mathbf{p}}(\mathbf{h}) = f(\mathbf{p} + \mathbf{h}) - f(\mathbf{p}), \qquad \mathbf{h} \in D_{\mathbf{p}}.$$

Compare with Definitions 2.10.1 and 3.3.3.

4.3.2 Definition.   *Let* $g : N \subseteq \mathbb{R}^m \to \mathbb{R}^n$ *and* $g^* : M \subseteq \mathbb{R}^m \to \mathbb{R}^n$ *be two functions whose open domains both contain* $\mathbf{0}$. *We will say that* g *and* g^* *closely approximate each other near* $\mathbf{0}$ *if there is a function*

$\eta : N \cap M \subseteq \mathbb{R}^m \to \mathbb{R}^n$ *such that*

   [i] $g(\mathbf{h}) - g^*(\mathbf{h}) = \|\mathbf{h}\| \eta(\mathbf{h}),$ $\mathbf{h} \in N \cap M,$

and

   [ii] $\lim_{\mathbf{h} \to 0} \eta(\mathbf{h}) = 0.$

4.3.3 Definition. *A function* $f : D \subseteq \mathbb{R}^m \to \mathbb{R}^n$ *is* differentiable *at* $\mathbf{p} \in D$ *if the difference function* $\delta_{f, \mathbf{p}} : D_{\mathbf{p}} \subseteq \mathbb{R}^m \to \mathbb{R}^n$ *can be closely approximated by a linear function* $L : \mathbb{R}^m \to \mathbb{R}^n$ *near* **0.** *The function is said to be* differentiable *if it is differentiable everywhere in D.*

This definition leads to those given in Sections 2.10 and 3.3 in the particular cases considered there. Notice that f is differentiable at $\mathbf{p}$ if and only if there is a linear function $L : \mathbb{R}^m \to \mathbb{R}^n$ and a function $\eta : D_{\mathbf{p}} \subseteq \mathbb{R}^m \to \mathbb{R}^n$ such that

4.3.4 $f(\mathbf{p} + \mathbf{h}) - f(\mathbf{p}) = L(\mathbf{h}) + \|\mathbf{h}\| \eta(\mathbf{h}),$ $\mathbf{h} \in D_{\mathbf{p}}$

and

4.3.5 $\lim_{\mathbf{h} \to 0} \eta(\mathbf{h}) = 0.$

The following theorem enables us to use the work done in Chapter 3 to study the differentiability of vector-valued functions.

4.3.6 Theorem. *The function* $f : D \subseteq \mathbb{R}^m \to \mathbb{R}^n$ *is differentiable at* $\mathbf{p} \in D$ *if and only if each of its coordinate functions* $f_i : D \subseteq \mathbb{R}^m \to \mathbb{R},$ $i = 1, \ldots, n,$ *is differentiable at* $\mathbf{p} \in D.$

Proof. Remember that a function $L : \mathbb{R}^m \to \mathbb{R}^n$ is linear if and only if each of its coordinate functions is linear.

Assume firstly that f is differentiable at $\mathbf{p} \in D.$ Choose a linear function L and a function η satisfying 4.3.4 and 4.3.5. By considering the ith coordinates of the vectors involved in 4.3.4 we obtain the following expression involving coordinate functions for each $i = 1, \ldots, n,$

4.3.7 $f_i(\mathbf{p} + \mathbf{h}) - f_i(\mathbf{p}) = L_i(\mathbf{h}) + \|\mathbf{h}\| \eta_i(\mathbf{h}),$ $\mathbf{h} \in D_{\mathbf{p}}.$

Furthermore, from 4.3.5,

4.3.8 $\lim_{\mathbf{h} \to 0} \eta_i(\mathbf{h}) = 0,$

since $|\eta_i(\mathbf{h})| \leqslant \|\eta(\mathbf{h})\|$ for each $i.$

These two expressions, 4.3.7 and 4.3.8, imply that f_i is differentiable at $\mathbf{p}$ for each i.

Conversely, assume that each coordinate function of f is differentiable at $\mathbf{p} \in D$. There therefore exists for each $i = 1, \ldots, n$ a linear function $L_i : \mathbb{R}^m \to \mathbb{R}$ and a function $\eta_i : D_{\mathbf{p}} \subseteq \mathbb{R}^m \to \mathbb{R}$ satisfying 4.3.7 and 4.3.8. Define a linear function $L : \mathbb{R}^m \to \mathbb{R}^n$ by

4.3.9 $L(\mathbf{h}) = (L_1(\mathbf{h}), \ldots, L_n(\mathbf{h})), \qquad \mathbf{h} \in \mathbb{R}^m,$

and a function $\eta : D_{\mathbf{p}} \subseteq \mathbb{R}^m \to \mathbb{R}^n$ by

4.3.10 $\eta(\mathbf{h}) = (\eta_1(\mathbf{h}), \ldots, \eta_n(\mathbf{h})), \qquad \mathbf{h} \in D_{\mathbf{p}}.$

Now 4.3.7 and 4.3.9 imply 4.3.4. Finally, since

$$\|\eta(\mathbf{h})\|^2 = |\eta_1(\mathbf{h})|^2 + \cdots + |\eta_n(\mathbf{h})|^2,$$

4.3.8 and 4.3.10 imply 4.3.5. Therefore f is differentiable at $\mathbf{p} \in D$.

It follows immediately from the definition of differentiability that linear functions are differentiable (they are their own close linear approximation). Theorem 4.3.6 implies that if $f : D \subseteq \mathbb{R}^m \to \mathbb{R}^n$ and $g : D \subseteq \mathbb{R}^m \to \mathbb{R}^n$ and $\phi : D \subseteq \mathbb{R}^m \to \mathbb{R}$ are differentiable at $\mathbf{p} \in D$, then so are the functions $f + g$, $f \cdot g$, ϕf and (provided $n = 3$) so is $f \wedge g$. It is enough to consider the coordinates of the given combinations and use the result of Exercise 3.3.13.

4.3.11 Corollary.   *If $f : D \subseteq \mathbb{R}^m \to \mathbb{R}^n$ is differentiable at $\mathbf{p} \in D$, then f is continuous at $\mathbf{p}$.*

Proof.   Since f is differentiable at $\mathbf{p}$ its coordinate functions are differentiable at $\mathbf{p}$. By Theorem 3.3.11 the coordinate functions are continuous at $\mathbf{p} \in D$. Hence by Theorem 4.2.2 f is continuous at $\mathbf{p}$.

4.3.12 Corollary.   *Let $f : D \subseteq \mathbb{R}^m \to \mathbb{R}^n$ be differentiable at $\mathbf{p} \in D$. Then there is only one close linear approximation to $\delta_{f, \mathbf{p}}$ near $\mathbf{0}$. It is the linear function $L : \mathbb{R}^m \to \mathbb{R}^n$ given by*

4.3.13 $L(\mathbf{h}) = (L_{f_1, \mathbf{p}}(\mathbf{h}), \ldots, L_{f_n, \mathbf{p}}(\mathbf{h})), \qquad \mathbf{h} \in \mathbb{R}^m.$

Proof.   If L is any close linear approximation to $\delta_{f, \mathbf{p}}$ near $\mathbf{0}$, then by the first part of the proof of Theorem 4.3.6 and in particular by 4.3.7 and 4.3.8, the coordinate functions of L are the differentials $L_{f_i, \mathbf{p}}, i = 1, \ldots, n$. The result follows.

4.3.14 Definition. *Let* $f : D \subseteq \mathbb{R}^m \to \mathbb{R}^n$ *be differentiable at* $\mathbf{p} \in D$. *Then the (unique) close linear approximation to* $\delta_{f, \mathbf{p}}$ *at* $\mathbf{0}$ *is denoted by* $L_{f, \mathbf{p}}$ *and is called the* differential *of* f *at* $\mathbf{p}$.

4.3.15 Theorem. *If the function* $f : D \subseteq \mathbb{R}^m \to \mathbb{R}^n$ *is differentiable at* $\mathbf{p} \in D$, *then all the partial derivatives* $(\partial f_i / \partial x_j)(\mathbf{p})$ *exist and the matrix representing the differential* $L_{f, \mathbf{p}}$ *with respect to the standard bases of* $\mathbb{R}^m$ *and* $\mathbb{R}^n$ *is the* $n \times m$ *matrix*

4.3.16
$$
J_{f, \mathbf{p}} = \left[\frac{\partial f_i}{\partial x_j}(\mathbf{p}) \right] = \begin{bmatrix} \dfrac{\partial f}{\partial x_1}(\mathbf{p}) & \cdots & \dfrac{\partial f_1}{\partial x_m}(\mathbf{p}) \\ \vdots & & \vdots \\ \dfrac{\partial f_n}{\partial x_1}(\mathbf{p}) & \cdots & \dfrac{\partial f_n}{\partial x_m}(\mathbf{p}) \end{bmatrix}.
$$

Proof. If f is differentiable at $\mathbf{p}$, then so is each of its coordinate function f_i for $1 \leqslant i \leqslant n$. Therefore by Theorem 3.3.20(i) the partial derivatives $(\partial f_i / \partial x_j)(\mathbf{p})$ exist for each $1 \leqslant i \leqslant n$ and $1 \leqslant j \leqslant m$.

For each $1 \leqslant j \leqslant m$, by 4.3.13 and Theorem 3.3.20(ii),

$$
L_{f, \mathbf{p}}(\mathbf{e}_j) = (L_{f_1, \mathbf{p}}(\mathbf{e}_j), \ldots, L_{f_n, \mathbf{p}}(\mathbf{e}_j)) = \left(\frac{\partial f_1}{\partial x_j}(\mathbf{p}), \ldots, \frac{\partial f_n}{\partial x_j}(\mathbf{p}) \right).
$$

But the coordinates of $L_{f, \mathbf{p}}(\mathbf{e}_j)$ with respect to the standard basis of $\mathbb{R}^n$ form the jth column of the matrix representing $L_{f, \mathbf{p}}$. The result follows.

4.3.17 Definition. *Let* $f : D \subseteq \mathbb{R}^m \to \mathbb{R}^n$ *be differentiable at* $\mathbf{p} \in D$. *The* $n \times m$ *matrix* $J_{f, \mathbf{p}}$ *defined in 4.3.16 is called the* Jacobian *of* f *at* $\mathbf{p}$.

Notice that the Jacobian matrix of a differentiable function from $\mathbb{R}^m$ to $\mathbb{R}^n$ is an $n \times m$ matrix, as is any matrix representing a linear function from $\mathbb{R}^m$ to $\mathbb{R}^n$.

The vectors $L_{f, \mathbf{p}}(\mathbf{e}_j) \in \mathbb{R}^n$, $j = 1, \ldots, m$, whose coordinates form the columns of $J_{f, \mathbf{p}}$ are very significant in the study of a function $f : D \subseteq \mathbb{R}^m \to \mathbb{R}^n$ which is differentiable at $\mathbf{p} \in D$. They are denoted by

$$
\frac{\partial f}{\partial x_j}(\mathbf{p}) = \left(\frac{\partial f_1}{\partial x_j}(\mathbf{p}), \ldots, \frac{\partial f_n}{\partial x_j}(\mathbf{p}) \right) = L_{f, \mathbf{p}}(\mathbf{e}_j).
$$

Since $L_{f, \mathbf{p}}$ is linear, it follows that for all $\mathbf{h} \in \mathbb{R}^m$,

$$
L_{f, \mathbf{p}}(\mathbf{h}) = h_1 \frac{\partial f}{\partial x_1}(\mathbf{p}) + \cdots + h_m \frac{\partial f}{\partial x_m}(\mathbf{p}),
$$

and that there exists a function $\eta : D_{\mathbf{p}} \subseteq \mathbb{R}^m \to \mathbb{R}^n$ such that $\lim_{\mathbf{h} \to \mathbf{0}} \eta(\mathbf{h}) = \mathbf{0}$ and

$$f(\mathbf{p} + \mathbf{h}) - f(\mathbf{p}) = h_1 \frac{\partial f}{\partial x_1}(\mathbf{p}) + \cdots + h_m \frac{\partial f}{\partial x_m}(\mathbf{p}) + \|\mathbf{h}\| \eta(\mathbf{h}), \qquad \mathbf{h} \in D_{\mathbf{p}}.$$

This last expression is an identity between vectors in $\mathbb{R}^n$. It should be compared with the special case considered in Section 3.3.

We have seen (Example 3.3.27) that a function $f : D \subseteq \mathbb{R}^m \to \mathbb{R}^n$ may not be differentiable at $\mathbf{p} \in D$ even though $(\partial f_i / \partial x_j)(\mathbf{p})$ exists for all i and j. The linear transformation represented by the matrix $J_{f, \mathbf{p}}$ of 4.3.16 may not be a close linear approximation to $\delta_{f, \mathbf{p}}$ near $\mathbf{0}$. However, we have the following extension of Theorem 3.3.29.

4.3.18 Theorem.   *Consider a function* $f : D \subseteq \mathbb{R}^m \to \mathbb{R}^n$. *If all the partial derivatives* $\partial f_i / \partial x_j$ *exist throughout* D, $1 \leqslant i \leqslant n$, $1 \leqslant j \leqslant m$, *and if they are all continuous at* $\mathbf{p} \in D$, *then* f *is differentiable at* $\mathbf{p}$.

Proof.   Exercise.

4.3.19 Definition.   *A function* $f : D \subseteq \mathbb{R}^m \to \mathbb{R}^n$ *all of whose partial derivatives are continuous in* D *is said to be* continuously differentiable *on* D. *Any such function is also said to be a* C^1 *function.*

It follows from Theorem 4.3.18 that any continuously differentiable function on D is also differentiable.

4.3.20 Example.   The function $f : \mathbb{R}^2 \to \mathbb{R}^2$ given by

$$f(x, y) = (|x - y|, x + y), \qquad (x, y) \in \mathbb{R}^2,$$

is continuously differentiable on any open subset of $\mathbb{R}^2$ excluding the line $x = y$.

4.3.21 Example.   Consider the linear function $f : \mathbb{R}^3 \to \mathbb{R}^2$ defined by

$$f(\mathbf{x}) = (2x_1 + 2x_2 + x_3, x_1 - x_2) \qquad \mathbf{x} = (x_1, x_2, x_3) \in \mathbb{R}^2.$$

The coordinate functions $f_i : \mathbb{R}^3 \to \mathbb{R}$ are defined by $f_1(\mathbf{x}) = 2x_1 + 2x_2 + x_3$ and $f_2(\mathbf{x}) = x_1 - x_2$. Since the function f is linear it is continuously differentiable at every point $\mathbf{p} \in \mathbb{R}^3$. By taking $\eta(\mathbf{h}) = \mathbf{0}$ for all $\mathbf{h}$, 4.3.5 is certainly satisfied and 4.3.4 becomes

$$f(\mathbf{p} + \mathbf{h}) - f(\mathbf{p}) = f(\mathbf{h}) + \|\mathbf{h}\| \mathbf{0}, \qquad \mathbf{h} \in \mathbb{R}^3.$$

Therefore, for all $\mathbf{p} \in \mathbb{R}^3$, $L_{f, \mathbf{p}} = f$. The Jacobian matrix is

$$J_{f, \mathbf{p}} = \left[\frac{\partial f_i}{\partial x_j}\right](\mathbf{p}) = \begin{bmatrix} 2 & 2 & 1 \\ 1 & -1 & 0 \end{bmatrix}, \qquad \text{for all } \mathbf{p} \in \mathbb{R}^3.$$

As expected, the Jacobian matrix is just the matrix representing f with respect to the standard bases.

4.3.22 Example. The function $f : \mathbb{R}^3 \to \mathbb{R}^2$ given by

$$f(x_1, x_2, x_3) = (x_1^2 + x_2^2 + x_3^2, x_1 + x_2 + x_3)$$

is continuously differentiable in $\mathbb{R}^3$. The Jacobian matrix of f at $\mathbf{p} \in \mathbb{R}^3$ is given by

$$J_{f, \mathbf{p}} = \begin{bmatrix} 2p_1 & 2p_2 & 2p_3 \\ 1 & 1 & 1 \end{bmatrix}.$$

It is sometimes necessary to consider vector-valued functions whose domains are not open. It may not be possible to define the partial derivatives of the coordinate functions of such a function $g : S \subseteq \mathbb{R}^m \to \mathbb{R}^n$ at some points of S. In this case we have the following extension of Definition 4.3.19.

4.3.23 Definition. *A function $g : S \subseteq \mathbb{R}^m \to \mathbb{R}^n$ whose domain S is not an open subset of R^m is said to be a C^1 function if g can be extended to a C^1 function $f : D \subseteq \mathbb{R}^m \to \mathbb{R}^n$ defined on an open set D containing S, such that f and g agree at all points in S.*

We shall need the following generalization of the idea of smoothness introduced in Definitions 2.8.4 and 3.8.14.

4.3.24 Definition. *A function $f : D \subseteq \mathbb{R}^m \to \mathbb{R}^n$ is smooth if f is a C^1 function and if for all $\mathbf{p} \in D$, the Jacobian $J_{f, \mathbf{p}}$ is of maximum possible rank $\min(m, n)$. A function $g : S \subseteq \mathbb{R}^m \to \mathbb{R}^n$ whose domain is not an open subset of $\mathbb{R}^m$ is said to be smooth if g can be extended to a smooth function on an open domain containing S.*

4.3.25 Example. (a) A C^1 function $f : D \subseteq \mathbb{R} \to \mathbb{R}^n$ is smooth if and only if

$$J_{f, p} = [f_1'(p) \ldots f_n'(p)]^t \neq [0 \ldots 0]^t \qquad \text{for all } p \in D.$$

(b) A C^1 function $f : D \subseteq \mathbb{R}^m \to \mathbb{R}$ is smooth if and only if

$$J_{f, \mathbf{p}} = \left[\frac{\partial f}{\partial x_1}(\mathbf{p}) \ldots \frac{\partial f}{\partial x_m}(\mathbf{p})\right] \neq [0 \ldots 0] \qquad \text{for all } \mathbf{p} \in D.$$

4.3.26 Example. The linear function $f : \mathbb{R}^3 \to \mathbb{R}^2$ defined in Example 4.3.21 is smooth since f is a C^1 function and rank $J_{f,\mathbf{p}} = 2$ for all $\mathbf{p} \in \mathbb{R}^3$.

4.3.27 Example. The C^1 function $f : \mathbb{R}^3 \to \mathbb{R}^2$ defined in Example 4.3.22 is not smooth since rank $J_{f,\mathbf{p}} = 1$ at any point $\mathbf{p}$ on the straight line $x_1 = x_2 = x_3$ in $\mathbb{R}^3$.

Let $f : D \subseteq \mathbb{R}^m \to \mathbb{R}^n$ and $g : D \subseteq \mathbb{R}^m \to \mathbb{R}^n$ be two differentiable functions such that $f(\mathbf{x}) = g(\mathbf{x}) + \mathbf{k}$ for some fixed $\mathbf{k} \in \mathbb{R}^n$ and all $\mathbf{x} \in D$. Since $\delta_{f,\mathbf{p}} = \delta_{g,\mathbf{p}}$ for all $\mathbf{p} \in D$, the differentials $L_{f,\mathbf{p}}$ and $L_{g,\mathbf{p}}$ are equal (see Corollary 4.3.12). The converse result is a corollary of the following theorem.

4.3.28 Theorem. *Let $f : D \subseteq \mathbb{R}^m \to \mathbb{R}^n$ be a differentiable function defined on an open path connected subset D of $\mathbb{R}^m$. If the differential $L_{f,\mathbf{p}}$ is the zero function for all $\mathbf{p} \in D$ then f is a constant function.*

Proof. Consider the Jacobian matrix $J_{f,\mathbf{p}}$. Let $1 \leqslant i \leqslant n$. By definition, the elements of the ith row of $J_{f,\mathbf{p}}$ are the coordinates of $(\operatorname{grad} f_i)(\mathbf{p})$ where $f_i : D \subseteq \mathbb{R}^m \to \mathbb{R}$ is the ith coordinate function.

If $L_{f,\mathbf{p}}$ is the zero function for all $\mathbf{p} \in D$, then $J_{f,\mathbf{p}}$ is the zero $n \times m$ matrix. In particular the ith row of $J_{f,\mathbf{p}}$ consists of m zeros for each $\mathbf{p}$. Hence $\operatorname{grad} f_i : D \subseteq \mathbb{R}^m \to \mathbb{R}^m$ is the zero vector field. Therefore, by Theorem 3.8.22, f_i is a constant function for each i. Hence f is a constant function.

4.3.29 Corollary. *Let $f : D \subseteq \mathbb{R}^m \to \mathbb{R}^n$ and $g : D \subseteq \mathbb{R}^m \to \mathbb{R}^n$ be differentiable functions on an open path-connected subset D of $\mathbb{R}^m$. If the differentials $L_{f,\mathbf{p}}$ and $L_{g,\mathbf{p}}$ are equal for all $\mathbf{p} \in D$, then there exists $\mathbf{k} \in \mathbb{R}^n$ such that $f(\mathbf{x}) = g(\mathbf{x}) + \mathbf{k}$ for all $\mathbf{x} \in D$.*

Proof. Exercise.

4.3.30 Example. The identity function $\mathbf{l} : \mathbb{R}^n \to \mathbb{R}^n$ is defined by $\mathbf{l}(\mathbf{x}) = \mathbf{x}$ for all $\mathbf{x} \in \mathbb{R}^n$. Being linear, $\mathbf{l}$ is differentiable and $L_{\mathbf{l},\mathbf{p}} = \mathbf{l}$. Furthermore $J_{\mathbf{l},\mathbf{p}}$ is the $n \times n$ identity matrix I for each $\mathbf{p}$.

Consider a differentiable function $f : D \subseteq \mathbb{R}^n \to \mathbb{R}^n$, where D is an open path-connected subset of $\mathbb{R}^n$. If $L_{f,\mathbf{p}} = \mathbf{l}$ for all $\mathbf{p} \in D$, then $L_{f,\mathbf{p}} = L_{\mathbf{l},\mathbf{p}}$ for all $\mathbf{p}$. Hence, by Corollary 4.3.29, there exists a vector $\mathbf{k} \in \mathbb{R}^n$ such that $f(\mathbf{x}) = \mathbf{x} + \mathbf{k}$ for all $\mathbf{x} \in D$.

Exercises 4.3

1. Let $f : \mathbb{R}^3 \to \mathbb{R}^2$ be defined as in Example 4.3.22 by

$$f(x_1, x_2, x_3) = (x_1^2 + x_2^2 + x_3^2, x_1 + x_2 + x_3).$$

Write down an expression defining $L_{f,\mathbf{p}} : \mathbb{R}^3 \to \mathbb{R}^2$, and determine the remainder term $\|\mathbf{h}\| \eta(\mathbf{h})$ in the expression $f(\mathbf{p} + \mathbf{h}) - f(\mathbf{p}) = L_{f,\mathbf{p}}(\mathbf{h}) + \|\mathbf{h}\| \eta(\mathbf{h})$. Prove that $\eta(\mathbf{h}) \to 0$ as $\mathbf{h} \to 0$.

Answer: $L_{f,\mathbf{p}}(\mathbf{h}) = (2p_1 h_1 + 2p_2 h_2 + 2p_3 h_3, h_1 + h_2 + h_3)$ and
$\|\mathbf{h}\| \eta(\mathbf{h}) = (h_1^2 + h_2^2 + h_3^2, 0) = \|\mathbf{h}\|(\|\mathbf{h}\|, 0).$

2. Repeat Exercise 1 with the function $f : \mathbb{R}^2 \to \mathbb{R}^3$ defined by
$f(x_1, x_2) = (x_1^3 + x_2^3, e^{x_1 x_2}, x_1 - x_2).$

3. Find the Jacobian matrix $J_{f,\mathbf{p}}$ for each of the following differentiable functions $f : \mathbb{R}^3 \to \mathbb{R}^2$:
   (a) $f(x_1, x_2, x_3) = (x_2^2 + 2x_2, 2\sin^2 x_1 x_2 x_3)$
   (b) $f(x_1, x_2, x_3) = ((x_2 + 1)^2, -\cos 2x_1 x_2 x_3)$

4. Find (a) the Jacobian matrix $J_{f,(r,\theta)}$ where the function $f : \mathbb{R}^2 \to \mathbb{R}^2$ is defined by

$$f(r, \theta) = (r\cos \theta, r\sin \theta);$$

   (b) the Jacobian matrix $J_{f,(r,\phi,\theta)}$ where $f : \mathbb{R}^3 \to \mathbb{R}^3$ is defined by

$$f(r, \phi, \theta) = (r\sin \phi \cos \theta, r\sin \phi \sin \theta, r\cos \phi).$$

   Show also that the determinants of these matrices take the value (a) r, (b) $r^2 \sin \phi$.

5. Prove that if the function $f : \mathbb{R}^m \to \mathbb{R}^n$ is linear, then $L_{f,\mathbf{p}} = f$. Discuss the nature of the Jacobian matrix of f at $\mathbf{p}$.

6. Prove Theorem 4.3.18. (Apply Theorem 3.3.29.)

7. Prove that if $f : D \subseteq \mathbb{R}^m \to \mathbb{R}^n$, $g : D \subseteq \mathbb{R}^m \to \mathbb{R}^n$ and $\phi : D \subseteq \mathbb{R}^m \to \mathbb{R}$ are differentiable at $\mathbf{p} \in D$, then so are the functions $f + g$, $f \cdot g$, ϕf and (provided $n = 3$) $f \wedge g$. Prove also the following relations on the differentials at $\mathbf{p}$.

$$L_{f+g,\mathbf{p}} = L_{f,\mathbf{p}} + L_{g,\mathbf{p}}$$
$$L_{f \cdot g,\mathbf{p}}(\mathbf{h}) = f(\mathbf{p}) \cdot L_{g,\mathbf{p}}(\mathbf{h}) + L_{f,\mathbf{p}}(\mathbf{h}) \cdot g(\mathbf{p})$$
$$L_{\phi f,\mathbf{p}}(\mathbf{h}) = \phi(\mathbf{p}) L_{f,\mathbf{p}}(\mathbf{h}) + L_{\phi,\mathbf{p}}(\mathbf{h}) f(\mathbf{p})$$
$$L_{f \wedge g,\mathbf{p}}(\mathbf{h}) = f(\mathbf{p}) \wedge L_{g,\mathbf{p}}(\mathbf{h}) + L_{f,\mathbf{p}}(\mathbf{h}) \wedge g(\mathbf{p}).$$

   Verify these formulae for the case $m = 2, n = 3$ and

$$f(x_1, x_2) = (x_1^2, x_2^2, x_1 x_2)$$
$$g(x_1, x_2) = (x_2, x_1, 0)$$
$$\phi(x_1, x_2) = x_1 x_2.$$

8. There are difficulties in using Definition 4.3.3 to define the differentiability of a function $f : S \subset \mathbb{R}^m \to \mathbb{R}^n$ when S is not an open subset of $\mathbb{R}^m$.

For example, let S be the x, y plane in $\mathbb{R}^3$ and let $f : S \subseteq \mathbb{R}^3 \to \mathbb{R}^3$ be defined by $f(\mathbf{x}) = \mathbf{x}$ for all $\mathbf{x} \in S$. Prove that for each $\mathbf{p} \in S$ and each $(a, b, c) \in \mathbb{R}^3$ the linear function $L : \mathbb{R}^3 \to \mathbb{R}^3$ defined by $L(x, y, z) = (x + az, y + bz, cz)$, $(x, y, z) \in \mathbb{R}^3$ satisfies

$$f(\mathbf{p} + \mathbf{h}) - f(\mathbf{p}) = L(\mathbf{h}), \qquad \text{all } \mathbf{h} \in S_\mathbf{p}.$$

Deduce that the 'differential' L is not unique. Where does the proof of Corollary 4.3.12 break down?

4.4   The Chain Rule

The Chain Rule of elementary calculus and Theorems 2.6.11 and 3.6.4 are special cases of the following important result.

4.4.1 Theorem.   *The Chain Rule. Let* $g : E \subseteq \mathbb{R}^l \to \mathbb{R}^m$ *be defined on an open subset E of* $\mathbb{R}^l$ *and let* $f : D \subseteq \mathbb{R}^m \to \mathbb{R}^n$ *be defined on an open subset D of* $\mathbb{R}^m$ *such that* $g(E) \subseteq D$. *Define* $F : E \subseteq \mathbb{R}^l \to \mathbb{R}^n$ *to be the composite function given by*

$$F(\mathbf{t}) = (f \circ g)(\mathbf{t}) = f(g(\mathbf{t})), \qquad \mathbf{t} \in E.$$

Suppose that g is differentiable at $\mathbf{a} \in E$ *and that f is differentiable at* $g(\mathbf{a}) \in D$. *Then F is differentiable at* $\mathbf{a}$ *and its differential is given by*

4.4.2 $$L_{F,\,\mathbf{a}} = L_{f,\,g(\mathbf{a})} \circ L_{g,\,\mathbf{a}}.$$

Furthermore, the Jacobian matrix of F at $\mathbf{a}$ *is the matrix product*

4.4.3 $$J_{F,\,\mathbf{a}} = J_{f,\,g(\mathbf{a})} J_{g,\,\mathbf{a}}.$$

We prove the theorem by appealing to the following lemma.

4.4.4 Lemma.   *Suppose that* $G : \mathbb{R}^l \to \mathbb{R}^m$ *is closely approximated near* $\mathbf{0} \in \mathbb{R}^l$ *by a linear function* $M : \mathbb{R}^l \to \mathbb{R}^m$ *and that* $F : \mathbb{R}^m \to \mathbb{R}^n$ *is closely approximated near* $\mathbf{0} \in \mathbb{R}^m$ *by a linear function* $L : \mathbb{R}^m \to \mathbb{R}^n$. *Then* $F \circ G : \mathbb{R}^l \to \mathbb{R}^n$ *is closely approximated near* $\mathbf{0} \in \mathbb{R}^l$ *by the linear function* $L \circ M : \mathbb{R}^l \to \mathbb{R}^n$.

Proof of Lemma.   There exist functions $\mu : \mathbb{R}^l \to \mathbb{R}^m$ and $\eta : \mathbb{R}^m \to \mathbb{R}^n$ such that

[i] $G(\mathbf{k}) = M(\mathbf{k}) + \|\mathbf{k}\| \mu(\mathbf{k})$ for all $\mathbf{k} \in \mathbb{R}^l$ and $\lim\limits_{\mathbf{k} \to 0} \mu(\mathbf{k}) = \mathbf{0}$

[ii] $F(\mathbf{h}) = L(\mathbf{h}) + \|\mathbf{h}\| \eta(\mathbf{h})$ for all $\mathbf{h} \in \mathbb{R}^m$ and $\lim\limits_{\mathbf{h} \to 0} \eta(\mathbf{h}) = \mathbf{0}$.

It follows from (i) that

4.4.5 $$\frac{\|G(\mathbf{k})\|}{\|\mathbf{k}\|} \leqslant \frac{1}{\|\mathbf{k}\|} \|M(\mathbf{k})\| + \|\mu(\mathbf{k})\| \text{ for all } \mathbf{k} \neq \mathbf{0}, \mathbf{k} \in \mathbb{R}^l.$$

Therefore (see Exercise 4.4.6)

[iii] there exists an open neighbourhood U of $\mathbf{0} \in \mathbb{R}^l$ such that $\|G(\mathbf{k})\|/\|\mathbf{k}\|$ is bounded for all $\mathbf{k} \in U, \mathbf{k} \neq \mathbf{0}$.

To test how close $F \circ G$ and $L \circ M$ are near $\mathbf{0} \in \mathbb{R}^l$, we consider, for $\mathbf{k} \in \mathbb{R}^l$,

$$\begin{aligned} F(G(\mathbf{k})) - L(M(\mathbf{k})) &= F(G(\mathbf{k})) - L(G(\mathbf{k})) + L(G(\mathbf{k})) - L(M(\mathbf{k})) \\ &= \|G(\mathbf{k})\|\eta(G(\mathbf{k})) + L(G(\mathbf{k}) - M(\mathbf{k})) \\ &\qquad \text{(by (ii) and the linearity of } L) \\ &= \|G(\mathbf{k})\|\eta(G(\mathbf{k})) + \|\mathbf{k}\| L(\mu(\mathbf{k})) \\ &\qquad \text{(by (i) and the linearity of } L) \end{aligned}$$

Hence, for all $\mathbf{k} \in U, \mathbf{k} \neq \mathbf{0}$,

4.4.6 $$\frac{F(G(\mathbf{k})) - L(M(\mathbf{k}))}{\|\mathbf{k}\|} = \frac{\|G(\mathbf{k})\|}{\|\mathbf{k}\|}\eta(G(\mathbf{k})) + L(\mu(\mathbf{k})).$$

Now by [i] $\lim_{\mathbf{k} \to \mathbf{0}} G(\mathbf{k}) = \mathbf{0}$ and therefore by [ii], $\lim_{\mathbf{k} \to \mathbf{0}} \eta(G(\mathbf{k})) = \mathbf{0}$. Similarly, since L is linear, $\lim_{\mathbf{k} \to \mathbf{0}} L(\mu(\mathbf{k})) = \mathbf{0}$. Therefore by [iii], the right-hand side of 4.4.6 tends to $\mathbf{0} \in \mathbb{R}^n$ as $\mathbf{k}$ tends to $\mathbf{0}$. Hence the left-hand side tends to $\mathbf{0}$ and this completes the proof of the lemma.

Proof of Theorem 4.4.1.   The function $\delta_{g,\mathbf{a}} : E_{\mathbf{a}} \subseteq \mathbb{R}^l \to \mathbb{R}^m$ is closely approximated by $L_{g,\mathbf{a}} : \mathbb{R}^l \to \mathbb{R}^m$ near $\mathbf{0} \in \mathbb{R}^l$, and the function $\delta_{f,g(\mathbf{a})} : D_{g(\mathbf{a})} \subseteq \mathbb{R}^m \to \mathbb{R}^n$ is closely approximated by $L_{f,g(\mathbf{a})} : \mathbb{R}^m \to \mathbb{R}^n$ near $\mathbf{0} \in \mathbb{R}^m$. It follows from Lemma 4.4.4 that $\delta_{f,g(\mathbf{a})} \circ \delta_{g,a}$ is closely approximated by $L_{f,g(\mathbf{a})} \circ L_{g,\mathbf{a}}$ near $\mathbf{0} \in \mathbb{R}^l$. A simple calculation (see 3.6.6) shows that

4.4.7 $$\delta_{f \circ g, \mathbf{a}} = \delta_{f,g(\mathbf{a})} \circ \delta_{g,\mathbf{a}}.$$

Therefore $\delta_{f \circ g, \mathbf{a}}$ is closely approximated by the linear function $L_{f,g(\mathbf{a})} \circ L_{g,\mathbf{a}}$ near $\mathbf{0} \in \mathbb{R}^l$. It follows that $F = f \circ g$ is differentiable at $\mathbf{a}$ and that the differential $L_{f \circ g, \mathbf{a}}$ is $L_{f,g(\mathbf{a})} \circ L_{g,\mathbf{a}}$. Expression 4.4.3 follows immediately, thus completing the proof of the theorem.

From 4.4.3 the (i, j) entry of $J_{F,\mathbf{a}}$ is the dot product of the ith row of $J_{f,g(\mathbf{a})}$ and the jth column of $J_{g,\mathbf{a}}$. Denoting variables in E by $\mathbf{t}$

and variables in D by $\mathbf{x}$ we therefore have, for each $\mathbf{a} \in E$,

4.4.8 $$\frac{\partial F_i}{\partial t_j}(\mathbf{a}) = \frac{\partial f_i}{\partial x_1}(g(\mathbf{a}))\frac{\partial g_1}{\partial t_j}(\mathbf{a}) + \cdots + \frac{\partial f_i}{\partial x_m}(g(\mathbf{a}))\frac{\partial g_m}{\partial t_j}(\mathbf{a}).$$

One often meets 4.4.8 in a less precise but perhaps more con-venient form. In considering a vector-valued function f of m vari-ables $x_1, \ldots, x_m$, each of which is a function of l variables $t_1, \ldots, t_l$, the expression

4.4.9 $$f(x_1(t_1, \ldots, t_l), \ldots, x_m(t_1, \ldots, t_l))$$

can be thought of as defining f as a function of $t_1, \ldots, t_l$. In the terms set out in Theorem 4.4.1, if we define a function $g : E \subseteq \mathbb{R}^l \to \mathbb{R}^m$ by

$$g(t_1, \ldots, t_l) = (x_1(t_1, \ldots, t_l), \ldots, x_m(t_1, \ldots, t_l)), (t_1, \ldots, t_l) \in E,$$

then 4.4.9 gives the values of $F(t_1, \ldots, t_l)$.

The Chain Rule is then simplified to the identity (compare 4.4.8)

4.4.10 $$\frac{\partial f_i}{\partial t_j} = \frac{\partial f_i}{\partial x_1}\frac{\partial x_1}{\partial t_j} + \cdots + \frac{\partial f_i}{\partial x_m}\frac{\partial x_m}{\partial t_j}.$$

Of course $\partial f_i/\partial t_j$ is really $\partial F_i/\partial t_j$ and $\partial x_k/\partial t_j$ is really $\partial g_k/\partial t_j$. If $\partial f_i/\partial t_j$ is to be evaluated at $\mathbf{t} \in \mathbb{R}^l$ using 4.4.10, then $\partial x_k/\partial t_j$ must be eva-luated at $\mathbf{t}$ and $\partial f_i/\partial x_k$ must be evaluated at $(x_1(\mathbf{t}), \ldots, x_m(\mathbf{t}))$.

We now have a complete generalisation of the Chain Rule of elementary calculus in its conventional form $dy/dt = (dy/dx)(dx/dt)$. This special case is considered further in our first example.

4.4.11 *Example*.   Let $g : \mathbb{R} \to \mathbb{R}$ be differentiable at $a \in \mathbb{R}$. The differential $L_{g,a}$ is defined by $L_{g,a}(h) = (g'(a))h$ and the Jacobian of g at a is the 1×1 matrix $J_{g,a} = [g'(a)]$. Suppose now that $f : \mathbb{R} \to \mathbb{R}$ is differentiable at $g(a)$; then the Chain Rule implies that $f \circ g$ is differentiable at a. Furthermore, since $J_{f,g(a)} = [f'(g(a))]$ and $J_{f \circ g,a} = [(f \circ g)'(a)]$, expression 4.4.3 is a statement about 1×1 matrices:

$$[(f \circ g)'(a)] = [f'(g(a))][g'(a)],$$

which is effectively the elementary form of the Chain Rule.

4.4.12 *Example*.   Define functions $g : \mathbb{R}^3 \to \mathbb{R}^2$ and $f : \mathbb{R}^2 \to \mathbb{R}^2$ as follows:

$$g(t_1, t_2, t_3) = (t_1 t_2, t_2 t_3), \qquad (t_1, t_2, t_3) \in \mathbb{R}^3$$
$$f(x_1, x_2) = (2x_1 + x_2^2, 3x_1^2 - x_2), \quad (x_1, x_2) \in \mathbb{R}^2.$$

The composite function $F = f \circ g : \mathbb{R}^3 \to \mathbb{R}^2$ is given by

4.4.13
$$F(t_1, t_2, t_3) = f(g(t_1, t_2, t_3)) = f(t_1 t_2, t_2 t_3)$$
$$= (2t_1 t_2 + t_2^2 t_3^2, 3t_1^2 t_2^2 - t_2 t_3).$$

We could of course work out the partial derivatives of F directly from this. Alternatively, by informally putting $x_1 = t_1 t_2$ and $x_2 = t_2 t_3$, we could use 4.4.10 to obtain (with the conventions noted there) for example

$$\frac{\partial f_1}{\partial t_2} = \frac{\partial f_1}{\partial x_1}\frac{\partial x_1}{\partial t_2} + \frac{\partial f_1}{\partial x_2}\frac{\partial x_2}{\partial t_2} = 2t_1 + 2x_2 t_3 = 2t_1 + 2t_2 t_3^2.$$

A little more formally, applying 4.4.3 at $\mathbf{t} = (t_1, t_2, t_3) \in \mathbb{R}^3$,

$$J_{F,\mathbf{t}} = \begin{bmatrix} 2 & 2x_2(\mathbf{t}) \\ 6x_1(\mathbf{t}) & -1 \end{bmatrix} \begin{bmatrix} t_2 & t_1 & 0 \\ 0 & t_3 & t_2 \end{bmatrix}$$

$$= \begin{bmatrix} 2 & 2t_2 t_3 \\ 6t_1 t_2 & -1 \end{bmatrix} \begin{bmatrix} t_2 & t_1 & 0 \\ 0 & t_3 & t_2 \end{bmatrix}$$

$$= \begin{bmatrix} 2t_2 & 2t_1 + 2t_2 t_3^2 & 2t_2^2 t_3 \\ 6t_1 t_2^2 & 6t_1^2 t_2 - t_3 & -t_2 \end{bmatrix}.$$

These entries may be checked directly from 4.4.13.

4.4.14 Example. Let $g : E \subseteq \mathbb{R}^2 \to \mathbb{R}^2$ and $f : \mathbb{R}^2 \to \mathbb{R}^2$, where $E = \{(t_1, t_2) | t_1 > t_2\}$, be defined as follows:

$$g(t_1, t_2) = (\sqrt{(t_1 - t_2)}, t_1 + t_2), \qquad (t_1, t_2) \in E,$$
$$f(x_1, x_2) = (\tfrac{1}{2}(x_2 + x_1^2), \tfrac{1}{2}(x_2 - x_1^2)), \qquad (x_1, x_2) \in \mathbb{R}^2.$$

The composite function $F = f \circ g : E \subseteq \mathbb{R}^2 \to \mathbb{R}^2$ is differentiable since both g and f are differentiable throughout their domains. We can calculate the Jacobian matrix $J_{F,\mathbf{t}}$ by putting $x_1 = \sqrt{(t_1 - t_2)}$ and $x_2 = t_1 + t_2$ in the usual informal way. We find that

$$\frac{\partial F_1}{\partial t_1} = \frac{\partial f_1}{\partial x_1}\frac{\partial x_1}{\partial t_1} + \frac{\partial f_1}{\partial x_2}\frac{\partial x_2}{\partial t_1} = x_1 \frac{1}{2\sqrt{(t_1 - t_2)}} + \tfrac{1}{2} \cdot 1 = 1$$

$$\frac{\partial F_1}{\partial t_2} = \frac{\partial f_1}{\partial x_1}\frac{\partial x_1}{\partial t_2} + \frac{\partial f_1}{\partial x_2}\frac{\partial x_2}{\partial t_2} = x_1 \frac{-1}{2\sqrt{(t_1 - t_2)}} + \tfrac{1}{2} \cdot 1 = 0.$$

Similarly $\partial F_2 / \partial t_1 = 0$ and $\partial F_2 / \partial t_2 = 1$ (check this). Therefore the Jacobian matrix $J_{F,\mathbf{t}}$ is the 2×2 identity matrix I. Thus the differential $L_{F,\mathbf{t}} : \mathbb{R}^2 \to \mathbb{R}^2$ is the identity function, and, by Example 4.3.30, there is a vector $\mathbf{k} \in \mathbb{R}^2$ such that $F(\mathbf{t}) = \mathbf{t} + \mathbf{k}$ for all $\mathbf{t} \in E$. From a direct computation

$$F(t_1, t_2) = f(g(t_1, t_2)) = f(\sqrt{(t_1 - t_2)}, t_1 + t_2)$$
$$= (\tfrac{1}{2}(t_1 + t_2 + t_1 - t_2), \tfrac{1}{2}(t_1 + t_2 - t_1 + t_2)) = (t_1, t_2),$$

we see that in fact F is the identity function on E. So we have

4.4.15 $F = f \circ g = I.$

In a sense the functions f and g are inverse to each other. This is a very important idea which we consider in some detail in the next two sections.

In Example 4.4.12 we observed that with the particular functions there defined we could find the partial derivatives of $f \circ g$ without using the Chain Rule, by calculating an expression 4.4.13 for $(f \circ g)(\mathbf{t})$ in terms of $t_1, \ldots, t_n$. This is always possible where f and g are *explicitly* defined. The Chain Rule is of great importance in theoretical situations where such a direct approach is not possible. We use it for example in the following generalization of the elementary Mean-Value Theorem which we shall need in our study of inverse functions.

4.4.16 *Mean-Value Theorem.*   Let $f : D \subseteq \mathbb{R}^m \to \mathbb{R}^n$ be a differentiable function whose open domain D contains the points $\mathbf{q}$ and $\mathbf{q} + \mathbf{h}$ and the segment joining them. Then corresponding to any vector $\mathbf{u} \in \mathbb{R}^n$ there is $0 < \theta < 1$ such that

4.4.17 $(f(\mathbf{q} + \mathbf{h}) - f(\mathbf{q})) \cdot \mathbf{u} = L_{f, \mathbf{q} + \theta\mathbf{h}}(\mathbf{h}) \cdot \mathbf{u}$

Proof.   The function $f^* : D \subseteq \mathbb{R}^m \to \mathbb{R}$ defined by

$$f^*(\mathbf{x}) = (f(\mathbf{x}) - f(\mathbf{q})) \cdot \mathbf{u}, \qquad \mathbf{x} \in D$$

is differentiable (see Exercise 4.3.7). Let $\mathbf{e}_1, \ldots, \mathbf{e}_m$ be the standard basis of $\mathbb{R}^m$. It is easy to check from the definition of partial derivatives that for each $k = 1, \ldots, m,$

4.4.18 $\dfrac{\partial f^*}{\partial x_k}(\mathbf{x}) = \dfrac{\partial f}{\partial x_k}(\mathbf{x}) \cdot \mathbf{u} = L_{f, \mathbf{x}}(\mathbf{e}_k) \cdot \mathbf{u}, \qquad \mathbf{x} \in D.$

Now consider a function $F : E \subseteq \mathbb{R} \to \mathbb{R}$, where $[0, 1] \subseteq E$ and

$$F(t) = (f(\mathbf{q} + t\mathbf{h}) - f(\mathbf{q})) \cdot \mathbf{u}, \qquad t \in E.$$

Then, for all $t \in E$, $F(t) = f^*(\mathbf{q} + t\mathbf{h})$ and so (by the Chain Rule), F is differentiable. Furthermore, by 4.4.8, for all $t \in E$

$$\begin{aligned}
F'(t) &= h_1 \frac{\partial f^*}{\partial x_1}(\mathbf{q} + t\mathbf{h}) + \cdots + h_m \frac{\partial f^*}{\partial x_m}(\mathbf{q} + t\mathbf{h}) \\
&= (h_1 L_{f, \mathbf{q} + t\mathbf{h}}(\mathbf{e}_1) + \cdots + h_m L_{f, \mathbf{q} + t\mathbf{h}}(\mathbf{e}_m)) \cdot \mathbf{u} \qquad \text{(by 4.4.18)} \\
&= L_{f, \mathbf{q} + t\mathbf{h}}(\mathbf{h}) \cdot \mathbf{u}.
\end{aligned}$$

The elementary Mean-Value Theorem applied to F implies that there exists $0 < \theta < 1$ such that

$$(f(\mathbf{q} + \mathbf{h}) - f(\mathbf{q})) \cdot \mathbf{u} = F(1) - F(0) = F'(\theta) = L_{f, \mathbf{q} + \theta\mathbf{h}}(\mathbf{h}) \cdot \mathbf{u}.$$

This completes the proof of the theorem.

4.4.19 *Example.* Taking $n = 1$ and $u = 1$ in Theorem 4.4.16, we find that for any two points $\mathbf{q}$ and $\mathbf{q} + \mathbf{h}$ in the domain of a differentiable function $f : D \subseteq \mathbb{R}^m \to \mathbb{R}$ there exists $0 < \theta < 1$ such that

4.4.20 $f(\mathbf{q} + \mathbf{h}) - f(\mathbf{q}) = L_{f, \mathbf{q} + \theta\mathbf{h}}(\mathbf{h})$

$$= h_1 \frac{\partial f}{\partial x_1}(\mathbf{q} + \theta\mathbf{h}) + \cdots + h_m \frac{\partial f}{\partial x_m}(\mathbf{q} + \theta\mathbf{h}).$$

This is merely a restatement of Theorem 3.9.1. Clearly the elementary Mean-Value Theorem corresponds to the case $m = 1$.

4.4.21 *Remark.* There is no hope of identity 4.4.20 being generally true for functions $f : D \subseteq \mathbb{R}^m \to \mathbb{R}^n$. For example, it is easy to construct a differentiable path $f : [a, b] \subseteq \mathbb{R} \to \mathbb{R}^3$ such that at no point $t \in [a, b]$ is the tangent vector $f'(t)$ parallel to $f(b) - f(a)$. (Consider the circular helix of Example 2.1.7.)

Exercises 4.4

1. Define the functions $g : \mathbb{R}^2 \to \mathbb{R}^3$ and $f : \mathbb{R}^3 \to \mathbb{R}^3$ by

$$g(u, v) = (u^2 + v^2, u^2 - v^2, 2uv), \qquad (u, v) \in \mathbb{R}^2$$
$$f(x, y, z) = (x + y, y + z, z + x), \qquad (x, y, z) \in \mathbb{R}^3$$

By direct substitution obtain a formula defining the function $F = f \circ g : \mathbb{R}^2 \to \mathbb{R}^3$. Calculate the entries $(\partial F_i / \partial u)(\mathbf{p})$ and $(\partial F_i / \partial v)(\mathbf{p})$ of the Jacobian matrix $J_{F, \mathbf{p}}$, where $\mathbf{p} = (u, v)$, (a) by the Chain Rule 4.4.8, (b) from your formula for $F(u, v)$.

2. Let $g : \mathbb{R}^n \to \mathbb{R}^m$ and $f : \mathbb{R}^m \to \mathbb{R}^n$ be differentiable functions such that $f \circ g$ is the identity function $\mathbf{1} : \mathbb{R}^n \to \mathbb{R}^n$. Regard f as acting on vectors $(x_1, \ldots, x_m) \in \mathbb{R}^m$ and put

$$g(\mathbf{t}) = (x_1(\mathbf{t}), \ldots, x_m(\mathbf{t}))$$

where

$$\mathbf{t} = (t_1, \ldots, t_n) \in \mathbb{R}^n.$$

Prove that

$$\frac{\partial f_i}{\partial x_1} \frac{\partial x_1}{\partial t_j} + \cdots + \frac{\partial f_i}{\partial x_m} \frac{\partial x_m}{\partial t_j} = \begin{cases} 1 & \text{if} \quad i = j \\ 0 & \text{if} \quad i \neq j. \end{cases}$$

For an illustration, see Example 4.4.14.

3. The expressions

    $$z = x^2 + y^2 + xy, \qquad x = r\cos\theta, \qquad y = r\sin\theta,$$

    effectively define z as a function of r and θ. Calculate $\partial z/\partial r$ from the Chain Rule in the informal notation

    $$\frac{\partial z}{\partial r} = \frac{\partial z}{\partial x}\frac{\partial x}{\partial r} + \frac{\partial z}{\partial y}\frac{\partial y}{\partial r}.$$

    Similarly calculate $\partial z/\partial\theta$. Check the results by direct substitution.
    Reformulate the exercise in precise notation. (Start by defining $f : \mathbb{R}^2 \to \mathbb{R}$ by $f(x, y) = x^2 + y^2 + xy$.)

4. Let f and g be real-valued functions of x and y. The expressions

    $$z = (f(x,y), g(x,y)), \qquad x = u(t), \qquad y = v(t), \qquad t \in \mathbb{R},$$

    effectively define z as a function of t. Justify the Chain Rule

    $$\frac{dz}{dt} = \frac{\partial z}{\partial x}\frac{dx}{dt} + \frac{\partial z}{\partial y}\frac{dy}{dt}.$$

    and use it in the case $z = (x^2 + y^2, x^2 - y^2)$, $x = \sin t$, $y = \cos t$.
    Reformulate the exercise in precise notation.

5. Criticise the following argument. If $z = f(x, y)$ and $y = g(x, t)$, where f and g are real valued functions, then z is effectively defined as a function of x and t. By the Chain Rule

    $$\frac{\partial z}{\partial x} = \frac{\partial z}{\partial x}\frac{\partial x}{\partial x} + \frac{\partial z}{\partial y}\frac{\partial y}{\partial x} = \frac{\partial z}{\partial x} + \frac{\partial z}{\partial y}\frac{\partial y}{\partial x}.$$

    Hence

    $$\frac{\partial z}{\partial y}\frac{\partial y}{\partial x} = 0.$$

    In particular, if $z = x^2 + y$ and $y = x + t$, then $\partial z/\partial y = 1$, $\partial y/\partial x = 1$. Therefore $1 = 0$.

6. In relation to the proofs of Theorem 4.4.1 and Lemma 4.4.4,
    (a) establish identity 4.4.7;
    (b) prove statement (iii) in Lemma 4.4.4.

    Hint: in 4.4.5, $\lim_{\mathbf{k} \to \mathbf{0}} \mu(\mathbf{k}) = \mathbf{0}$ and

    $$\|M(\mathbf{k})\| \leqslant |k_1| \|M(\mathbf{e}_1)\| + \cdots + |k_l| \|M(\mathbf{e}_l)\|.$$

7. The following example illustrates that in Lemma 4.4.4 the linearity condition on the functions L and M cannot be dropped. Let G, M, F, L

be functions from $\mathbb{R}$ to $\mathbb{R}$ defined by

$$G(x) = x(1 + x^{1/3}), \qquad M(x) = x$$
$$F(x) = x^{1/3}, \qquad L(x) = x^{1/3}.$$

Prove that G is closely approximated near 0 by M and that F is closely approximated near 0 by L, but that $F \circ G$ is not closely approximated near 0 by $L \circ M$. In fact,

$$\frac{(F \circ G)(h) - (L \circ M)(h)}{|h|} \to \infty \qquad \text{as } h \to 0.$$

4.5 One-to-one functions and their inverses

4.5.1 Definition. *Let U and V be sets. A function $f : U \to V$ is said to be* one-to-one *(written $1-1$) when no two points of U have the same image under f.*

When U and V are subsets of $\mathbb{R}$ a sketch of the graph of $f : U \subseteq \mathbb{R} \to \mathbb{R}$ will reveal the property. The function is $1-1$ if and only if every line of the form $y = k$ intersects the graph in at most one point.

4.5.2 Example. Let f and h be continuous real-valued functions of $\mathbb{R}$ defined by $f(x) = (x - 2)^2 + 1$ and $h(x) = x^3(x - 5)^2/50$. The graphs of f and h are shown in Figs. 4.2 and 4.3 respectively. Neither f nor h is $1-1$, in particular $f(1) = f(3) = 2$ and $h(0) = h(5) = 0$.

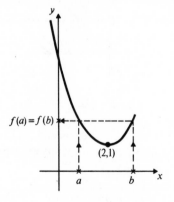

Fig. 4.2 $y = (x - 2)^2 + 1$

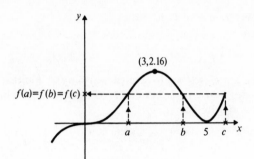

Fig. 4.3 $50y = x^3(x-5)^2$

4.5.3 Example.   Any real number x can be expressed in the form $n + \varepsilon$, where $n \in \mathbb{Z}$ and $0 \leqslant \varepsilon < 1$. The integer n is called the integer part of x and is denoted by $[x]$. The discontinuous function $f : \mathbb{R} \to \mathbb{R}$ defined by $f(x) = x - 2[x]$, whose graph is sketched in Fig. 4.4, is 1–1. No two x-values lead to the same y-value.

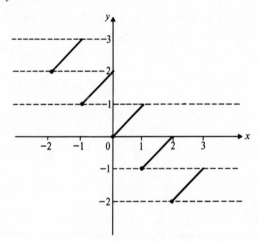

Fig. 4.4 $y = x - 2[x]$

A function which is both continuous and 1–1 has to be more straightforward than those of the previous examples as the following theorem shows.

4.5.4 Theorem.   *Let D be an open interval in* $\mathbb{R}$ *and consider a continuous function* $f : D \subseteq \mathbb{R} \to \mathbb{R}$. *The following three conditions are equivalent:*

[i] f is 1–1,

[ii] $f(N)$ is an open interval wherever N is an open interval in D,

[iii] f is strictly monotone.

Proof. We shall prove the three implications **[i]** $\Rightarrow$ **[ii]**, **[ii]** $\Rightarrow$ **[iii]** and **[iii]** $\Rightarrow$ **[i]**, from which the theorem follows.

[i] $\Rightarrow$ **[ii]**. Assuming that f is 1–1, consider an open interval $N \subseteq D$, and put $f(N) = M$. Since f is continuous, the Intermediate Value Theorem implies that M is an interval of some sort. We will show that M is an open interval. Suppose that M contains its greatest lower bound p. Then there exists $c \in N$ such that $f(c) = p$. Find an interval $[a, b] \subseteq N$ such that $c \in]a, b[$. Then $f(a) > f(c)$ and $f(b) > f(c)$. (Equality is ruled out since f is 1–1.) Let q be a number such that

$$f(a) > q > f(c) \quad \text{and} \quad f(c) < q < f(b)$$

(see Fig. 4.5(i)).

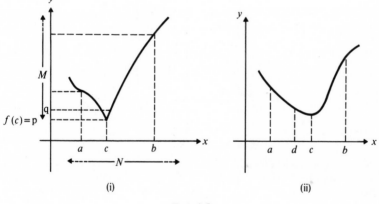

Fig. 4.5

The Intermediate Value Theorem implies that there are two points, one between a and c and the other between c and b, at which the function takes the value q, and so f is not 1–1. This contradiction establishes that M does not contain its greatest lower bound. Similarly M does not contain its least upper bound either, and so M is an open interval.

[ii] $\Rightarrow$ **[iii]**. Suppose that the images under f of open intervals are open. If $f : D \subseteq \mathbb{R} \to \mathbb{R}$ is not strictly monotone, then there exist three

points $a < d < b$ in D such that either $f(a) \geqslant f(d) \leqslant f(b)$ (see
Fig. 4.5(ii)) or $f(a) \leqslant f(d) \geqslant f(b)$. In the former case the function
$f : [a, b] \subseteq \mathbb{R} \to \mathbb{R}$ attains its infimum at some point $c \in]a, b[$. Hence
the image under f of the open interval $]a, b[$ contains its greatest
lower bound and it is therefore not an open interval. A similar
contradiction follows from the second inequality. Therefore $f : D \subseteq \mathbb{R}$
$\to \mathbb{R}$ is strictly monotone.

(iii) $\Rightarrow$ (i).   This is immediate.

4.5.5 Example.   Figure 4.6 shows the graph of the exponential function
$\exp : \mathbb{R} \to \mathbb{R}$ given by $\exp(x) = e^x$. Clearly exp is strictly increasing and 1–1.
To illustrate property [ii] of the theorem, $\exp(\mathbb{R}) = \mathbb{R}^+ = \{y \,|\, y > 0\}$ and
$\exp(]0, 1[) =]1, e[$.

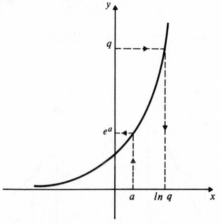

Fig. 4.6 $y = \exp x; \quad x = \ln y$

4.5.6 Example.   The function $f : \mathbb{R} \to \mathbb{R}$ given by $f(x) = (x - 2)^2 + 1$
considered in Example 4.5.2 is not 1–1. In this case we find that
$f(\mathbb{R}) = [1, \infty[$ and $f(]1, 3[) = [1, 2[$, for example.

A 1–1 function $f : U \to V$ establishes a 1–1 correspondence between U and $f(U)$. We can therefore define, unambiguously, a
function $g : f(U) \subseteq V \to U$ which simply reverses the effect of f. (The
reader should consider this process in relation to Fig. 4.5 and notice
the difficulty of defining a function that reverses the effect of the
function suggested by the figure.) More formally we have the following definition.

4.5.7 Definition.   *Let* $f : U \to V$ *be a* 1–1 *function. The* inverse *of f is the
function* $g : f(U) \subseteq V \to U$ *defined by*

4.5.8 $\qquad\qquad\qquad g(f(u)) = u, \qquad f(u) \in f(U).$

In agreement with arithmetic and matrix notation, the inverse of a function f is sometimes denoted by f^{-1}. Clearly f^{-1} is also a 1–1 function. The functions $f^{-1} \circ f : U \to U$ and $f \circ f^{-1} : f(U) \to f(U)$ are both identity functions, and $(f^{-1})^{-1} = f : U \to V$.

4.5.9 Example. The image of the exponential function considered in Example 4.5.5 is $\mathbb{R}^+ = \{y | y > 0\} \subseteq \mathbb{R}$. Its inverse is the natural logarithm function $\ln : \mathbb{R}^+ \to \mathbb{R}$ (see Fig. 4.6).

4.5.10 Example. The function $f : \mathbb{R} \to \mathbb{R}$ given by $f(x) = x - 2[x]$ considered in Example 4.5.3 is its own inverse. Using the notation introduced there, for any $x = n + \varepsilon \in \mathbb{R}$,

$$f(f(x)) = f(f(n + \varepsilon)) = f(n + \varepsilon - 2n) = f(-n + \varepsilon)$$
$$= -n + \varepsilon - 2(-n) = n + \varepsilon.$$

Hence $f^{-1} = f : \mathbb{R} \to \mathbb{R}$. This property is by no means as exceptional as it might appear. It can be shown (Exercise 4.5.1) that the graph of the inverse function of any 1–1 function $f : \mathbb{R} \to \mathbb{R}$ is just the reflection of the graph of f in the line $y = x$. Any 1–1 function whose graph is symmetric about this line is therefore its own inverse.

Further consideration of the functions defined in Example 4.5.2 and of their graphs suggests that a function may become 1–1 if its domain is restricted in some way. Theorem 4.5.4 implies that a continuous function $f : D \subseteq \mathbb{R} \to \mathbb{R}$ is 1–1 on an open interval $N \subseteq D$ if and only if f is strictly monotone on N.

4.5.11 Example. We have seen that the function $f : \mathbb{R} \to \mathbb{R}$ defined by the rule $f(x) = (x - 2)^2 + 1$ is not 1–1. The graph of f (Fig. 4.2) indicates that the function is strictly decreasing (and therefore 1–1) on the open interval $]-\infty, 2[$. If we use the same rule to define a function $f_1 :]-\infty, 2[\to \mathbb{R}$ by $f_1(x) = f(x)$ for all $x \in]-\infty, 2[$, then f_1 is 1–1. Furthermore $f_1(]-\infty, 2[) =]1, \infty[$ and its inverse $f_1^{-1} :]1, \infty[\to]-\infty, 2[$ is given by $f_1^{-1}(y) = 2 - \sqrt{(y-1)}$.

Similarly we can define a function $f_2 :]2, \infty[\subseteq \mathbb{R} \to \mathbb{R}$ by $f_2(x) = f(x), x \in]2, \infty[$. The function f_2 is strictly increasing and is therefore 1–1. The inverse of f_2 is the function $f_2^{-1} :]1, \infty[\to]2, \infty[$ given by $f_2^{-1}(y) = 2 + \sqrt{(y-1)}$.

We are led to the following definition.

4.5.12 Definition. *The function $f : D \subseteq \mathbb{R}^n \to \mathbb{R}^n$ is said to be* locally 1–1 *at* $\mathbf{p} \in D$ *if there is an open set N in $\mathbb{R}^n$ with $\mathbf{p} \in N \subseteq D$ such that f*

is $1-1$ *on* N. *We also say under these circumstances that* f *is* locally *invertible at* **p** *and, where there is no possible ambiguity, denote the local inverse by* $f^{-1} : f(N) \subseteq \mathbb{R}^n \to \mathbb{R}^n$.

4.5.13 Theorem.   *A differentiable function* $f : D \subseteq \mathbb{R} \to \mathbb{R}$ *is not locally* $1-1$ *at any of its extreme points.*

Proof.   Exercise.

4.5.14 Example.   The function $f : \mathbb{R} \to \mathbb{R}$ considered in Examples 4.5.2 and 4.5.11 is locally $1-1$ at all points in $]-\infty, 2[$ and $]2, \infty[$. We have denoted the local inverses on these two intervals by f_1^{-1} and f_2^{-1} respectively. The function is not locally $1-1$ at its extreme point 2 since it is not monotone on any open interval containing 2 (see Fig. 4.2).

4.5.15 Example.   The function $f : \mathbb{R} \to \mathbb{R}$ defined by $f(x) = \sin x$ is not locally $1-1$ at its extreme points $(2n+1)\pi/2$, $n \in \mathbb{Z}$. See Fig. 4.7. The function is not monotone in any open interval containing $\pi/2$, for example. It is, however, locally $1-1$ between the extreme points. In the notation of Definition 4.5.12 the open interval $]-\pi/2, \pi/2[$ is an appropriate choice for N corresponding to any point which it contains. The local inverse function there is arc sin : $]-1, 1[\to]-\pi/2, \pi/2[$. Similarly $]\pi/2, 3\pi/2[$ is an appropriate choice for N corresponding to any point in $]\pi/2, 3\pi/2[$, but the local inverse in this case is $g :]-1, 1[\to]\pi/2, 3\pi/2[$ defined by $g(y) = \pi - \arcsin y$.

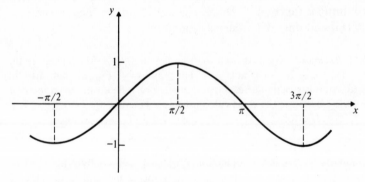

Fig. 4.7 $y = \sin x$

We shall see in Exercise 4.5.5 that a differentiable function $f : \mathbb{R} \to \mathbb{R}$ may fail to be locally $1-1$ at $p \in \mathbb{R}$ even if $f'(p) \neq 0$ since it can happen that *every* open interval containing p contains an extreme point of f. The added condition that f is continuously differentiable is sufficient, however, to ensure that f is locally $1-1$ at non-extreme points.

4.5.16 Theorem.   Let $f : D \subseteq \mathbb{R} \to \mathbb{R}$ be continuously differentiable and let $p \in D$ be such that $f'(p) \neq 0$. Then there is an open interval N containing p such that f is $1-1$ on N, $f(N)$ is an open interval and the function $g : f(N) \subseteq \mathbb{R} \to \mathbb{R}$ locally inverse to f is also continuously differentiable.

Furthermore,

4.5.17 $g'(f(x))f'(x) = 1, \qquad x \in N.$

Proof.   Suppose that $f'(p) > 0$. Since $f' : D \subseteq \mathbb{R} \to \mathbb{R}$ is continuous at p, there exists an open interval N containing p such that

4.5.18 $f'(x) > \tfrac{1}{2}f'(p) > 0$ for all $x \in N.$

Therefore f is strictly increasing on N and so, by Theorem 4.5.4, f is $1-1$ on N and $f(N)$ is an open interval. Let the local inverse of f be $g : M \to N$, where $M = f(N)$.

We will prove that g is differentiable. Given y and $y + k$ in M, there are unique points x and $x + h$ in N such that

4.5.19 $y = f(x), \quad x = g(y), \quad y + k = f(x + h), \quad x + h = g(y + k).$

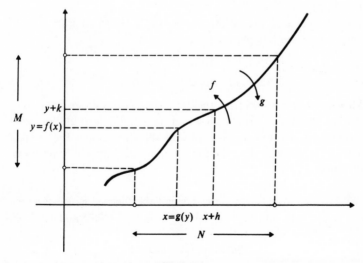

Fig. 4.8

See Fig. 4.8. By the Mean-Value Theorem,

$$k = f(x + h) - f(x) = hf'(x + \theta h) \text{ for some } \theta, 0 < \theta < 1.$$

Hence, by 4.5.18, $|k| \geqslant |h| f'(p)/2$. Therefore

$$\lim_{k \to 0} \frac{g(y + k) - g(y)}{k} = \lim_{k \to 0} \frac{h}{f(x + h) - f(x)}$$

$$= \lim_{h \to 0} \frac{h}{f(x + h) - f(x)} = \frac{1}{f'(x)}.$$

This proves that g is differentiable at $f(x)$ and also establishes the identity 4.5.17. Using that identity and the notation of 4.5.19 again,

$$\lim_{k \to 0} g'(y + k) = \lim_{k \to 0} g'(f(x + h)) = \lim_{k \to 0} \frac{1}{f'(x + h)}$$

$$= \lim_{h \to 0} \frac{1}{f'(x + h)} = g'(y).$$

Therefore g' is continuous and the proof is complete.

Notice that 4.5.17 is the consequence of applying the Chain Rule to the identity function $g \circ f = 1 : N \to N$. The rule can only be applied, however, if it is known that both functions are differentiable; it would not therefore be of any help to us in the proof of Theorem 4.5.16.

With reference to the notation $y = f(x)$, $x = g(y)$, identity 4.5.17 is often given in the less precise form

$$\frac{dy}{dx} \frac{dx}{dy} = 1.$$

Theorem 4.5.16 guarantees the *existence* of an inverse function under the stated conditions. However, an *explicit* formula for the inverse function is not necessarily available. Sometimes functions are invented expressly to describe the inverse – the 'arc sin' function is an example.

4.5.20 Example. The continuously differentiable function $h : \mathbb{R} \to \mathbb{R}$ given by $50h(x) = x^3(x - 5)^2$ was considered in Example 4.5.2 and its graph sketched in Fig. 4.3. Since

$$10h'(x) = x^2(x - 3)(x - 5),$$

the only extreme points are 3 and 5 (the point 0 is a point of inflection). By appealing to the above theorem, or by just looking at the graph, we can see that h is locally invertible at 2, for example. An appropriate open interval containing this point is $]-\infty, 3[$, and $h(]-\infty, 3[) =]-\infty, 2.16[$. Let the corresponding local inverse of h be $g:]-\infty, 2.16[\to]-\infty, 3[$. We cannot find a simple formula for g since the quintic equation $x^3(x-5)^2 = 50y$ has no elementary solution for x in terms of y. However, 4.5.17 gives us information about the derivative of g, for example

$$g'(h(2)) = g'(72) = \frac{1}{h'(2)} = \frac{1}{60}.$$

Notice that h is strictly increasing on $]-\infty, 3[$ even through $h'(0) = 0$. The function h is locally invertible at 0 but the inverse function g is not differentiable at $h(0) = 0$ since if it were we would have, by applying the Chain Rule to $g \circ h = 1 :]-\infty, 3[\to]-\infty, 3[$, that

4.5.21 $\qquad\qquad g'(h(0))h'(0) = g'(0).0 = 1.$

The graph of g is the reflection of the graph of $h:]-\infty, 3[\to]-\infty, 2.16[$ in the line $y = x$. The point of inflection of h at 0 becomes a point of infinite slope of g. This supports 4.5.21.

Exercises 4.5

1. (a) Sketch the graphs of the exponential function $y = e^x$, $x \in \mathbb{R}$ and the logarithmic function $y = \ln x$, $x \in \mathbb{R}^+$ on the same paper. Show that the second graph is a reflection of the first in the line $y = x$.
   (b) Prove generally that the graph of a $1-1$ function $f : D \subseteq \mathbb{R} \to \mathbb{R}$ and the graph of its inverse function $f^{-1} : f(D) \to D$ are reflections of each other in the line $y = x$.

2. Sketch the graphs of the following functions $f : D \subseteq \mathbb{R} \to \mathbb{R}$. Find the inverse function $f^{-1} : f(D) \to D$, if it exists, and sketch its graph.

   (a) $f(x) = x^3,$ $\qquad x \in \mathbb{R},$ $\qquad$ (b) $f(x) = x^2,$ $\qquad x \in \mathbb{R},$
   (c) $f(x) = x^2$ $\qquad x \in \mathbb{R}^+$ $\qquad$ (d) $f(x) = x^2,$ $\qquad x \in \mathbb{R}^-,$
   (e) $f(x) = \cos x,$ $\qquad x \in \mathbb{R},$ $\qquad$ (f) $f(x) = \cos x,$ $\qquad x \in]0, \pi[.$

Answer: inverse functions exist in cases (a), (c), (d), (f).

3. Sketch the graphs of the following functions $f : D \subseteq \mathbb{R} \to \mathbb{R}$. Prove that the inverse functions $f^{-1} : f(D) \to D$ exist. In these examples there is no simple formula for the inverse functions. Roughly sketch the graphs of the inverse functions.

   (a) $f(x) = x \ln x,$ $\quad x \in]0, 1/e[,$ $\quad$ (b) $f(x) = 3x^5 - 5x^3 + 2,$ $\quad x \in]-1, 1[,$
   $\qquad$ (c) $f(x) = x - \sin x,$ $\qquad x \in \mathbb{R}.$

Prove that the inverse function of Example (b) is not differentiable at the point $f(0) = 2$. At which points is the inverse function of Example (c) differentiable?

4. Prove Theorem 4.5.13. (Consider as domain of f an interval containing an extreme point.)

5. Define $f : \mathbb{R} \to \mathbb{R}$ by $f(x) = x^2 \sin(1/x) + x$, $x \neq 0$, and $f(0) = 0$. Sketch its graph. Prove that
   (a) f is differentiable on $\mathbb{R}$, and in particular, $f'(0) = 1$,
   (b) f is not locally $1-1$ at 0 (show that every open interval containing 0 contains an extreme point of f),
   (c) f' is discontinuous at 0.
   This example shows that the assumption that f is differentiable and that $f'(p) \neq 0$ does not imply that f is locally invertible at p.

6. Prove that the inverse of a $1-1$ continuous function $f : D \subseteq \mathbb{R} \to \mathbb{R}$ is continuous on its domain $f(D)$.

Hint: consider $(f^{-1})^{-1}(N)$, where N is an open subset of D, and apply Theorems 4.5.4(ii) and 4.2.10.

4.6   The Inverse Function Theorem

We now turn to the problem of generalizing Theorem 4.5.16 and consider what properties of a function $f : D \subseteq \mathbb{R}^n \to \mathbb{R}^n$ will guarantee that f has a "well behaved" local inverse at some point $\mathbf{p}$ in the open domain D. Since the effect of f near $\mathbf{p}$ is closely described by the linear function $L_{f, \mathbf{p}}$, one would expect a close relationship between the local invertibility of f near $\mathbf{p}$ and the invertibility of $L_{f, \mathbf{p}}$. Now $L_{f, \mathbf{p}}$ is invertible if and only if the Jacobian matrix $J_{f, \mathbf{p}}$ is non-singular or equivalently if and only if det $J_{f, \mathbf{p}} \neq 0$. Notice that when $n = 1$ this last condition reduces to $f'(p) \neq 0$, a property which was part of the hypothesis of Theorem 4.5.16. The generalization we are looking for involves the assumptions that det $J_{f, \mathbf{p}} \neq 0$ and that f is continuously differentiable (in order to avoid the problem illustrated in Exercise 4.5.5). The result is the celebrated Inverse Function Theorem – one of the most important theorems of vector calculus. We prove it by first showing that under the above assumptions there is a neighbourhood of $\mathbf{p}$ on which f is $1-1$ and smooth (that is, det $J_{f, \mathbf{q}} \neq 0$ for all $\mathbf{q}$ in the neighbourhood). We need two lemmas. The first one is a fundamental result about linear functions.

4.6.1 *Lemma.* *If the linear function* $T : \mathbb{R}^n \to \mathbb{R}^n$ *is an isomorphism* *(and so is invertible) then there exists $\mu > 0$ such that, for all $\mathbf{x} \in \mathbb{R}^n$,*

4.6.2 $$\|T(\mathbf{x})\| \leqslant \mu\|\mathbf{x}\| \qquad and \qquad \|T^{-1}(\mathbf{x})\| \geqslant \frac{1}{\mu}\|\mathbf{x}\|.$$

Proof.   Let $\mathbf{e}_1, \ldots, \mathbf{e}_n$ be the standard basis of $\mathbb{R}^n$. For any $\mathbf{x} \in \mathbb{R}^n$

$$T(\mathbf{x}) = T(x_1\mathbf{e}_1 + \cdots + x_n\mathbf{e}_n) = x_1 T(\mathbf{e}_1) + \cdots + x_n T(\mathbf{e}_n).$$

The triangle inequality implies that

$$\begin{aligned}\|T(\mathbf{x})\| &\leqslant |x_1|\|T(\mathbf{e}_1)\| + \cdots + |x_n|\|T(\mathbf{e}_n)\| \\ &= (|x_1|, \ldots, |x_n|) \cdot (\|T(\mathbf{e}_1)\|, \ldots, \|T(\mathbf{e}_n)\|),\end{aligned}$$

and therefore it follows from the Cauchy–Schwarz inequality that

$$\|T(\mathbf{x})\|^2 \leqslant \sum_1^n |x_i|^2 \sum_1^n \|T(\mathbf{e}_i)\|^2.$$

Setting $\mu^2 = \sum_1^n \|T(e_i)\|^2$ gives the first part of 4.6.2.

The second inequality follows by replacing $\mathbf{x}$ by $T^{-1}(\mathbf{x})$ in the first one.

The second lemma shows that the continuous differentiability of f leads to a continuous variation of the differentials $L_{f,\mathbf{x}}$.

4.6.3 Lemma.   *Let $f : D \subseteq \mathbb{R}^n \to \mathbb{R}^n$ be a C^1 function and let $\mathbf{p}$ be a point in the open set D. Then to each $\varepsilon > 0$ there corresponds a neighbourhood $N(\mathbf{p}, \delta) \subseteq D$ such that for all $\mathbf{q} \in N(\mathbf{p}, \delta)$,*

[i] $\|(L_{f,\mathbf{q}} - L_{f,\mathbf{p}})(\mathbf{h})\| \leqslant \varepsilon\|\mathbf{h}\|$ *for all $\mathbf{h} \in \mathbb{R}^n$,*

[ii] $\|f(\mathbf{q} + \mathbf{h}) - f(\mathbf{q}) - L_{f,\mathbf{p}}(\mathbf{h})\| \leqslant \varepsilon\|\mathbf{h}\|$

       for all $\mathbf{h} \in \mathbb{R}^n$ such that $\mathbf{q} + \mathbf{h} \in N(\mathbf{p}, \delta)$.

Proof.   For all $\mathbf{q} \in D$ and $\mathbf{h} \in \mathbb{R}^n$,

$$L_{f,\mathbf{q}}(\mathbf{h}) - L_{f,\mathbf{p}}(\mathbf{h}) = h_1\left(\frac{\partial f}{\partial x_1}(\mathbf{q}) - \frac{\partial f}{\partial x_1}(\mathbf{p})\right) + \cdots + h_n\left(\frac{\partial f}{\partial x_n}(\mathbf{q}) - \frac{\partial f}{\partial x_n}(\mathbf{p})\right).$$

Therefore for all such $\mathbf{q}$ and $\mathbf{h}$,

4.6.4
$$\|L_{f,\mathbf{q}}(\mathbf{h}) - L_{f,\mathbf{p}}(\mathbf{h})\| \leqslant |h_1| \left\| \frac{\partial f}{\partial x_1}(\mathbf{q}) - \frac{\partial f}{\partial x_1}(\mathbf{p}) \right\| + \cdots$$

$$+ |h_n| \left\| \frac{\partial f}{\partial x_n}(\mathbf{q}) - \frac{\partial f}{\partial x_n}(\mathbf{p}) \right\|.$$

The partial derivatives of f are continuous in D. Therefore, corresponding to any $\varepsilon > 0$ there is a neighbourhood $N(\mathbf{p}, \delta) \subseteq D$ such that for all $i = 1, \ldots, n$

$$\left\| \frac{\partial f}{\partial x_i}(\mathbf{q}) - \frac{\partial f}{\partial x_i}(\mathbf{p}) \right\| \leqslant \frac{\varepsilon}{n} \qquad \text{whenever } \mathbf{q} \in N(\mathbf{p}, \delta).$$

[*i*] By the choice of δ and by 4.6.4

$$\|L_{f,\mathbf{q}}(\mathbf{h}) - L_{f,\mathbf{p}}(\mathbf{h})\| \leqslant \frac{\varepsilon}{n}(|h_1| + \cdots + |h_n|) \leqslant \varepsilon \|\mathbf{h}\|$$

whenever $\mathbf{q} \in N(\mathbf{p}, \delta)$.

[*ii*] For any $\mathbf{q}$ and $\mathbf{q} + \mathbf{h}$ in $N(\mathbf{p}, \delta)$ let

$$\mathbf{u} = f(\mathbf{q} + \mathbf{h}) - f(\mathbf{q}) - L_{f,\mathbf{p}}(\mathbf{h}).$$

The Mean-Value Theorem 4.4.16 implies that there exists $0 < \theta < 1$ such that
$$(f(\mathbf{q} + \mathbf{h}) - f(\mathbf{q})) \cdot \mathbf{u} = L_{f,\mathbf{q} + \theta\mathbf{h}}(\mathbf{h}) \cdot \mathbf{u}.$$
Hence

$$(f(\mathbf{q} + \mathbf{h}) - f(\mathbf{q}) - L_{f,\mathbf{p}}(\mathbf{h})) \cdot \mathbf{u} = (L_{f,\mathbf{q} + \theta\mathbf{h}}(\mathbf{h}) - L_{f,\mathbf{p}}(\mathbf{h})) \cdot \mathbf{u}.$$

Therefore, substituting for $\mathbf{u}$ and applying the Cauchy–Schwarz inequality,

$$\|f(\mathbf{q} + \mathbf{h}) - f(\mathbf{q}) - L_{f,\mathbf{p}}(\mathbf{h})\| \leqslant \|(L_{f,\mathbf{q} + \theta\mathbf{h}} - L_{f,\mathbf{p}})(\mathbf{h})\|.$$

The result follows from (i).

We can now prove our first main result, that if a C^1 function is smooth at a point, then it is smooth and 1–1 in a neighbourhood of the point.

4.6.5 Theorem.   *Let* $f : D \subseteq \mathbb{R}^n \to \mathbb{R}^n$ *be a* C^1 *function on an open set* D *in* $\mathbb{R}^n$ *and let* $\mathbf{p}$ *be a point in* D *such that* $\det J_{f,\mathbf{p}} \neq 0$. *Then there exists neighbourhood* $N(\mathbf{p}, \delta) \subseteq D$ *such that*
[**i**] $\det J_{f,\mathbf{q}} \neq 0$ *for all* $\mathbf{q} \in N(\mathbf{p}, \delta)$,
[**ii**] $f : N(\mathbf{p}, \delta) \subseteq \mathbb{R}^n \to \mathbb{R}^n$ *is* 1–1.

Proof. Since $L_{f,\mathbf{p}}$ is invertible, by Lemma 4.6.1 there exists $\mu > 0$ such that for all $\mathbf{x} \in \mathbb{R}^n$

4.6.6 $$\|L_{f,\mathbf{p}}^{-1}(\mathbf{x})\| \leqslant \mu \|\mathbf{x}\| \quad \text{and} \quad \|L_{f,\mathbf{p}}(\mathbf{x})\| \geqslant \frac{1}{\mu} \|\mathbf{x}\|$$

We shall prove that the neighbourhood $N(\mathbf{p}, \delta)$ which corresponds in Lemma 4.6.3 to $\varepsilon = 1/2\mu$ has the properties stated in the theorem.

[*i*] Suppose that for some $\mathbf{q} \in N(p, \delta)$, $\det J_{f,\mathbf{q}} = 0$. Then there exists $\mathbf{h} \neq \mathbf{0}$ in $\mathbb{R}^n$ such that $L_{f,\mathbf{q}}(\mathbf{h}) = 0$. But, by Lemma 4.6.3(i), since $\varepsilon = 1/2\mu$

$$\| -L_{f,\mathbf{p}}(\mathbf{h})\| = \|(L_{f,\mathbf{q}} - L_{f,\mathbf{p}})(\mathbf{h})\| \leqslant \frac{1}{2\mu} \|\mathbf{h}\|.$$

This contradicts 4.6.6.

[*ii*] Suppose similarly that there are two distinct points $\mathbf{q}$ and $\mathbf{q} + \mathbf{h}$ in $N(\mathbf{p}, \delta)$ such that $f(\mathbf{q} + \mathbf{h}) = f(\mathbf{q})$. Then by Lemma 4.6.3[ii],

$$\| -L_{f,\mathbf{p}}(\mathbf{h})\| = \|f(\mathbf{q} + \mathbf{h}) - f(\mathbf{q}) - L_{f,\mathbf{p}}(\mathbf{h})\| \leqslant \frac{1}{2\mu} \|\mathbf{h}\|,$$

and again we have a contradiction.

Theorem 4.6.5 tells us that if the Jacobian of a continuously differentiable function f is non-singular at a point $\mathbf{p}$ in the domain of f, then f is locally invertible at $\mathbf{p}$. It tells us nothing about the function g inverse to f. The remarkable result which we now prove is that the set $f(N(\mathbf{p}, \delta))$ contains a neighbourhood V of $f(\mathbf{p})$ on which the inverse function g is itself continuously differentiable. Lemma 4.6.3 again gives the appropriate information about the function f to facilitate the proof.

4.6.7 Theorem. The Inverse Function Theorem. *Let* $f : D \subseteq \mathbb{R}^n \to \mathbb{R}^n$ *be continuously differentiable on an open set D in $\mathbb{R}^n$ and let* $\det J_{f,\mathbf{p}} \neq 0$ *at a point* $\mathbf{p} \in D$. *Then*

[**i**] *there exists an open set U in $\mathbb{R}^n$ containing $\mathbf{p}$ and an open set V in $\mathbb{R}^n$ containing $f(\mathbf{p})$ such that $U \subseteq D$, $f(U) = V$ and f is 1–1 on U;*

[**ii**] *the function $g : V \subseteq \mathbb{R}^n \to \mathbb{R}^n$ locally inverse to f on U is continuously differentiable;*

[**iii**] $J_{g,f(\mathbf{p})} J_{f,\mathbf{p}} = I.$

Proof. Preliminaries. Denote the linear function $L_{f,\mathbf{p}}$ by L. Since $\det J_{f,\mathbf{p}} \neq 0$ the function L has an inverse $L^{-1} : \mathbb{R}^n \to \mathbb{R}^n$. Let $\mu > 0$ be such that (see 4.6.2)

4.6.8 $\|L^{-1}(\mathbf{z})\| \leqslant \mu\|\mathbf{z}\|,$ for all $\mathbf{z} \in \mathbb{R}^n.$

Let $N(\mathbf{p}, \delta) \subseteq D$ be the neighbourhood (see Lemma 4.6.3 with $\varepsilon = 1/2\mu$) such that whenever $\mathbf{q}$ and $\mathbf{q} + \mathbf{h}$ lie in $N(\mathbf{p}, \delta)$,

4.6.9 $\|f(\mathbf{q} + \mathbf{h}) - f(\mathbf{q}) - L(\mathbf{h})\| \leqslant \dfrac{1}{2\mu}\|\mathbf{h}\|.$

It was shown in Theorem 4.6.5 that f is 1–1 on $N(\mathbf{p}, \delta)$ and that $L_{f,\mathbf{q}}$ is an isomorphism on $\mathbb{R}^n$ for all $\mathbf{q} \in N(\mathbf{p},\delta)$.

We shall show that there exists a neighbourhood $V = N(f(\mathbf{p}), \sigma)$ of $f(\mathbf{p})$ in $\mathbb{R}^n$ such that for each $\mathbf{y}$ in V there is a (unique) $\mathbf{x} \in N(\mathbf{p}, \delta)$ such that $\mathbf{y} = f(\mathbf{x})$. This is equivalent to showing that

4.6.10 $V \subseteq f(N(\mathbf{p}, \delta)).$

Once this is established part [i] of the theorem will follow since the set $U = f^{-1}(V) \cap N(\mathbf{p}, \delta)$ is open in D (and therefore in $\mathbb{R}^n$) and 4.6.10 implies that $f(U) = V$. See Fig. 4.9.

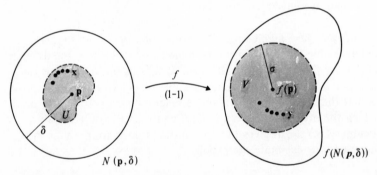

Fig. 4.9

For each $\mathbf{y} \in N(f(\mathbf{p}), \sigma)$ we shall find $\mathbf{x} \in N(\mathbf{p}, \delta)$ such that $\mathbf{y} = f(\mathbf{x})$ by a method of successive approximation. Starting with $\mathbf{x}_1 = \mathbf{p}$ we find a sequence $(\mathbf{x}_k)$ in $N(\mathbf{p}, \delta)$ such that $\mathbf{y} - f(\mathbf{x}_k) \to 0$ in $f(N(\mathbf{p}, \delta))$. If $(\mathbf{x}_k)$ converges to $\mathbf{x}$ in $N(\mathbf{p}, \delta)$, then the continuity of f implies that $\mathbf{y} = f(\mathbf{x})$. The number σ has to be small enough to guarantee that for each $\mathbf{y} \in N(f(\mathbf{p}), \sigma)$ the corresponding sequence $(\mathbf{x}_k)$ converges in $N(\mathbf{p}, \delta)$.

Before deciding what σ is to be, it is useful to consider how the sequence $(\mathbf{x}_k)$ might be chosen. Suppose we already have $\mathbf{x}_k$ in

$N(\mathbf{p}, \delta)$. How should we choose $\mathbf{x}_{k+1} = \mathbf{x}_k + \mathbf{h}$ in $N(\mathbf{p}, \delta)$ so that $f(\mathbf{x}_{k+1})$ is a better approximation to $\mathbf{y}$ than is $f(\mathbf{x}_k)$? Since f is differentiable, we have

$$f(\mathbf{x}_k + \mathbf{h}) \approx f(\mathbf{x}_k) + L_{f,\mathbf{x}_k}(\mathbf{h}).$$

But $L_{f,\mathbf{x}_k}(\mathbf{h})$ is not far from $L(\mathbf{h})$ (see Lemma 4.6.3) and it therefore seems plausible to choose $\mathbf{h}$ such that

$$\mathbf{y} = f(\mathbf{x}_k) + L(\mathbf{h}).$$

Taking $\mathbf{h} = L^{-1}(\mathbf{y} - f(\mathbf{x}_k))$ we are led to define

4.6.11 $$\mathbf{x}_{k+1} = \mathbf{x}_k + L^{-1}(\mathbf{y} - f(\mathbf{x}_k)).$$

We need to check of course that $\mathbf{x}_{k+1}$ is also in $N(\mathbf{p}, \delta)$ before proceeding to the next stage.

Notice that if the terms of the sequence $(\mathbf{x}_k)$ satisfy 4.6.11 for each $k \in \mathbb{N}$ and if $(\mathbf{x}_k)$ converges to $\mathbf{x}$ in $N(\mathbf{p}, \delta)$, then, since L^{-1} and f are continuous,

$$\mathbf{x} = \mathbf{x} + L^{-1}(\mathbf{y} - f(\mathbf{x})).$$

But L^{-1} is an isomorphism. Therefore $\mathbf{y} = f(\mathbf{x})$.

In studying the convergence of $(\mathbf{x}_k)$ we shall consider vectors $\mathbf{x}_{k+1} - \mathbf{x}_k$, for each $\mathbf{k} \in \mathbb{N}$. There exists $\mathbf{z}_k \in \mathbb{R}^n$ for each $k \in \mathbb{N}$ such that

4.6.12 $$f(\mathbf{x}_{k+1}) - f(\mathbf{x}_k) = L(\mathbf{x}_{k+1} - \mathbf{x}_k) + \|\mathbf{x}_{k+1} - \mathbf{x}_k\|\mathbf{z}_k,$$

where by 4.6.9,

4.6.13 $$\|\mathbf{z}_k\| \leqslant \frac{1}{2\mu}.$$

It follows from 4.6.12 that for each $k \in \mathbb{N}$,

4.6.14 $$\mathbf{x}_{k+1} - \mathbf{x}_k = L^{-1}(f(\mathbf{x}_{k+1}) - f(\mathbf{x}_k)) - \|\mathbf{x}_{k+1} - \mathbf{x}_k\|L^{-1}(\mathbf{z}_k).$$

Proof of $[i]$ Let $\sigma = \delta/4\mu$ and choose $\mathbf{y} \in N(f(\mathbf{p}), \sigma)$. With initial value $\mathbf{x}_1 = \mathbf{p} \in N(\mathbf{p}, \delta)$ we consider the next two terms of a sequence $(\mathbf{x}_k)$ defined by the recurrence relation 4.6.11. Putting $k = 1$ and $\mathbf{x}_1 = \mathbf{p}$ in 4.6.11 we obtain

$$\|\mathbf{x}_2 - \mathbf{p}\| = \|L^{-1}(\mathbf{y} - f(\mathbf{p}))\|,$$

and from 4.6.8

$$\|L^{-1}(\mathbf{y} - f(\mathbf{p}))\| \leqslant \mu\|\mathbf{y} - f(\mathbf{p})\| < \mu\sigma = \frac{\delta}{4}.$$

Hence

4.6.15 $$\|\mathbf{x}_2 - \mathbf{x}_1\| = \|\mathbf{x}_2 - \mathbf{p}\| < \frac{\delta}{4}$$

and therefore $\mathbf{x}_2 \in N(\mathbf{p}, \delta)$.

Since $\mathbf{x}_2 \in D$, the recurrence relation 4.6.11 defines $\mathbf{x}_3$, and

$$\begin{aligned}\mathbf{x}_3 - \mathbf{x}_2 &= (\mathbf{x}_2 + L^{-1}(\mathbf{y} - f(\mathbf{x}_2))) - (\mathbf{x}_1 + L^{-1}(\mathbf{y} - f(\mathbf{x}_1))) \\ &= (\mathbf{x}_2 - \mathbf{x}_1) - L^{-1}(f(\mathbf{x}_2) - f(\mathbf{x}_1)) \\ &= -\|\mathbf{x}_2 - \mathbf{x}_1\| L^{-1}(\mathbf{z}_1) \qquad \text{(by 4.6.14)}.\end{aligned}$$

Therefore by 4.6.8 and 4.6.13

4.6.16 $$\|\mathbf{x}_3 - \mathbf{x}_2\| \leqslant \tfrac{1}{2}\|\mathbf{x}_2 - \mathbf{x}_1\| < \frac{\delta}{8}.$$

Now by the triangle inequality, and by 4.6.16 and 4.6.15.

$$\|\mathbf{x}_3 - \mathbf{p}\| \leqslant \|\mathbf{x}_3 - \mathbf{x}_2\| + \|\mathbf{x}_2 - \mathbf{x}_1\| < (\tfrac{1}{8} + \tfrac{1}{4})\delta < \tfrac{1}{2}\delta.$$

The above argument can be used step by step to show that for all $k \geqslant 2$

4.6.17 $$\|\mathbf{x}_k - \mathbf{x}_{k-1}\| < \frac{\delta}{2^k}$$

and that

4.6.18 $$\|\mathbf{x}_k - \mathbf{p}\| < \left(\frac{1}{2^k} + \cdots + \frac{1}{2^2}\right)\delta < \tfrac{1}{2}\delta.$$

Furthermore from 4.6.17 and 4.6.18, for all $k > l \geqslant 1$,

4.6.19 $$\begin{aligned}\|\mathbf{x}_k - \mathbf{x}_l\| &\leqslant \|\mathbf{x}_k - \mathbf{x}_{k-1}\| + \cdots + \|\mathbf{x}_{l+1} - \mathbf{x}_l\| \\ &\leqslant \left(\frac{1}{2^k} + \cdots + \frac{1}{2^{l+1}}\right)\delta < \frac{\delta}{2^l}.\end{aligned}$$

Hence $(\mathbf{x}_k)$ is a Cauchy sequence in $N(\mathbf{p}, \delta)$ which therefore converges to say $\mathbf{x} \in \mathbb{R}^n$. By 4.6.18, $\|\mathbf{x} - \mathbf{p}\| \leqslant \tfrac{1}{2}\delta$ and therefore $\mathbf{x} \in N(\mathbf{p}, \delta)$. As observed earlier, 4.6.11 now implies that $f(\mathbf{x}) = \mathbf{y}$.

The conclusions of part [i] are therefore satisfied by $V = N(f(\mathbf{p}), \sigma)$ and $U = f^{-1}(V) \cap N(\mathbf{p}, \delta)$ (see the remarks following 4.6.9).

Remark. Our proof can be expressed in terms of a function $\phi : B \subseteq \mathbb{R}^n \to \mathbb{R}^n$ where B is a closed ball, centre $\mathbf{p}$, and

$$\phi(\mathbf{x}) = \mathbf{x} + L^{-1}(\mathbf{y} - f(\mathbf{x})), \qquad \mathbf{x} \in B$$

(compare 4.6.11). One can prove that, subject to certain restrictions,

$$\|\phi(\mathbf{x}') - \phi(\mathbf{x})\| \leqslant \tfrac{1}{2}\|\mathbf{x}' - \mathbf{x}\|, \qquad \mathbf{x}, \mathbf{x}' \in B,$$

and $\phi(B) \subset B$. The function ϕ is a *contraction mapping* on B and as such has a unique fixed point $\mathbf{x}$ in B (such that $\phi(\mathbf{x}) = \mathbf{x}$). Therefore $\mathbf{y} = f(\mathbf{x})$. For details of this approach see for example Rudin, *Principles of Analysis*.

Proof of [*ii*] *and* [*iii*]. Let U and V be the open subsets of $\mathbb{R}^n$ considered in part [i]. We know that $f : U \to V$ is 1–1 and maps U onto V. Let $g : V \to U$ be the local inverse of f on U. Suppose that $\mathbf{y}$ and $\mathbf{y} + \mathbf{k}$ are both in V. Then there exist unique $\mathbf{x}$ and $\mathbf{x} + \mathbf{h}$ in U such that

4.6.20
$$\begin{aligned} f(\mathbf{x}) &= \mathbf{y}, & \mathbf{x} &= g(\mathbf{y}) \\ f(\mathbf{x} + \mathbf{h}) &= \mathbf{y} + \mathbf{k}, & \mathbf{x} + \mathbf{h} &= g(\mathbf{y} + \mathbf{k}). \end{aligned}$$

Since f is differentiable at $\mathbf{x}$ there is a function $\eta : D_{\mathbf{x}} \subseteq \mathbb{R}^n \to \mathbb{R}^n$ such that (by 4.6.20).

4.6.21
$$\mathbf{k} = f(\mathbf{x} + \mathbf{h}) - f(\mathbf{x}) = L_{f,\mathbf{x}}(\mathbf{h}) + \|\mathbf{h}\|\eta(\mathbf{h})$$

and

$$\lim_{\mathbf{h} \to 0} \eta(\mathbf{h}) = \mathbf{0}.$$

By Theorem 4.6.5[i], $L_{f,\mathbf{x}}$ is an isomorphism on $\mathbb{R}^n$. Let $S = L_{f,\mathbf{x}}^{-1} : \mathbb{R}^n \to \mathbb{R}^n$. Then applying S to 4.6.21

$$S(\mathbf{k}) = \mathbf{h} + S(\|\mathbf{h}\|\eta(\mathbf{h})).$$

Therefore

4.6.22
$$g(\mathbf{y} + \mathbf{k}) - g(\mathbf{y}) = \mathbf{h} = S(\mathbf{k}) + \|\mathbf{k}\|S\left(-\frac{\|\mathbf{h}\|}{\|\mathbf{k}\|}\eta(\mathbf{h})\right).$$

But by 4.6.9

$$\|L(\mathbf{h})\| - \|f(\mathbf{x} + \mathbf{h}) - f(\mathbf{x})\| \leqslant \frac{1}{2\mu}\|\mathbf{h}\|.$$

So by 4.6.8 and 4.6.21,

$$\frac{1}{\mu}\|\mathbf{h}\| - \|\mathbf{k}\| \leqslant \frac{1}{2\mu}\|\mathbf{h}\|,$$

that is

$$\|\mathbf{k}\| \geqslant \frac{1}{2\mu}\|\mathbf{h}\|.$$

Hence, since S is continuous at $\mathbf{0}$,

4.6.23 $$\lim_{\mathbf{k} \to 0} S\left(-\frac{\|\mathbf{h}\|}{\|\mathbf{k}\|}\eta(\mathbf{h})\right) = \mathbf{0}.$$

Expressions 4.6.22 and 4.6.23 imply that g is differentiable at $\mathbf{y}$ with differential $L_{g,\mathbf{y}} = S = L_{f,\mathbf{x}}^{-1}$. Therefore $J_{g,\mathbf{y}}$ is non-singular and

4.6.24 $$J_{g,\mathbf{y}} = (J_{f,\mathbf{x}})^{-1}, \qquad \mathbf{x} \in U, \ \mathbf{y} = f(\mathbf{x}) \in V.$$

Part [iii] of the theorem follows taking $\mathbf{x} = \mathbf{p}$ and $\mathbf{y} = f(\mathbf{p})$.

The (i,j) entry of $(J_{f,\mathbf{x}})^{-1}$ is a rational combination of $(\partial f_k/\partial x_l)(\mathbf{x})$, $k, l = 1, \ldots, n$ (Cramer's Rule).

From 4.6.24, $(\partial g_i/\partial y_i)(\mathbf{y}) = (\partial g_i/\partial y_j)(f(\mathbf{x}))$ is therefore a continuous function of $\mathbf{x}$. But $\mathbf{x} = g(\mathbf{y})$ is a continuous function of $\mathbf{y}$ and therefore

$$\frac{\partial g_i}{\partial y_j}(f(g(\mathbf{y}))) = \frac{\partial g_i}{\partial y_j}(\mathbf{y})$$

is a continuous function of $\mathbf{y}$. Hence g is continuously differentiable on V.

4.6.25 *Remark.* Part [iii] of the theorem is a consequence of applying the Chain Rule (Theorem 4.4.1) to the identity function $\mathbf{l} = g \circ f : U \to U$.

4.6.26 *Example.* The function $f : \mathbb{R}^2 \to \mathbb{R}^2$ given by

$$f(\mathbf{r}) = f(x, y) = (e^x \cos y, e^x \sin y), \qquad (x, y) \in \mathbb{R}^2$$

is continuously differentiable in $\mathbb{R}^2$, and

$$J_{f,\mathbf{r}} = \begin{bmatrix} e^x \cos y & -e^x \sin y \\ e^x \sin y & e^x \cos y \end{bmatrix}.$$

Hence

$$\det J_{f,\mathbf{r}} = e^x \neq 0,$$

and so f is locally invertible at every point in $\mathbb{R}^2$. Indeed, given any $\mathbf{p} \in \mathbb{R}^2$ there is a formula for the inverse of f which applies when the domain of f is restricted to a sufficiently small open set containing $\mathbf{p}$.

For example, f is invertible on the open rectangle

$$R_1 = \{(x, y)\in\mathbb{R}^2| -1 < x < 1, -\tfrac{1}{2}\pi < y < \tfrac{1}{2}\pi\},$$

and $f(R_1) = A$, as illustrated in Fig. 4.10.

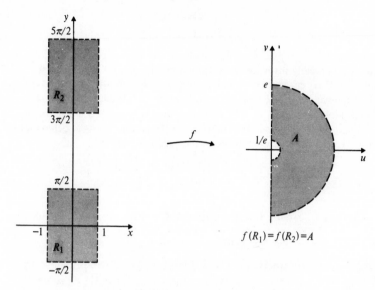

Fig. 4.10 $f(x, y) = (e^x\cos y, e^x\sin y)$

The inverse of $f : R_1 \to A$ is $g : A \to R_1$ given by the formula $g(u, v) = (x, y)\in R_1$, where

$$x = \ln\sqrt{(u^2 + v^2)}, \qquad y = \arctan\frac{v}{u}, \qquad (u, v)\in A.$$

Again, f is invertible on

$$R_2 = \{(x, y)\in\mathbb{R}^2| -1 < x < 1, \tfrac{3}{2}\pi < y < \tfrac{5}{2}\pi\},$$

and $f(R_2) = A$. The inverse of $f : R_2 \to A$ is $g^* : A \to R_2$ given by the formula $g^*(u, v) = (x, y)\in R_2$, where

$$x = \ln\sqrt{(u^2 + v^2)}, \qquad y = \left(\arctan\frac{v}{u}\right) + 2\pi, \qquad (u, v)\in A.$$

This example illustrates the *local* nature of the Inverse Function Theorem. Although $\det J_{f, \mathbf{r}} \neq 0$ for all $\mathbf{r}\in\mathbb{R}^2$ and f is locally invertible at every point in $\mathbb{R}^2$, the function f is not *globally* invertible. By this we mean that f is not invertible on the whole of its domain. This is clearly so because f is not 1–1 on $\mathbb{R}^2$.

4.6.27 *Example.* The function $f : \mathbb{R}^2 \to \mathbb{R}^2$ given by

$$f(\mathbf{r}) = f(x, y) = (y \sin x, \, x + y + 1), \qquad (x, y) \in \mathbb{R}^2$$

is continuously differentiable in $\mathbb{R}^2$, and

$$J_{f, \mathbf{r}} = \begin{bmatrix} y \cos x & \sin x \\ 1 & 1 \end{bmatrix}.$$

Therefore $\det J_{f, \mathbf{r}} = y \cos x - \sin x$. In particular, if $\mathbf{a} = (0, 1)$, then $\det J_{f, \mathbf{a}} = 1$ and so f is locally invertible at $\mathbf{a}$. Put $\mathbf{b} = f(\mathbf{a}) = (0, 2)$. By the Inverse Function Theorem there exist open sets U and V with $\mathbf{a} \in U$ and $\mathbf{b} \in V$ such that f is invertible on U and the inverse of $f : U \to V$ is a continuously differentiable function $g : V \to U$. Although the existence of g is guaranteed, there is no simple formula that describes it. However, the local behaviour of g near the point $\mathbf{b}$ is known through the Jacobian matrix

$$J_{g, \mathbf{b}} = (J_{f, \mathbf{a}})^{-1} = \begin{bmatrix} 1 & 0 \\ 1 & 1 \end{bmatrix}^{-1} = \begin{bmatrix} 1 & 0 \\ -1 & 1 \end{bmatrix}.$$

Note the following interpretation of Example 4.6.27: the equations

$$u = y \sin x, \qquad v = x + y + 1$$

can be solved uniquely for x and y with (x, y) sufficiently close to $(0, 1)$ in terms of u and v for values of (u, v) sufficiently close to $(0, 2)$, and the solutions $x = g_1(u, v)$, $y = g_2(u, v)$ are continuously differentiable.

Exercises 4.6

1. Let $f : \mathbb{R}^2 \to \mathbb{R}^2$ be defined by

    $$f(\mathbf{r}) = f(x, y) = (x^2 - y^2, \, 2xy), \qquad (x, y) \in \mathbb{R}^2.$$

    (a) Calculate the Jacobian matrix $J_{f, \mathbf{r}}$ and prove that f is locally invertible except possibly at the origin.
    (b) Let $U \subseteq \mathbb{R}^2$ be a neighbourhood of the point $\mathbf{p} = (1, 1) \in \mathbb{R}^2$ as in Theorem 4.6.7 (so that f is 1–1 on U), and denote the inverse of $f : U \to \mathbb{R}^2$ by $g : f(U) \to U$. Find the Jacobian matrix $J_{g, \, f(\mathbf{p})}$.

    Hint: apply Theorem 4.6.7(iii).

    (c) Let $U^* \subseteq \mathbb{R}^2$ be a neighbourhood of the point $\mathbf{q} = (-1, -1) \in \mathbb{R}^2$ as in Theorem 4.6.7 and denote the inverse of $f : U^* \to \mathbb{R}^2$ by $g^* : f(U^*) \to U^*$. Find the Jacobian matrix $J_{g^*, \, f(\mathbf{q})}$.
    (d) Observe that $f(\mathbf{p}) = f(\mathbf{q}) = (0, 2)$, but that $J_{g, (0, 2)} \neq J_{g^*, (0, 2)}$. Conclude that although f is locally invertible at every $\mathbf{r} \in \mathbb{R}^2 \setminus \{0\}$, it is not globally invertible on $\mathbb{R}^2 \setminus \{0\}$.

Direct proof: f is not 1–1 on $\mathbb{R}^2\backslash\{0\}$.

(e) Put $f(x, y) = (u, v)$ and find an expression for $g(u, v)$, $(u, v) \in f(U)$ and an expression for $g^*(u, v)$, $(u, v) \in f(U)$.

Answer: The equations $u = x^2 - y^2$, $v = 2xy$ are solved by

$$x = \pm[\tfrac{1}{2}(u + \sqrt{(u^2 + v^2)})]^{1/2}, \qquad y = \pm[\tfrac{1}{2}(-u + \sqrt{(u^2 + v^2)})]^{1/2}.$$

The plus or minus sign must be chosen in the definitions of g and g^* such that $g(0, 2) = (1, 1)$ and $g^*(0, 2) = (-1, -1)$.

(f) Is f locally invertible at $(0, 0)$?

Hint: is there a neighbourhood of $(0, 0)$ on which f is 1–1?

2. Without solving the equations

$$u = x^2 - y^2, \qquad v = 2xy,$$

prove that they effectively define x and y (a) as continuously differentiable functions of u and v in a neighbourhood of $(u, v) = (0, 2)$ such that $x = 1$, $y = 1$ when $(u, v) = (0, 2)$, and also (b) as continuously differentiable functions of u and v in a neighbourhood of $(u, v) = (0, 2)$ such that $x = -1$, $y = -1$ when $(u, v) = (0, 2)$. By considering appropriate Jacobian matrices show that in case (a),

$$\frac{\partial x}{\partial v}(0, 2) = \tfrac{1}{4}$$

and in case (b),

$$\frac{\partial x}{\partial v}(0, 2) = -\tfrac{1}{4}.$$

(This is a rephrasing of part of Exercise 1, and illustrates a possible ambiguity encountered in solving functional equations.)

3. Prove that the equations

$$u = y\sin x, \qquad v = x + y + 1$$

effectively define x and y as continuously differentiable functions of u and v in a neighbourhood of $(u, v) = (0, 2)$ with (x, y) taking values in a neighbourhood of $(1, 0)$. If the functional relationship is described by $(x, y) = g^*(u, v)$, calculate the Jacobian matrix $J_{g^*, (0, 2)}$. Compare with Example 4.6.27.

4. Let $f : \mathbb{R}^2 \to \mathbb{R}^2$ be defined by

$$f(x, y) = (x^3 + y^3, x^3 - y^3), \qquad (x, y) \in \mathbb{R}^2.$$

Prove that the Jacobian matrix $J_{f, (0, 0)}$ is the zero matrix. Show that nevertheless f is globally invertible on $\mathbb{R}^2$.

Hint: prove that f is 1–1 on $\mathbb{R}^2$.

Show also that the inverse function is not differentiable at $f(0, 0) = (0, 0)$.

5. Compute the Jacobian matrix $J_{f,(x,y)}$ and discuss the local behaviour of the functions $f : \mathbb{R}^2 \to \mathbb{R}^2$, where
   (a) $f(x, y) = (x \cos y, x \sin y)$,
   (b) $f(x, y) = (x^2 + 2xy + y^2, 3x + 3y)$,
   (c) $f(x, y) = \dfrac{1}{\sqrt{2}}(x + y, x - y)$.

4.7   Implicitly defined functions

A rule such as

4.7.1 $f(x) = \sqrt{(1 - x^2)}, \qquad x \in [-1, 1]$

defines a function f explicitly. By this we mean that at each point in its domain the value of f is calculated by direct substitution in the formula. The graph of f is also explicitly determined. In the present example it is the set of points

$$S = \{(x, \sqrt{(1 - x^2)}) \in \mathbb{R}^2 \,|\, x \in [-1, 1]\}$$

(see Fig. 4.11(i)).

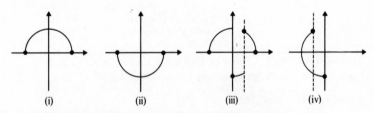

Fig. 4.11 (i) $y = f(x)$; (ii) $y = f^*(x)$; (iii) $y = f^{\dagger}(x)$

The graph S is a subset of the circle

4.7.2 $C = \{(x, y) \in \mathbb{R}^2 \,|\, x^2 + y^2 - 1 = 0\}$,

for if we substitute $y = f(x) = \sqrt{(1 - x^2)}$, then the equation

$$x^2 + y^2 - 1 = 0$$

is satisfied whenever $x \in [-1, 1]$. This equation is said to define the function f *implicitly*. If we put $F(x, y) = x^2 + y^2 - 1$, $(x, y) \in \mathbb{R}^2$, then we have

$$F(x, f(x)) = 0, \qquad x \in [-1, 1].$$

This means that the graph of f is a subset of the level set of F corresponding to the value 0. Generalizing this example, we are led to the following definition.

4.7.3 Definition. *Given a real-valued function $F : D \subseteq \mathbb{R}^m \to \mathbb{R}$, where $m \geqslant 2$, if there exists a real-valued function $f : D^* \subseteq \mathbb{R}^{m-1} \to \mathbb{R}$ such that for all $(x_1, \ldots x_{m-1}) \in D^*$,*

4.7.4
$$F(x_1, \ldots, x_{m-1}, f(x_1, \ldots, x_{m-1})) = 0,$$

then the function f is said to be defined implicitly *on D^* by the equation*

4.7.5
$$F(x_1, \ldots, x_m) = 0.$$

The condition 4.7.4 can be expressed in the form

4.7.6
$$F(\mathbf{x}, f(\mathbf{x})) = 0 \qquad \mathbf{x} \in D^* \subseteq \mathbb{R}^{m-1}.$$

We observe that equation 4.7.5 defines a real-valued function f implicitly if the level set of F corresponding to the value 0 contains the graph of f as a subset.

4.7.7 Example. An equation of the form 4.7.5 does not in general lead to the implicit definition of just one function. For example, if

$$F(x, y) = x^2 + y^2 - 1, \qquad (x, y) \in \mathbb{R}^2,$$

then the level set of F corresponding to 0 is the circle C of 4.7.2 which contains an infinity of different graphs. We have illustrated just three in Fig. 4.11(i)–(iii). They are the graphs of the following functions:

(i) $\quad f(x) = \sqrt{(1 - x^2)}, \qquad x \in [-1, 1];$

(ii) $\quad f^*(x) = -\sqrt{(1 - x^2)}, \qquad x \in [-1, 1];$

(iii) $f^\dagger(x) = \begin{cases} \sqrt{(1 - x^2)}, & x \in [-1, 0[; \\ -\sqrt{(1 - x^2)}, & x \in [0, \frac{1}{2}[; \\ \sqrt{(1 - x^2)}, & x \in [\frac{1}{2}, 1]. \end{cases}$

All functions defined implicitly by the equation $x^2 + y^2 - 1 = 0$ have as their domain a subset of the interval $[-1, 1]$.

The curve of Fig. 4.11(iv) illustrates a subset of the level set C which is not the graph of a function, because for any $x \in]-1, -\frac{1}{2}]$ there are two values of y such that $(x, y) \in C$. We observe, however, that this curve is the graph of a function when the roles of the x and y coordinates are interchanged, for it consists of the points $(g(y), y)$ where

4.7.8
$$g(y) = -\sqrt{(1 - y^2)}, \qquad y \in [-1, \tfrac{1}{2}\sqrt{3}].$$

In this way the equation $F(x, y) = 0$ may also be regarded as implicitly defining the function $g : [-1, \tfrac{1}{2}\sqrt{3}] \subseteq \mathbb{R} \to \mathbb{R}$ given in 4.7.8.

4.7.9 *Example.* The equation

4.7.10
$$x_1^2 + \tfrac{1}{2}x_2^2 + x_3^2 - 1 = 0$$

implicitly defines (among others) the function $f : D \subseteq \mathbb{R}^2 \to \mathbb{R}$, where

$$D = \{(x_1, x_2) \in \mathbb{R}^2 \,|\, x_1^2 + \tfrac{1}{2}x_2^2 \leqslant 1\}$$

and

$$f(x_1, x_2) = -\sqrt{(1 - x_1^2 - \tfrac{1}{2}x_2^2)}, \qquad (x_1, x_2) \in D.$$

The graph of f is part of the surface of the ellipsoid which is defined by Equation 4.7.10.

It is in the nature of the equation $x^2 + y^2 - 1 = 0$ considered above that the functions it defines implicitly can also be described explicitly. It is simply a case of "solving" for y (or for x) and making a selection of the possibilities. The following example illustrates an implicitly defined function that has no simple explicit presentation.

4.7.11 *Example.* Consider the function $F : \mathbb{R}^2 \to \mathbb{R}$ defined by

4.7.12
$$F(x, y) = x^5 + y^5 - 5x^3 y.$$

The level set of F corresponding to the value 0,

$$S = \{(x, y) \in \mathbb{R}^2 \,|\, F(x, y) = 0\},$$

is illustrated in Fig. 4.12.

Here we cannot "solve" for y as a function of x (nor for x as function of y) and yet the equation

4.7.13
$$x^5 + y^5 - 5x^3 y = 0$$

implicitly defines a number of real-valued functions on various subsets of $\mathbb{R}$. Our sketch of the solution set of the equation suggests that there are three different continuously differentiable functions defined implicitly by the equation 4.7.13 in a neighbourhood of $x = 1$. By putting $x = 1$ in 4.7.13 we find that the corresponding values of y are approximately 1.44, 0.20 and -1.54.

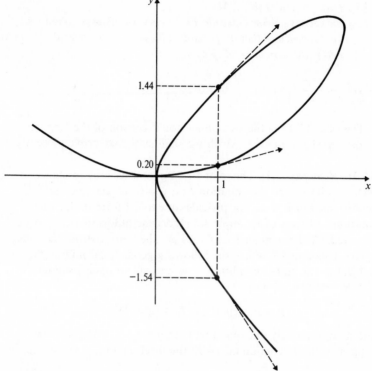

Fig. 4.12 $\{(x, y)\in\mathbb{R}^2 \,|\, x^5 + y^5 - 5x^3y = 0\}$

Our examples illustrate the *Implicit Function Theorem* 4.7.14, which asserts that if an equation $F(x, y) = 0$ has a solution $x = a$, $y = b$, then under not too severe restrictions the equation implicitly defines in a neighbourhood of $x = a$ a unique continuously differentiable function that takes the value b at $x = a$. Its generalization has many applications, as we shall see in the next section.

4.7.14 Theorem.   *Let $F : D \subseteq \mathbb{R}^2 \to \mathbb{R}$ be a real-valued continuously differentiable function defined in a neighbourhood D of a point $(a, b)\in\mathbb{R}^2$. Suppose that*

[i] $F(a, b) = 0$,

[ii] $\dfrac{\partial F}{\partial y}(a, b) \neq 0$.

Then there exists a neighbourhood N of $a\in\mathbb{R}$, a neighbourhood M of $b\in\mathbb{R}$, and a continuously differentiable function $f : N \subseteq \mathbb{R} \to \mathbb{R}$, such that

[1] $f(a) = b$, and $f(N) \subseteq M$;

[2] *for each* $x \in N$ *the equation* $F(x, y) = 0$ *is uniquely solved by*
$y = f(x) \in M$, *provided that the possible values of* y *are restricted to lie in* M.
Moreover, the derivative of f *is given by*

4.7.15 $$f'(t) = -\frac{\partial F}{\partial x}(t, f(t)) \bigg/ \frac{\partial F}{\partial y}(t, f(t)), \qquad t \in N.$$

Theorem 4.7.14 is the two-dimensional version of the Implicit
Function Theorem 4.8.1, which we shall state and prove presently.

4.7.16 Remarks. **[i]** Theorem 4.7.14 guarantees the existence of
certain solutions of the equation $F(x, y) = 0$ subject to certain
conditions, but it does not provide an explicit formula for the
solutions. In view of Example 4.7.11, a general formula cannot be
expected. (A theorem such as 4.7.14 is called an *existence theorem*.)

[ii] Theorem 4.7.14 has the following geometrical interpretation.
Subject to the stated conditions, there exists an open rectangle
$R = N \times M$ centred at (a, b),

$$R = \{(x, y) \in \mathbb{R}^2 \,|\, x \in N \subseteq \mathbb{R}, \, y \in M \subseteq \mathbb{R}\},$$

and a continuously differentiable function $f : N \to M$ such that
subject to the restriction $(x, y) \in R$, the level set $F(x, y) = 0$ is the

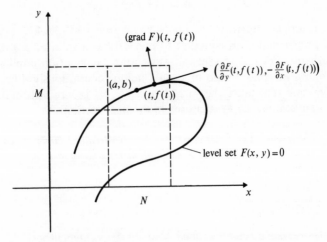

Fig. 4.13 Level set $F(x, y) = 0$ is graph of f in rectangle $N \times M$

graph of f. See Fig. 4.13. Since

$$(\text{grad } F)(t, f(t)) = \left(\frac{\partial F}{\partial x}(t, f(t)), \frac{\partial F}{\partial y}(t, f(t))\right),$$

the tangent line to the level set (graph) at $(t, f(t))$ is in the direction

4.7.17 $\left(\dfrac{\partial F}{\partial y}(t, f(t)), -\dfrac{\partial F}{\partial x}(t, f(t))\right),$ $t \in N.$

The slope of this line is indeed the slope of the graph of f at $(t, f(t))$ as given by 4.7.15, for if 4.7.15 is satisfied, then the vector 4.7.17 is a non-zero scalar multiple of $(1, f'(t))$.

[iii] Once the existence of a differentiable function $f : N \subseteq \mathbb{R} \to \mathbb{R}$ satisfying $F(t, f(t)) = 0, t \in N$ has been established, expression 4.7.15 for its derivative is obtained by the Chain Rule as follows.

Put $g(t) = (t, f(t)), t \in N$. Then $(F \circ g)(t) = F(g(t)) = 0$. Hence on differentiating we obtain

$$0 = \frac{\partial F}{\partial x}(t, f(t)).1 + \frac{\partial F}{\partial y}(t, f(t)).f'(t), \qquad t \in N$$

and Formula 4.7.15 follows. The requirement $(\partial F/\partial y)(t, f(t)) \neq 0, t \in N$ is a consequence of the continuity of $\partial F/\partial y$ and the condition $(\partial F/\partial y)(a, b) \neq 0$, as stated in the theorem.

The following example illustrates the application of 4.7.15.

4.7.18 *Example*.   [i] Let f be the function defined implicitly near $x = 1$ by the equation $F(x, y) = 0$, where

$$F(x, y) = x^5 + y^5 - 5x^3y \qquad (x, y) \in \mathbb{R}^2$$

and by the condition $f(1) = 1.44$ (see Example 4.7.11). Find the slope of the tangent vector to the graph of f at $x = 1$.

[ii] Repeat with the functions defined implicitly near $x = 1$ by $F(x, y) = 0$ and taking respectively the values 0.20 and -1.54 at $x = 1$.

Solution.   [i] we have for $(x, y) \in \mathbb{R}^2$

$$\frac{\partial F}{\partial x}(x, y) = 5x^4 - 15x^2y, \qquad \frac{\partial F}{\partial y}(x, y) = 5y^4 - 5x^3.$$

Hence, by Formula 4.7.15, the slope of the tangent vector to the graph of f at $x = 1$ is

$$f'(1) = -\frac{\partial F}{\partial x}(1, f(1)) \Big/ \frac{\partial F}{\partial y}(1, f(1))$$

$$= -\frac{5 - 15(1.44)}{5(1.44)^2 - 5} = 1.01$$

correct to 2 decimal places.

Alternatively, the Chain Rule of elementary calculus can be applied directly as follows. The function f satisfies the equation

$$x^5 + (f(x))^5 - 5x^3 f(x) = 0$$

for all x in a neighbourhood of 1. Differentiating with respect to x we obtain

$$5x^4 + 5(f(x))^4 f'(x) - 15x^2 f(x) - 5x^3 f'(x) = 0,$$

and hence $f'(1)$ is calculated by substituting $x = 1$ and $f(x) = 1.44$.

[ii] Similar calculations lead to tangent vectors with slopes 0.40 and -1.22.

The tangent vectors for the three cases are indicated in Fig. 4.12.

Exercises 4.7

1. Consider the folium of Descartes defined by the equation $F(x, y) = 0$, where

$$F(x, y) = x^3 + y^3 - 3xy, \qquad (x, y) \in \mathbb{R}^2.$$

   (See Example 3.1.7 and Fig. 3.2.)

   Find the slope of the tangent vector to the graph of the function f at $x = \frac{2}{3}$ defined implicitly by the equation $F(x, y) = 0$ and the condition (a) $f(x) = \frac{4}{3}$; (b) $f(x) = (-2 + \sqrt{6})/3$; (c) $f(x) = (-2 - \sqrt{6})/3$.

   Sketch the curve and the tangent vectors.

2. (a) Let $F(x, y) = x + y^2 + \sin(xy)$. Prove that in a sufficiently small neighbourhood of $(0, 0)$ the equation $F(x, y) = 0$ defines implicitly a continuously differentiable function g such that $g(0) = 0$ and $F(x, y) = 0$ if and only if $x = g(y)$. Show also that $g'(0) = 0$. (Apply Theorem 4.7.14 with the roles of x and y reversed.)

   (b) According to part (a) of this exercise, the condition $x + y^2 + \sin(xy) = 0$, with (x, y) sufficiently close to $(0, 0)$, implies that $x = g(y)$. Does it also imply that $y = f(x)$ for some continuously differentiable function f such that $f(0) = 0$?

   Answer: no. Observe that near $(0, 0)$ the equation $F(x, y) = 0$ behaves like $x + y^2 + xy = 0$.

3. As in Exercise 1, let $F(x, y) = x^3 + y^3 - 3xy$. Observe that (a) $F(0, 0) = 0$, but (b) $(\partial F/\partial y)(0, 0) = (\partial F/\partial x)(0, 0) = 0$. Therefore condition (ii) of

Theorem 4.7.14 fails. Note from your sketch of the curve $F(x, y) = 0$ (or from Fig. 3.2) that the conclusion (2) of Theorem 4.7.14 also fails. The curve crosses itself at $(0, 0)$ and therefore the equation $F(x, y) = 0$ is clearly not solved *uniquely* in the form $y = f(x)$ or $x = g(y)$ near the origin. The sketch suggests that there are two continuously differentiable function, f and g such that $f(0) = g(0) = 0$, and near $(0, 0)$ if $F(x, y) = 0$ then either $y = f(x)$ or $x = g(y)$. Approximations to the functions f and g are given by $f(x) = \frac{1}{3}x^2$, $g(y) = \frac{1}{3}y^2$.

4. Describe explicitly all continuously differentiable functions f defined in a neighbourhood N of 1 and such that $F(x, f(x)) = 0$ for all $x \in N$, where

   (a) $F(x, y) = y^2 - x^2 - 1$;
   (b) $F(x, y) = x - 2\cos y$.

   In each case calculate $f'(1)$. Illustrate your answers with a sketch.

Answer: (b) $f(x) = 2k\pi \pm \arccos\frac{1}{2}x$, $k \in \mathbb{N}$, $f'(1) = \pm 1/\sqrt{3}$.

4.8 Implicit Function Theorems

In this section we first discuss the Implicit Function Theorem in a form which directly generalises Theorem 4.7.14. We then briefly consider further possible generalizations.

4.8.1 *The Implicit Function Theorem.* *Let $F : D \subseteq \mathbb{R}^m \to \mathbb{R}$ be a real-valued continuously differentiable function defined in a neighbourhood D of a point $(p_1, \ldots, p_m) \in \mathbb{R}^m$, $m \geq 2$. Suppose that*

  [i] $F(p_1, \ldots, p_m) = 0$, *and*

  [ii] $\dfrac{\partial F}{\partial x_m}(p_1, \ldots, p_m) \neq 0$.

Then there exists a neighbourhood N of $(p_1, \ldots, p_{m-1}) \in \mathbb{R}^{m-1}$, a neighbourhood M of $p_m \in \mathbb{R}$, and a continuously differentiable function $f : N \subseteq \mathbb{R}^{m-1} \to \mathbb{R}$ such that

  (1) $f(p_1, \ldots, p_{m-1}) = p_m$, *and* $f(N) \subseteq M$,
  (2) *for each $(x_1, \ldots, x_{m-1}) \in N$ the equation $F(x_1, \ldots, x_{m-1}, x_m) = 0$ is uniquely solved by $x_m = f(x_1, \ldots, x_{m-1}) \in M$, provided that the possible values of x_m are restricted to lie in M.*

Proof. For simplicity we give the proof for the case $m = 3$. The general case is proved along similar lines.

   The idea of the proof is to construct from the function $F : D \subseteq \mathbb{R}^3 \to \mathbb{R}$ a related function to which the Inverse Function Theorem 4.6.7

can be applied. Towards this end, define $F^* : D \subseteq \mathbb{R}^3 \to \mathbb{R}^3$ by

4.8.2 $F^*(x_1, x_2, x_3) = (x_1, x_2, F(x_1, x_2, x_3)), (x_1, x_2, x_3) \in D.$

Notice that $F^*(x_1, x_2, x_3)$ lies in the x_1, x_2 plane if and only if $F(x_1, x_2, x_3) = 0$. In particular, by condition (i),

4.8.3 $F^*(p_1, p_2, p_3) = (p_1, p_2, 0).$

The function F^* is continuously differentiable on D and its Jacobian matrix at $\mathbf{p} \in D$ is

$$J_{F^*, \mathbf{p}} = \begin{bmatrix} 1 & 0 & 0 \\ 0 & 1 & 0 \\ \dfrac{\partial F}{\partial x_1}(\mathbf{p}) & \dfrac{\partial F}{\partial x_2}(\mathbf{p}) & \dfrac{\partial F}{\partial x_3}(\mathbf{p}) \end{bmatrix}.$$

By condition (ii),

$$\det J_{F^*, \mathbf{p}} = \frac{\partial F}{\partial x_3}(\mathbf{p}) \neq 0,$$

and the Inverse Function Theorem may be applied to F^* in a neighbourhood of $\mathbf{p}$. The theorem implies that $\mathbf{p}$ lies in an open set $U \subseteq D$ in $\mathbb{R}^3$ such that F^* is invertible with C^1 inverse on U, and such that $F^*(U) = V$ is an open subset of $\mathbb{R}^3$ containing $F^*(p) = (p_1, p_2, 0)$. We may assume, by taking a further subset if necessary, that $U = N_1 \times M$ where N_1 is a neighbourhood of (p_1, p_2) in $\mathbb{R}^2$ and M is a neighbourhood of p_3 in $\mathbb{R}$. See Fig. 4.14.

Denote the C^1 inverse of $F^* : U \to V$ by $G^* : V \to U$. It is clear from 4.8.2 that G^* has the form

4.8.4

$$G^*(x_1, x_2, x_3) = (x_1, x_2, G(x_1, x_2, x_3)) \in N_1 \times M, (x_1, x_2, x_3) \in V,$$

where $G : V \subseteq \mathbb{R}^3 \to \mathbb{R}$ is a C^1 function. By 4.8.4,

4.8.5 $$G(V) \subseteq M.$$

Since V is an open subset of $\mathbb{R}^3$ containing $(p_1, p_2, 0)$, there is a neighbourhood N of (p_1, p_2) in $\mathbb{R}^2$ such that $N \times \{0\} \subseteq V$. We can now define a function $f : N \subseteq \mathbb{R}^2 \to \mathbb{R}$ by

4.8.6 $f(x_1, x_2) = G(x_1, x_2, 0)$ $(x_1, x_2) \in N.$

The function f is well defined since $(x_1, x_2, 0) \in N \times \{0\} \subseteq V$ whenever $(x_1, x_2) \in N$. Furthermore, since G is a C^1 function, f is a C^1

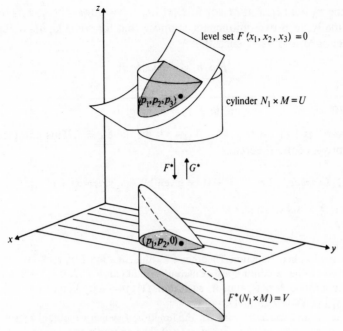

level set $F(x_1, x_2, x_3) = 0$

cylinder $N_1 \times M = U$

F^* ↓ G^* ↑

$(p_1, p_2, 0)$ •

$F^*(N_1 \times M) = V$

Fig. 4.14

function. We shall show that f has the required properties (1) and (2).

(1) Firstly $f(p_1, p_2) = p_3$ since by 4.8.6,

$$(p_1, p_2, f(p_1, p_2)) = (p_1, p_2, G(p_1, p_2, 0))$$
$$= G^*(p_1, p_2, 0) = (p_1, p_2, p_3).$$

Secondly, since $f(N) = G(N \times \{0\})$ and $N \times \{0\} \subseteq V$, expression 4.8.5 implies that

4.8.7 $f(N) \subseteq M.$

(2) It is clear from the definition of F^* that $V \subseteq N_1 \times \mathbb{R}$ and therefore, since $N \times \{0\} \subseteq V$ we have

4.8.8 $N \subseteq N_1$ and $N \times M \subseteq N_1 \times M.$

Therefore, for each $(x_1, x_2) \in N$, by 4.8.7, the vector $(x_1, x_2, f(x_1, x_2))$ lies in the domain of F. Now for each $(x_1, x_2) \in N$,

4.8.9 $(x_1, x_2, F(x_1, x_2, f(x_1, x_2))) = (x_1, x_2, F(x_1, x_2, G(x_1, x_2, 0))).$
$$= (F^* \circ G^*)(x_1, x_2, 0) = (x_1, x_2, 0).$$

Hence $x_3 = f(x_1, x_2) \in M$ solves $F(x_1, x_2, x_3) = 0$ for all $(x_1, x_2) \in N$.

Finally, to prove uniqueness, suppose that for some $(a, b) \in N$ there exists $c \in M$ and $d \in M$ such that

$$F(a, b, c) = F(a, b, d).$$

Then

4.8.10 $$F^*(a, b, c) = F^*(a, b, d).$$

Since F^* is 1–1 on $N \times M \subseteq N_1 \times M$, we have $c = d$. This completes the proof of the theorem.

4.8.11 *Example.* Let $F : \mathbb{R}^3 \to \mathbb{R}$ be given by $F(x, y, z) = x^2 + y^2 + z^2 - 1$. Then

(a) $F(\frac{1}{2}, \frac{1}{2}, -\frac{1}{2}\sqrt{3}) = 0$ and

(b) $\dfrac{\partial F}{\partial z}(\frac{1}{2}, \frac{1}{2}, -\frac{1}{2}\sqrt{3}) = -\sqrt{3}.$

By the Implicit Function Theorem 4.8.1 the equation $F(x, y, z) = 0$ uniquely defines a continuously differentiable function $f : N \subseteq \mathbb{R}^2 \to \mathbb{R}$ in a neighbourhood N of $(\frac{1}{2}, \frac{1}{2})$ in $\mathbb{R}^2$ such that $f(\frac{1}{2}, \frac{1}{2}) = -\frac{1}{2}\sqrt{3}$ and $F(x, y, f(x, y)) = 0$ for all $(x, y) \in N$.

There is an explicit formula for the function f which we obtain by solving for z in the equation $x^2 + y^2 + z^2 - 1 = 0$. The appropriate solution is

$$f(x, y) = -\sqrt{(1 - x^2 - y^2)},$$

which satisfies the required condition $f(\frac{1}{2}, \frac{1}{2}) = -\frac{1}{2}\sqrt{3}$. The explicit formula for f shows that the neighbourhood N of $(\frac{1}{2}, \frac{1}{2})$ on which f is defined must be restricted at least by the condition $x^2 + y^2 < 1$.

A second solution for z of the equation $x^2 + y^2 + z^2 - 1 = 0$ leads to the function given by

$$g(x, y) = +\sqrt{(1 - x^2 - y^2)},$$

where we have $g(\frac{1}{2}, \frac{1}{2}) = \frac{1}{2}\sqrt{3}$.

The graphs of the functions f and g lie on the surface of the sphere $x^2 + y^2 + z^2 = 1$, centre the origin, radius 1 (Fig. 4.15).

As a final illustration, note that

(i) $F(1, 0, 0) = 0$ but   (ii) $\dfrac{\partial F}{\partial z}(1, 0, 0) = 0.$

Thus condition (ii) of the Implicit Function Theorem 4.8.1 fails at the point $(1, 0, 0)$. The conclusions of the theorem also fail, for there is no neighbourhood N of the point $(1, 0)$ on which a differentiable function $h : N \subseteq \mathbb{R}^2 \to \mathbb{R}$ can be defined such that $F(x, y, h(x, y)) = 0$ for all $(x, y) \in N$. A glance at Fig. 4.15 should suggest why this is so. Note, however, that $(\partial F/\partial x)(1, 0, 0) = 2 \neq 0$. By switching the roles of the first and third coordinates we can infer the existence of a continuously differentiable function $h : N \subseteq \mathbb{R}^2 \to \mathbb{R}$

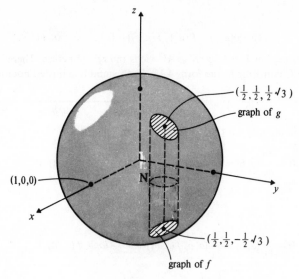

$$\left(\tfrac{1}{2}, \tfrac{1}{2}, \tfrac{1}{2}\sqrt{3}\right)$$

graph of g

$(1,0,0)$

N

$$\left(\tfrac{1}{2}, \tfrac{1}{2}, -\tfrac{1}{2}\sqrt{3}\right)$$

graph of f

Fig. 4.15

defined in a neighbourhood N of $(0, 0)$ such that $h(0, 0) = 1$ and $F(h(y, z), y, z) = 0$ for all $(y, z) \in N$. The function h can be defined explicitly (Exercise 4.8.2).

4.8.12 Example. The equation

4.8.13 $$x + y + z - \sin(xyz) = 0, \qquad (x, y, z) \in \mathbb{R}^3,$$

is satisfied by $(x, y, z) = (0, 0, 0)$. We can apply the Implicit Function Theorem 4.8.1 to justify the process of solving for z as a function of x and y close to the origin. Define $F : \mathbb{R}^3 \to \mathbb{R}$ by $F(x, y, z) = x + y + z - \sin(xyz)$, $(x, y, z) \in \mathbb{R}^3$. Then F is continuously differentiable on $\mathbb{R}^3$ and

$$\text{(i) } F(0, 0, 0) = 0 \quad \text{and} \quad \text{(ii) } \frac{\partial F}{\partial z}(0, 0, 0) = 1 \neq 0.$$

Hence there exists a neighbourhood $N \subseteq \mathbb{R}^2$ of $(0, 0)$, a neighbourhood $M \subseteq \mathbb{R}$ of 0, and a continuously differentiable function $f : N \subseteq \mathbb{R}^2 \to \mathbb{R}$ such that Equation 4.8.13 is uniquely solved by $z = f(x, y)$ in the open cylinder $N \times M$.

The function f is defined implicitly and there is no explicit formula for it. However, given $(a, b) \in N$ it will of course be possible to calculate $f(a, b)$ by solving Equation 4.8.13 with $x = a$, $y = b$ by a numerical method.

We can obtain information about the partial derivatives of f as follows. Define $g : N \subseteq \mathbb{R}^2 \to \mathbb{R}^3$ by

$$g(u, v) = (u, v, f(u, v)), \qquad (u, v) \in N.$$

Then

4.8.14 $(F \circ g)(u, v) = F(u, v, f(u, v)) = 0,$ $(u, v) \in N.$

Thus the function $H = F \circ g : N \subseteq \mathbb{R}^2 \to \mathbb{R}$ is the zero function. Therefore, using the Chain Rule in the form 4.4.3, (with suitably adjusted notation) we obtain,

4.8.15 $0 = J_{H,(a, b)} = J_{F, g(a, b)} J_{g,(a, b)}$ $(a, b) \in N.$

The matrix identity 4.8.15 is equivalent to the system

$$0 = \frac{\partial H}{\partial u}(a, b) = \frac{\partial F}{\partial x}(a, b, f(a, b)) \cdot 1 + \frac{\partial F}{\partial y}(a, b, f(a, b)) \cdot 0$$

$$+ \frac{\partial F}{\partial z}(a, b, f(a, b)) \frac{\partial f}{\partial u}(a, b)$$

$$0 = \frac{\partial H}{\partial v}(a, b) = \frac{\partial F}{\partial x}(a, b, f(a, b)) \cdot 0 + \frac{\partial F}{\partial y}(a, b, f(a, b)) \cdot 1$$

$$+ \frac{\partial F}{\partial z}(a, b, f(a, b)) \frac{\partial f}{\partial v}(a, b).$$

These identities give us expressions for $(\partial f/\partial u)(a, b)$ and $(\partial f/\partial v)(a, b)$. See Exercise 4.8.3.

The Implicit Function Theorem 4.8.1 concerns the solution of one equation $F(x_1, \ldots, x_m) = 0$ for the "unknown" x_m. There is a generalization that deals with the solution of k equations in $x_1, \ldots, x_m$ for k unknowns, where $2 \leqslant k \leqslant m - 1$. The following theorem provides a typical illustration. It concerns conditions under which two equations in $x_1, \ldots, x_5$ can be solved for x_4 and x_5 in terms of x_1, x_2 and x_3.

4.8.16 Theorem.   *Let* $H : D \subseteq \mathbb{R}^5 \to \mathbb{R}$ *and* $K : D \subseteq \mathbb{R}^5 \to \mathbb{R}$ *be real-valued continuously differentiable functions defined in a neighbourhood D of a point* $\mathbf{p} = (p_1, \ldots, p_5) \in \mathbb{R}^5.$ *Suppose that*
   [i] $H(p_1, \ldots, p_5) = 0$ *and* $K(p_1, \ldots, p_5) = 0,$ *and*
   [ii] *the determinant*

$$\frac{\partial(H, K)}{\partial(x_4, x_5)}(\mathbf{p}) = \det \begin{bmatrix} \dfrac{\partial H}{\partial x_4}(\mathbf{p}) & \dfrac{\partial H}{\partial x_5}(\mathbf{p}) \\ \dfrac{\partial K}{\partial x_4}(\mathbf{p}) & \dfrac{\partial K}{\partial x_5}(\mathbf{p}) \end{bmatrix}$$

is non-zero.

Then there exists a neighbourhood N of $(p_1, p_2, p_3) \in \mathbb{R}^3$, *a neighbourhood M of* $(p_4, p_5) \in \mathbb{R}^2$, *and real-valued continuously differentiable functions* $f : N \subseteq \mathbb{R}^3 \to \mathbb{R}$, *and* $g : N \subseteq \mathbb{R}^3 \to \mathbb{R}$ *such that*

(1) $f(p_1, p_2, p_3) = p_4, \quad g(p_1, p_2, p_3) = p_5$

and

$$(f(x_1, x_2, x_3), g(x_1, x_2, x_3)) \in M \text{ for all } (x_1, x_2, x_3) \in N,$$

(2) *for each* $(x_1, x_2, x_3) \in N$ *the equations*

$$H(x_1, \ldots, x_5) = 0, \qquad K(x_1, \ldots, x_5) = 0$$

are simultaneously solved uniquely by

$$x_4 = f(x_1, x_2, x_3), \qquad x_5 = g(x_1, x_2, x_3),$$

provided that (x_4, x_5) *is restricted to lie in M.*

Sketch of Proof. Apply the Inverse Function Theorem 4.6.7 to the continuously differentiable function $F^* : D \subseteq \mathbb{R}^5 \to \mathbb{R}^5$ defined by

4.8.17
$$\begin{aligned} F^*(\mathbf{x}) &= F^*(x_1, x_2, x_3, x_4, x_5) \\ &= (x_1, x_2, x_3, H(\mathbf{x}), K(\mathbf{x})), \qquad \mathbf{x} \in D, \end{aligned}$$

so that, in particular, by condition (i),

4.8.18
$$F^*(\mathbf{p}) = (p_1, p_2, p_3, 0, 0).$$

It will be found that

$$\det J_{F^*, \mathbf{p}} = \frac{\partial(H, K)}{\partial(x_4, x_5)}(\mathbf{p}) \neq 0,$$

by condition (ii). Therefore by the Inverse Function Theorem 4.6.7 there exist open sets U and V in $\mathbb{R}^5$ containing $\mathbf{p}$ and $F^*(\mathbf{p})$ respectively such that $U \subseteq D$, $F^*(U) = V$, F^* is 1–1 on U, and the function $G^* : V \to U$ locally inverse to F^* on U is continuously differentiable.

From the form of 4.8.17 it is clear that

4.8.19 $\quad G^*(y_1, y_2, y_3, y_4, y_5) = (y_1, y_2, y_3, G_4^*(\mathbf{y}), G_5^*(\mathbf{y})), \qquad \mathbf{y} \in V,$

and, in particular, that

4.8.20
$$G^*(p_1, p_2, p_3, 0, 0) = (p_1, p_2, p_3, p_4, p_5).$$

The proof is completed by a method similar to that of Theorem 4.8.1.

The following example illustrates the solution of two equations in three unknowns:

4.8.21 *Example.* The point $\mathbf{p} = (\frac{1}{2}, \frac{1}{4}(1 + \sqrt{5}), \frac{1}{4}(1 - \sqrt{5}))$ satisfies the equations

4.8.22
$$\begin{cases} x + y + z = 1, \\ x^2 + y^2 + z^2 = 1. \end{cases}$$

We show that these equations implicitly define y and z as continuously differentiable functions of x in a neighbourhood of $x = \frac{1}{2}$ that take the values $\frac{1}{4}(1 + \sqrt{5})$ and $\frac{1}{4}(1 - \sqrt{5})$ respectively at $x = \frac{1}{2}$. Define $H : \mathbb{R}^3 \to \mathbb{R}$ and $K : \mathbb{R}^3 \to \mathbb{R}$ by

$$H(x, y, z) = x + y + z - 1, \quad K(x, y, z) = x^2 + y^2 + z^2 - 1,$$
$$(x, y, z) \in \mathbb{R}^3.$$

Then H, K are continuously differentiable on $\mathbb{R}^3$ and

$$\frac{\partial(H, K)}{\partial(y, z)}(x, y, z) = \det \begin{bmatrix} 1 & 1 \\ 2y & 2z \end{bmatrix} = 2(z - y).$$

This is non-zero at $\mathbf{p}$. Therefore, by The General Implicit Function Theorem, there exists a neighbourhood N of $\frac{1}{2} \in \mathbb{R}$, a neighbourhood M of $(\frac{1}{4}(1 + \sqrt{5}), \frac{1}{4}(1 - \sqrt{5}) \in \mathbb{R}^2$ and continuously differentiable functions $f : N \subseteq \mathbb{R} \to \mathbb{R}$ and $g : N \subseteq \mathbb{R} \to \mathbb{R}$ such that $f(\frac{1}{2}) = \frac{1}{4}(1 + \sqrt{5})$, $g(\frac{1}{2}) = \frac{1}{4}(1 - \sqrt{5})$ and Equations 4.8.22 are uniquely solved by

$$y = f(x), \qquad z = g(x), \qquad\qquad x \in N$$

in the open cylinder $N \times M$.

It turns out that Equations 4.8.22 can be solved explicitly for y and z as functions of x. The formulae

$$y = -\tfrac{1}{2}(x - 1) + \tfrac{1}{2}\sqrt{(1 + 2x - 3x^2)}, \qquad z = 1 - x - y$$

provide solutions of 4.8.22 in a neighbourhood of $x = \frac{1}{2}$.

The point $(1, 0, 0)$ also satisfies Equations 4.8.22, but, as

$$\frac{\partial(H, K)}{\partial(y, z)}(1, 0, 0) = 0,$$

for this case the Implicit Function Theorem is inconclusive. In fact Equations 4.8.22 do not implicitly define y and z as real-valued functions of x in a neighbourhood of $(1, 0, 0)$, for there are no solutions of 4.8.22 with $x > 1$.

Exercises 4.8

1. (a) Prove that the surface S in $\mathbb{R}^3$ whose equation is $xyz + e^{xz} = 1$ is the graph G of a continuously differentiable function in a neighbourhood of the point $(1, 0, 0) \in S$.

Hint: apply the Implicit Function Theorem 4.8.1 to the function $F(x, y, z) = xyz + e^{xz} - 1$ in a neighbourhood of $(1, 0, 0)$. There is an explicit formula for the graph G: it is the plane $z = 0$.

Does there exist a continuously differentiable function g with $g(0, 0) = 1$ such that $x = g(y, z)$ for all (x, y, z) in S close to $(1, 0, 0)$?

Hint: since $(\partial F/\partial x)(1, 0, 0) = 0$, the Implicit Function Theorem is inconclusive. The following alternative method establishes that there does not even exist a continuous function g with the stated properties. Suppose the contrary. Then $\lim_{z \to 0} g(0, z) = g(0, 0) = 1$. But also for $y = 0$ and all z close to 0

$$g(0, z) . 0 . z + \exp(g(0, z) . z) = 1$$

Deduce the contradiction $\lim_{z \to 0} g(0, z) = 0$.

(b) Is the surface S of part (a) the graph of a continuously differentiable function in a neighbourhood of the point (i) $(0, 0, 1) \in S$, (ii) $(0, 1, 0) \in S$?

Hint: The Implicit Function Theorem is inconclusive. By inspection, the plane $z = 0$ lies in S and contains $(0, 1, 0)$. But does this plane *describe S* in a neighbourhood of $(0, 1, 0)$? Try another plane.

2. Let $F(x, y, z) = x^2 + y^2 + z^2 - 1$. As suggested in Example 4.8.11, find a continuously differentiable function $h : N \subseteq \mathbb{R}^2 \to \mathbb{R}$ defined in a neighbourhood N of $(0, 0)$ such that $h(0, 0) = 1$ and $F(h(y, z), y, z) = 0$ for all $(y, z) \in N$.

3. Consider the continuously differentiable function $F : \mathbb{R}^3 \to \mathbb{R}$ defined by $F(x, y, z) = x + y + z - \sin(xyz)$. In Example 4.8.12 we proved the existence of a neighbourhood $N \subseteq \mathbb{R}^2$ of $(0, 0)$, a neighbourhood $M \subseteq \mathbb{R}$ of 0 and a continuously differentiable function $f : M \to N$ such that

$$F(u, v, f(u, v)) = 0, \qquad (u, v) \in N.$$

Prove that

$$\frac{\partial f}{\partial u}(0, 0) = \frac{\partial f}{\partial v}(0, 0) = -1.$$

4. Exercise 3 can be stated as follows. By the Implicit Function Theorem the equation $x + y + z - \sin(xyz) = 0$ is uniquely solved in a neighbourhood of $(0, 0, 0)$ by $z = f(x, y)$, where f is a continuously differentiable function. Find $(\partial f/\partial x)(0, 0)$ and $(\partial f/\partial y)(0, 0)$ from the identity

$$x + y + f(x, y) - \sin(xyf(x, y)) = 0.$$

5. For each of the following functions $F : \mathbb{R}^3 \to \mathbb{R}$, show that the equation $F(x, y, z) = 0$ defines implicitly a continuously differentiable function $z = f(x, y)$ in a neighbourhood of the given point (a, b, c). Find $(\partial f/\partial x)(a, b)$ and $(\partial f/\partial y)(a, b)$.
(a) $F(x, y, z) = x^3 + y^3 + z^3 - xyz - 2$ at $(1, 1, -1)$;
(b) $F(x, y, z) = x^2 + z^3 - z - xy\sin z$ at $(1, 1, 0)$.

Answer: (a) $-2, -2$;   (b) $1, 0$.

6. Show that the equation $F(x, y, z) = 0$ in Exercise 5(a) also defines implicitly y as a function of x, z, and x as a function of y, z in a neighbourhood of the given point (a, b, c).
   Is the same true in Exercise 5(b)?

7. Let $F : \mathbb{R}^2 \to \mathbb{R}$ be defined by $F(x_1, x_2) = x_1^9 - x_2^3$. Then (a) $F(0, 0) = 0$ and (b) $(\partial F/\partial x_1)(0, 0) = (\partial F/\partial x_2)(0, 0) = 0$. Hence condition (ii) of the Implicit Function Theorem 4.8.1 is not satisfied. Show that nevertheless the conclusions of the theorem hold, since the equation $F(x_1, x_2) = 0$ is uniquely solved by $x_2 = f(x_1) = x_1^3$.

8. Define the functions $H : \mathbb{R}^4 \to \mathbb{R}$ and $K : \mathbb{R}^4 \to \mathbb{R}$ by

$$H(x, y, z, t) = x^2 - yz, \qquad K(x, y, z, t) = xy - zt.$$

   Prove by the method of Theorem 4.8.16 that in a neighbourhood of $(-2, 2, 2, -2)$ the equations $H(x, y, z, t) = 0$, $K(x, y, z, t) = 0$ implicitly define z and t as continuously differentiable functions of x and y taking the values $z = 2$ and $t = -2$ at $(x, y) = (-2, 2)$. (Show that

$$\frac{\partial(H, K)}{\partial(z, t)}(-2, 2, 2, -2) \neq 0.$$

   There is an explicit formula for z and t as functions of x and y.)
   Are z and t defined as functions of x and y near $(0, 1, 0, 2)$?
   Prove that

   (a) $\dfrac{\partial(H, K)}{\delta(x, z)}(0, 1, 0, 2) \neq 0$ (b) $\dfrac{\partial(H, K)}{\delta(x, z)}(\tfrac{1}{2}, 1, \tfrac{1}{4}, 2) \neq 0$.

   Obtain explicit expressions for x and z as continuously differentiable functions of y and t in a neighbourhood of $(y, t) = (1, 2)$ such that

   (i) $x = z = 0$ at $(y, t) = (1, 2)$,
   (ii) $x = \tfrac{1}{2}$, $z = \tfrac{1}{4}$ at $(y, t) = (1, 2)$.

   Answer: (ii) $x = y^2/t$, $z = y^3/t^2$. The answer to (i) is different!

9. Prove that if $\mathbf{q}$ is a point of a surface S in $\mathbb{R}^m$, then the normal line to S at $\mathbf{q}$ (see Definition 3.8.18) is independent of which smooth function $f : D \subseteq \mathbb{R}^m \to \mathbb{R}$ is used to define S.

Hint: consider local graph like behaviour and follow the argument of Section 3.8.

10. Let $\mathbf{p}$ be a point in a surface S in $\mathbb{R}^m$. Prove that there is a 1–1 C^1 function $g : N(\mathbf{0}, \delta) \subseteq \mathbb{R}^{m-1} \to \mathbb{R}^m$ such that $g(\mathbf{0}) = \mathbf{p}$ and $g(N(\mathbf{0}, \delta)) \subseteq S$. It follows that S is locally a copy of $\mathbb{R}^{m-1}$.

4.9   Extreme values subject to constraints. The method of Lagrange multipliers

In Section 3.12 we considered a method of determining the extreme values (local maxima and minima) of a differentiable function $f : D \subseteq \mathbb{R}^m \to \mathbb{R}$, whose domain D is an open subset of $\mathbb{R}^m$. An important class of problems concerns the determination of the extreme values of f when its domain is restricted to a proper subset of D by the imposition of "constraints". Our first example is a simple illustration. It can be solved by the method of Section 3.12. However, in the general case an appeal to the Implicit Function Theorem is necessary.

4.9.1 *Example*.   Find the dimensions of a rectangular box such that the surface area of its base and vertical sides is a minimum subject to the condition that the box has prescribed volume V.

Solution.   The surface area of the base and sides of a rectangular box of base measurements $x > 0$, $y > 0$ and height $z > 0$ is given by the formula

4.9.2 $g(x, y, z) = xy + 2xz + 2yz,$ $(x, y, z) \in D,$

where the domain of the function $g : D \subseteq \mathbb{R}^3 \to \mathbb{R}$ is the open set

$$D = \{(x, y, z) \in \mathbb{R}^3 \mid x > 0, y > 0, z > 0\}.$$

The volume xyz of the box is subject to the constraint

4.9.3 $xyz = V$ $(x, y, z) \in D.$

We wish to find the minimum value of $g : D \subseteq \mathbb{R}^3 \to \mathbb{R}$ subject to the constraint 4.9.3. This is easily done by solving 4.9.3 for z and substituting in 4.9.2. Hence the required surface area of a box of volume V and base measurements $x > 0$, $y > 0$ is given by

4.9.4 $g\left(x, y, \dfrac{V}{xy}\right) = s(x, y) = xy + \dfrac{2V}{y} + \dfrac{2V}{x},$ $x > 0, \quad y > 0.$

The identity 4.9.4 defines the function $s : E \subseteq \mathbb{R}^2 \to \mathbb{R}$, where

$$E = \{(x, y) \in \mathbb{R}^2 \mid x > 0, y > 0\}.$$

We require the minimum value of s on E, and this can be found by an application of Corollary 3.12.4. The critical points of s are solutions of the equations

4.9.5 $0 = \dfrac{\partial s}{\partial x}(x, y) = y - \dfrac{2V}{x^2}$ and $0 = \dfrac{\partial s}{\partial y}(x, y) = x - \dfrac{2V}{y^2}, \ (x, y) \in E.$

The unique solution of 4.9.5, $x = y = (2V)^{1/3}$, determines a minimum of s.
Therefore the dimensions of the rectangular box of volume V and minimum
surface area of base and vertical sides are $(2V)^{1/3}, (2V)^{1/3}, \frac{1}{2}(2V)^{1/3}$.

4.9.6 Remarks. [i] It is instructive to interpret the solution of
Example 4.9.1 geometrically as follows. By application of the results
of Example 3.12.29 we see that the function $g : D \subseteq \mathbb{R}^3 \to \mathbb{R}$ given by
4.9.2 has no local maxima or minima. The constraint 4.9.3 restricts
the domain of g to a surface S in $\mathbb{R}^3$, where $S \subseteq D$. On this surface
the function g attains a minimum at the point

$$((2V)^{1/3}, (2V)^{1/3}, \tfrac{1}{2}(2V)) \in S.$$

In view of the above comment we speak of the *extreme points of g
on S* when the domain of g is restricted to S.

[ii] The constraint 4.9.3 allows us to solve for z and to redefine
the surface area of the box in terms of the function $s : E \subseteq \mathbb{R}^2 \to \mathbb{R}$ on
which the methods of Section 3.12 are applicable. The method would
fail with a constraint such as, for example,

$$x + y + z - \sin(xyz) = 0,$$

for then it is not possible to solve for z or for x or for y in terms of
the other two variables.

A different type of difficulty arises with a constraint such as

$$x^2 + \tfrac{1}{2}y^2 + z^2 - 1 = 0.$$

Here it is possible to solve for z in terms of x and y, but there is
more than one case to be considered. (See Example 4.7.9).

These difficulties are avoided by the so-called method of Lagrange
multiplier. The theorem on which the method is based concerns the
nature of the extreme points of a real-valued function $g : D \subseteq \mathbb{R}^m \to \mathbb{R}$
when its domain is restricted to a subset of D upon which some
function $F : D \subseteq \mathbb{R}^m \to \mathbb{R}$ takes only the value 0. For example, the
constraint 4.9.3 on the domain of the function g of Example 4.9.1 is
expressible in this form by defining $F(x, y, z) = xyz - V$. Define the
subset S of $D \subseteq \mathbb{R}^m$ by

$$S = \{ \mathbf{x} \in D \mid F(\mathbf{x}) = 0 \}.$$

We wish to consider the extreme points of the function g when its
domain is restricted to S. Let $\mathbf{p}$ be a point in S. The set

$$T = \{ \mathbf{x} \in D \mid g(\mathbf{x}) = g(\mathbf{p}) \}$$

is the boundary between subsets T^+ and T^- of $\mathbb{R}^m$, where

$$T^+ = \{\mathbf{x}{\in}D\,|\,g(\mathbf{x}) > g(\mathbf{p})\} \qquad \text{and} \qquad T^- = \{\mathbf{x}{\in}D\,|\,g(\mathbf{x}) < g(\mathbf{p})\}.$$

Notice that $\mathbf{p}$ lies in both S and T. If $\mathbf{p}$ is an extreme point of $g : S \subseteq \mathbb{R}^m \to \mathbb{R}$, then S cannot cross over T at $\mathbf{p}$ from T^+ to T^-. This means that the level set S of F and the level set T of g must be tangential at $\mathbf{p}$ and therefore that $(\operatorname{grad} F)(\mathbf{p})$ and $(\operatorname{grad} g)(\mathbf{p})$, if non-zero, are in the same direction (normal to S and T). The situation is illustrated for $m = 2$ in Fig. 4.16(i) and (ii). We therefore expect, under suitable conditions, to find all the extreme points of g on S among those points $\mathbf{p}$ at which $(\operatorname{grad} g)(\mathbf{p})$ and $(\operatorname{grad} F)(\mathbf{p})$ are linearly dependent. Figure 4.16(iii) shows however that some such points may not be extreme points. Here S and T are tangential at $\mathbf{p}$ but S crosses over T from T^+ to T^-.

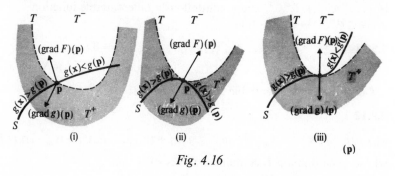

Fig. 4.16

4.9.7 Theorem.   *Let $g : D \subseteq \mathbb{R}^m \to \mathbb{R}$ be a differentiable function and let $F : D \subseteq \mathbb{R}^m \to \mathbb{R}$ be a C^1 function defined on an open set $D \subseteq \mathbb{R}^m$, where $m \geqslant 2$. Let S be the level set of F corresponding to the value 0, that is,*

$$S = \{(x_1, \ldots, x_m){\in}D\,|\,F(x_1, \ldots, x_m) = 0\}.$$

Suppose that $\mathbf{p} = (p_1, \ldots, p_m){\in}S$ satisfies the condition

$$(\operatorname{grad} F)(\mathbf{p}) \neq \mathbf{0}.$$

If $\mathbf{p}$ is an extreme point of $g : S \subseteq \mathbb{R}^m \to \mathbb{R}$ (where the domain of g is restricted to S), then there exists $\lambda{\in}\mathbb{R}$ such that

4.9.8 $$(\operatorname{grad} g)(\mathbf{p}) = \lambda(\operatorname{grad} F)(\mathbf{p}).$$

Proof.   Let $\mathbf{p}$ be an extreme point of $g : S \subseteq \mathbb{R}^m \to \mathbb{R}$. Expression 4.9.8 is trivially satisfied by $\lambda = 0$ if $(\operatorname{grad} g)(\mathbf{p}) = \mathbf{0}$ (any such point is a critical point of g on D). Assume then that $(\operatorname{grad} g)(\mathbf{p}) \neq \mathbf{0}$. We establish 4.9.8 by contradiction. Assume that $(\operatorname{grad} g)(\mathbf{p})$ and (grad F)($\mathbf{p}$) are linearly independent. Let $\mathbf{u} = (u_1, \ldots, u_m) \in \mathbb{R}^m$ be a vector such that $\{(\text{grad } F)(\mathbf{p}), \mathbf{u}\}$ is an orthogonal basis of the plane spanned by (grad F)($\mathbf{p}$) and (grad g)($\mathbf{p}$). Then

4.9.9 $(\text{grad } F)(\mathbf{p}) \cdot \mathbf{u} = 0,$

4.9.10 $(\text{grad } g)(\mathbf{p}) \cdot \mathbf{u} \neq 0.$

We now construct a curve in S whose tangent at $\mathbf{p}$ is in the direction of $\mathbf{u}$. The condition $(\text{grad } F)(\mathbf{p}) \neq \mathbf{0}$ means that we can assume $(\partial F / \partial x_m)(\mathbf{p}) \neq 0$. (Otherwise $(\partial F / \partial x_i)(\mathbf{p}) \neq 0$ for some i, $1 \leqslant i \leqslant m - 1$, and we interchange the roles of the x_i and x_m coordinates.) The function F satisfies the conditions of the Implicit Function Theorem 4.8.1. Therefore there exists a neighbourhood N of $(p_1, \ldots, p_{m-1}) \in \mathbb{R}^{m-1}$, and a continuously differentiable function $f : N \subseteq \mathbb{R}^{m-1} \to \mathbb{R}$ such that

4.9.11 $F(x_1, \ldots, x_{m-1}, f(x_1, \ldots, x_{m-1})) = 0,$

$$\text{for all } (x_1, \ldots, x_{m-1}) \in N.$$

Consider the differentiable function $\alpha : E \subseteq \mathbb{R} \to \mathbb{R}^m$ defined by

4.9.12

$$\alpha(t) = (p_1 + tu_1, \ldots, p_{m-1} + tu_{m-1}, f(p_1 + tu_1, \ldots, p_{m-1} + tu_{m-1})), t \in E,$$

whose open domain E contains 0 and is such that $(p_1 + tu_1, \ldots, p_{m-1} + tu_{m-1})$ lies in N for all $t \in E$.

The image of α lies in S (by 4.9.11) and $\alpha(0) = \mathbf{p}$. In fact $\alpha(E)$ is the projection parallel to the x_m-axis of the line $\{\mathbf{p} + t\mathbf{u} \in \mathbb{R}^m | t \in \mathbb{R}\}$ onto S. We will show that $\alpha'(0) = \mathbf{u}$. From 4.9.12, for some $w \in \mathbb{R}$,

4.9.13 $\alpha'(0) = (u_1, \ldots, u_{m-1}, w).$

Now $F(\alpha(t)) = 0$ for all $t \in E$. Hence $(F \circ \alpha)'(0) = 0$ and so, by the Chain Rule and 4.9.13

4.9.14 $(\text{grad } F)(\mathbf{p}) \cdot (u_1, \ldots, u_{m-1}, w) = 0.$

Subtracting 4.9.14 from 4.9.9 gives

4.9.15 $(\text{grad } F)(\mathbf{p}) \cdot (0, \ldots, 0, u_m - w) = 0.$

Therefore, since $(\partial F / \partial x_m)(\mathbf{p}) \neq 0$, $u_m = w$. It follows from 4.9.13 that $\alpha'(0) = \mathbf{u}$.

The required contradiction now follows. Since $\mathbf{p}$ is an assumed extreme point of g on S and since $\alpha(E) \subseteq S$ and $\alpha(0) = \mathbf{p}$, the function $(g \circ \alpha) : E \subseteq \mathbb{R} \to \mathbb{R}$ has an extreme point at 0. But by the Chain Rule and 4.9.10,

$$(g \circ \alpha)'(0) = (\operatorname{grad} g)(\mathbf{p}) \cdot \alpha'(0) = (\operatorname{grad} g)(\mathbf{p}) \cdot \mathbf{u} \neq 0.$$

This contradiction completes the proof of the theorem.

4.9.16 Remark. *The method of the Lagrange multiplier.* According to Theorem 4.9.7 there are two possibilities for an extreme point **p** of the function $g : S \subseteq \mathbb{R}^m \to \mathbb{R}$. *Either*

4.9.17 $F(\mathbf{p}) = 0$ and $(\operatorname{grad} F)(\mathbf{p}) = \mathbf{0}$,

or

4.9.18 $\begin{cases} F(\mathbf{p}) = 0, \quad (\operatorname{grad} F)(\mathbf{p}) \neq \mathbf{0} \text{ and} \\ (\operatorname{grad} g)(\mathbf{p}) = \lambda (\operatorname{grad} F)(\mathbf{p}), \end{cases}$

for some $\lambda \in \mathbb{R}$. The constant λ is called the *Lagrange multiplier* or *undetermined multiplier*. In the course of solution its value is usually left undetermined.

A solution **p** of either Equations 4.9.17 or Equations 4.9.18 is called a *critical point of g on S*. The set of critical points of g on S contains the extreme points of g on S. However, a critical point is not necessarily an extreme point. See Example 4.9.30 and 4.9.33.

4.9.19 Example. Let us apply the method of Lagrange multiplier to find the extreme values of

4.9.20 $g(x, y, z) = xy + 2xz + 2yz$, $x > 0, y > 0, z > 0$

subject to the constraint $F(x, y, z) = 0$, where

4.9.21 $F(x, y, z) = xyz - V$,

and V is a non-zero constant. (Compare Example 4.9.1.)

Here the restricted domain of g is

$$S = \{(x, y, z) \in \mathbb{R}^3 \mid F(x, y, z) = 0, x > 0, y > 0, z > 0\}.$$

We first calculate the gradient functions of g and F:

4.9.22 $(\operatorname{grad} g)(x, y, z) = (y + 2z, x + 2z, 2x + 2y)$,

and

4.9.23 $(\operatorname{grad} F)(x, y, z) = (yz, xz, xy)$.

By Remark 4.9.16, the critical points of g on S fall into two classes. *Class* 4.9.17: the set of solutions of the equations

4.9.24 $xyz - V = 0$, $yz = xz = xy = 0$, $(x, y, z) \in S$.

There are no solutions.

Class 4.9.18: the set of solutions for some $\lambda\in\mathbb{R}$ of the system

4.9.25
$$xyz - V = 0,$$

4.9.26
$$y + 2z = \lambda yz$$

4.9.27
$$x + 2z = \lambda xz$$

4.9.28
$$2x + 2y = \lambda xy$$

where $(x, y, z)\in S$ and $(yz, xz, xy)\neq(0, 0, 0)$.

In solving the system 4.9.25–28, note first that $\lambda\neq 0$, for otherwise $x = y = -2z$ and $x = -y$, and so $x = y = z = V = 0$, a contradiction. Next, multiply equations 4.9.26, 27, 28 by x, y, z respectively. Then

4.9.29 $\lambda xyz = \lambda V = xy + 2xz = xy + 2yz = 2xz + 2yz,$ $(x, y, z)\in S$.

It follows easily that the equations 4.9.29 have the unique solution

$$x = y = 2z = (2V)^{1/3}.$$

The function $g : S \subseteq \mathbb{R}^3 \to \mathbb{R}$ takes the value $3(4V^2)^{1/3}$ at the critical point $((2V)^{1/3}, (2V)^{1/3}, \frac{1}{2}(2V)^{1/3})$. It is a local minimum.

In general it is not an easy matter to decide whether a critical point which is found by the method of Remark 4.9.16 is a local maximum, a local minimum or neither. Frequently the physical nature of a problem makes a mathematical analysis unnecessary.

The following two examples illustrate the possibility that a critical point may be neither a maximum nor a minimum.

4.9.30 *Example.* Consider the critical points of the function g given by

4.9.31 $g(x, y, z) = x + y + z,$ $(x, y, z)\in\mathbb{R}^3$

on the restricted domain $S = \{(x, y, z)\in\mathbb{R}^3 \,|\, F(x, y, z) = 0\}$, where

$$F(x, y, z) = x^2 - y^2 - x - y - z.$$

It will be found that there is a unique critical point $(0, 0, 0)$. We show that this is neither a minimum nor a maximum as follows. Note that

$$(a, b, a^2 - b^2 - a - b)\in S, \qquad a, b\in\mathbb{R},$$

and that, by 4.9.31,

4.9.32 $g(a, b, a^2 - b^2 - a - b) = a^2 - b^2.$

Now $g(0, 0, 0) = 0$, and, by 4.9.32,

$$g(a, 0, a^2 - a) = a^2, \qquad g(0, b, -b^2 - b) = -b^2.$$

It follows that g takes positive and negative values at points in S arbitrarily close to its critical point $(0, 0, 0)$. Therefore $(0, 0, 0)$ is not an extreme point of g on S.

4.9.33 *Example*.   Find the minimum of the function g given by

$$g(x, y) = (x - 1)^2 + (y + 1)^2, \qquad (x, y) \in \mathbb{R}^2$$

on the restricted domain $S = \{(x, y) \in \mathbb{R}^2 \mid F(x, y) = 0\}$, where

$$F(x, y) = x^2 + y^2 - 2xy.$$

Applying the method of Lagrange multiplier, we calculate

$$(\text{grad } g)(x, y) = (2x - 2, 2y + 2)$$

and

$$(\text{grad } F)(x, y) = (2x - 2y, 2y - 2x).$$

From 4.9.17 we obtain critical points of g on S as solutions of the equations

$$x^2 + y^2 - 2xy = 0 \qquad \text{and} \qquad 2x - 2y = 2y - 2x = 0.$$

This system is solved by $x = y = a$, for any constant a. Now

$$g(a, a) = 2a^2 + 2,$$

and it follows that the critical point $(0, 0)$ is a minimum of g on S whereas the critical points (a, a), $a \neq 0$, are neither maxima nor minima.

The conditions 4.9.18 yield no further critical points.

Example 4.9.33 is easily solved without recourse to Theorem 4.9.7 (Exercise 4.9.4). Our purpose was to use it as an illustration that the conditions 4.9.17 of the method of the Lagrange multiplier must not be overlooked in the search for local maxima and minima of a function on a restricted domain.

Theorem 4.9.7 can be extended to functions whose domain is subject to more than one constraint. The generalization concerns a real-valued function $g : D \subseteq \mathbb{R}^m \to \mathbb{R}$ defined on an open set $D \subseteq \mathbb{R}^m$, whose domain is restricted by $r \, (< m)$ constraints to the set

$$S = \{\mathbf{x} \in \mathbb{R}^m \mid F_1(\mathbf{x}) = 0, \dots, F_r(\mathbf{x}) = 0\}$$

where the functions F_i, $i = 1, \dots, r$, are continuously differentiable on D. Suppose that $\mathbf{p}$ is a point in S such that the vectors $(\text{grad } F_1)(\mathbf{p}), \dots, (\text{grad } F_r)(\mathbf{p})$ are linearly independent. Then if $\mathbf{p}$ is an extreme point of g on S, there exist numbers (Lagrange multipliers) $\lambda_1, \dots, \lambda_r$ such that

$$(\text{grad } g)(\mathbf{p}) = \lambda_1 (\text{grad } F_1)(\mathbf{p}) + \cdots + \lambda_r (\text{grad } F_r)(\mathbf{p}).$$

We omit the proof, but here, to end the section, is an illustration.

4.9.34 *Example*.   The intersection of the sphere

$$\{(x, y, z) \in \mathbb{R}^3 \mid x^2 + y^2 + z^2 = 1\}$$

and the plane
$$\{(x, y, z) \in \mathbb{R}^3 \mid x + y + z = 1]$$
is a circle C. Find the shortest distance from the point $(0, 3, 3)$ to the circle C.

Solution. The square of the distance from $(0, 3, 3)$ to a point (x, y, z) on C is
$$g(x, y, z) = x^2 + (y - 3)^2 + (z - 3)^2.$$
We require the minimum value of g when its domain is restricted to the set
$$S = \{(x, y, z) \in \mathbb{R}^3 \mid F_1(x, y, z) = 0, F_2(x, y, z) = 0\}$$
where
$$F_1(x, y, z) = x^2 + y^2 + z^2 - 1$$
$$F_2(x, y, z) = x + y + z - 1.$$

We calculate the gradients:
$$(\mathrm{grad}\, g)(x, y, z) = (2x, 2y - 6, 2z - 6),$$
$$(\mathrm{grad}\, F_1)(x, y, z) = (2x, 2y, 2z),$$
$$(\mathrm{grad}\, F_2)(x, y, z) = (1, 1, 1).$$

Hence $(\mathrm{grad}\, F_1)(x, y, z)$ and $(\mathrm{grad}\, F_2)(x, y, z)$ are linearly independent, provided that (x, y, z) is not a multiple of $(1, 1, 1)$. In our problem the possibility $x = y = z = a$ does not arise, for the equations $F_1(a, a, a) = 0$ and $F_2(a, a, a) = 0$ cannot be simultaneously satisfied. Therefore the generalization of Theorem 4.9.7 applies, and the minimum of g on S occurs among the points $(x, y, z) \in \mathbb{R}^3$ which simultaneously solve the equations $F_i(x, y, z) = 0$, $i = 1, 2$ and
$$(\mathrm{grad}\, g)(x, y, z) = \lambda(\mathrm{grad}\, F_1)(x, y, z) + \mu(\mathrm{grad}\, F_2)(x, y, z)$$
for some constants λ, μ.

The equations are as follows:

4.9.35 $x^2 + y^2 + z^2 - 1 = 0$ and $x + y + z - 1 = 0$

4.9.36 $2x = \lambda(2x) + \mu$

4.9.37 $2y - 6 = \lambda(2y) + \mu$

4.9.38 $2z - 6 = \lambda(2z) + \mu.$

Eliminating μ from 4.9.36, 37 and from 4.9.37, 38 we obtain
$$(\lambda - 1)(x - y) = 3 \quad \text{and} \quad (\lambda - 1)(y - z) = 0.$$
Hence $\lambda - 1 \neq 0$ and $y = z$. The equations 4.9.35 reduce to
$$x^2 + 2y^2 = 1 \quad \text{and} \quad x + 2y = 1.$$

This leads to the solutions

$$(x, y, z) = (1, 0, 0) \qquad \text{and} \qquad (x, y, z) = (-\tfrac{1}{3}, \tfrac{2}{3}, \tfrac{2}{3}).$$

It will be found that $g(1, 0, 0) = 19$ and $g(-\tfrac{1}{3}, \tfrac{2}{3}, \tfrac{2}{3}) = 11$. Therefore the shortest distance from the point $(0, 3, 3)$ to the circle C is $\sqrt{11}$, and the point on C closest to $(0, 3, 3)$ is $(-\tfrac{1}{3}, \tfrac{2}{3}, \tfrac{2}{3})$. The second solution $(x, y, z) = (1, 0, 0)$ gives the point on C furthest from $(0, 3, 3)$.

Exercises 4.9

1. Find by the method of the Lagrange multiplier the dimensions of the rectangular parallelopiped of largest volume that can be inscribed in the ellipsoid $x^2/a^2 + y^2/b^2 + z^2/c^2 = 1$.

Hint: find the maximum of $g(x, y, z) = 8xyz$ subject to the constraint $F(x, y, z) = 0$, where $F(x, y, z) = x^2/a^2 + y^2/b^2 + z^2/c^2 - 1$.

Answer: $x = a/\sqrt{3}$, $y = b/\sqrt{3}$, $z = c/\sqrt{3}$.

2. (a) Find the maximum and minimum distance from the origin $(0, 0)$ to the ellipsoid $5x^2 - 6xy + 5y^2 = 8$.

Hint: consider the critical points of $x^2 + y^2$ subject to the ellipsoidal constraint.

Answer: max 2, min 1.

    (b) Find by the method of Lagrange multiplier the shortest distance from the point $(1, 0)$ to the parabola $y^2 = 4x$. Check your answer by a method of substitution.

Answer: 1.

3. Complete the calculations of Example 4.9.30.

4. Solve Example 4.9.33 by a direct method.

Hint: $x^2 + y^2 - 2xy = 0$ if and only if $x = y$.

5. Find by the method of Example 4.9.34 the point P nearest the origin on the line of intersection of the two planes $2x + 3y + z = 6$ and $x + 2y + 2z = 4$. Verify that the direction of OP is orthogonal to the line.

Answer: $(\tfrac{12}{13}, \tfrac{17}{13}, \tfrac{3}{13})$.

6. Verify that the point $\mathbf{p} = (0, \tfrac{1}{2}, 0)$ is a critical point of

$$g(x, y, z) = xz + (2y - 1)^3$$

subject to the constraint

$$x^2 + 4y^2 + z^2 - 4xy + 2x - 4y + 1 = 0.$$

Show also that it is neither a local maximum nor a local minimum.

Hint: show that in any neighbourhood of **p** there are points subject to the constraint at which g takes positive and negative values.

7. Verify that the critical point of g on S calculated in Example 4.9.19 is a local minimum.

8. The points P and P^* lie on non-intersecting C^1 surfaces S and S^* in $\mathbb{R}^3$. Prove that, when the distance PP^* has a local minimum or maximum, the line PP^* is normal to both surfaces.

Hint: define the surfaces as level sets of smooth functions F and F^*. Use (x, y, z) to denote points in S and (u, v, w) to denote points in S^*. Determine the critical points of

$$g(x, y, z, u, v, w) = (x - u)^2 + (y - v)^2 + (z - w)^2$$

on $S \times S^*$, given that $S \cap S^*$ is empty, that is, $(x, y, z) \neq (u, v, w)$. By the extension of Theorem 4.9.7, at a critical point there exist numbers λ and μ such that

$$(\operatorname{grad} g)(x, y, z, u, v, w) = \lambda(\operatorname{grad} F)(x, y, z) + \mu(\operatorname{grad} F^*)(u, v, w)$$

Deduce that $(x - u, y - v, z - w)$ is a scalar multiple of $(\operatorname{grad} F)(x, y, z)$ and of $(\operatorname{grad} F^*)(u, v, w)$.

9. Find the shortest distance from the hyperbola $x^2 - y^2 = 3$ to the line $y = 2x$.

Hint: treat the square of the distance between points (x, y) on the hyperbola and (u, v) on the line as a function of x, y, u, v.

Answer: $3/\sqrt{5}$.

Bibliography

The following list of books is intended for reference and as a guide to further reading.

Elementary analysis and linear algebra

Adamson, Iain T., *Elementary Mathematical Analysis.* Longman
Hadley, G., *Linear Algebra.* Addison-Wesley
Lang. S., *Linear Algebra.* Addison-Wesley
Spivak, M., *Calculus.* W. A. Benjamin

Vector calculus

Bartle, R. G., *The Elements of Real Analysis.* Wiley
Flett, T. M., *Mathematical Analysis.* McGraw-Hill
Fulks, W., *Advanced Calculus.* Wiley
Lang, S., *Calculus of Several Variables.* Addison-Wesley
Marsden, J. E. and **Tromba, A. J.**, *Vector Calculus.* Freeman
Nickerson, H. K., **Spencer D. C.** and **Steenrod, N. E.**, *Advanced Calculus.* Van Nostrand
Rudin, W., *Principles of Mathematical Analysis.* McGraw-Hill
Williamson, R. E., **Crowell, R. H.** and **Trotter, H. F.**, *Calculus of Vector Functions.* Prentice-Hall

Applied mathematics

Bourne, D. E. and **Kendall, P. C.**, *Vector Analysis and Cartesian Tensors.* Nelson
Cole, R. J., *Vector Methods.* Van Nostrand Reinhold
Marder, L., *Vector Analysis.* Allen and Unwin
Smith, R. C. and **Smith, P.**, *Mechanics.* Wiley
Sowerby, L., *Vector Field Theory with Applications.* Longman
Troup, G. J., *Mechanics.* Longman

Advanced analysis

Apostol, T. M., *Mathematical Analysis.* Addison-Wesley
Flett, T. M., *Differential Analysis.* Cambridge University Press

Lang, S., *Analysis I and II.* Addison-Wesley

Spivak, M., *Calculus on Manifolds.* W. A. Benjamin

Differential geometry

O'Neill, B., *Elementary Differential Geometry.* Academic Press

Index